M. EVANS MUNROE

University of New Hampshire, Durham, New Hampshire

IDEAS IN MATHEMATICS

ADDISON-WESLEY PUBLISHING COMPANY
Reading, Massachusetts · Menlo Park, California · London · Don Mills, Ontario

This book is in the
ADDISON-WESLEY SERIES IN INTRODUCTORY MATHEMATICS

Consulting Editors:
Richard S. Pieters and Gail S. Young

Copyright © 1968, Philippines copyright 1968 by Addison-Wesley Publishing Company, Inc. All rights reserved. No part of this publication may be reproduced, stored in a retrieval system, or transmitted, in any form or by any means, electronic, mechanical, photocopying, recording, or otherwise, without the prior written permission of the publisher. Printed in the United States of America. Published simultaneously in Canada. Library of Congress Catalog Card No. 68-18580.

PREFACE

This book is designed to present a course in pure mathematics for the nonmathematician.

First, I say that this is "pure" mathematics in that the aim of each chapter is to present a few important ideas of a purely mathematical nature. Illustrations are included to aid in the exposition of these ideas rather than as an end in themselves. In the second place, I say it is for nonmathematicians in that it is not specifically designed to develop problem-solving facility. There are exercises, but they are intended primarily to illustrate and amplify rather than to develop technique.

Mathematics has developed many ideas of real intellectual interest and genuine beauty. In a way this book is based on the premise that a few of these mathematical ideas should be in the repertoire of any well-educated person. Let me emphasize that this is not supposed to be a "mathematics appreciation" course. The student is expected really to come to grips with some genuine mathematical notions. However, these are introduced through simplified examples in which technical manipulative prerequisites are held to a minimum.

When I was choosing a title for this book I resisted the temptation to parody a well-used one and call it *Advanced Mathematics from an Elementary Standpoint*. However, this does describe something of what I have in mind. It is natural to ask how such a thing can be done. My plan of attack was inspired by a remark made by a colleague some years ago over coffee in the faculty lounge. This colleague is a biologist, but the remark might equally well have come from, say, a historian. He said, "Though my students need some mathematics, I am tempted to stop putting them in mathematics courses because you try to teach them a way of thinking alien to that they have to use in their major field. You try to mold them into your little mathematician's pattern of deductive reasoning as the be-all and end-all, while I beat my brains out trying to make them infer the general from the particular."

I do not agree that a standard mathematics course is bad for a biologist, but my friend did give me an idea. To teach mathematical ideas to a nonmathematician, roll with the punch and go at it inductively. This is the procedure I have generally adopted in this book. Discuss specific problems, each technically easy to solve but each illustrating an important principle. Once the principle has been amply illustrated and finally specifically formulated, that is the end of the line for this book. The aim here is not to develop advanced mathematical theories but to look at some of the basic ideas on which they are built.

This is not to say that I am trying to picture mathematics as an inductive science. Indeed, one of the big ideas that appears more than once here is that of a postulate system as the starting point of a mathematical discipline. However, I am not forcing the student to start this way. Rather, I am trying to teach him about deduction inductively.

The preparation expected is a good three-year high school mathematics sequence. Trigonometry is not needed.

Chapter 1 contains miscellany, most of which is found in the prerequisite high school courses. The instructor should check out the items mentioned there, though, before embarking on the main body of the book. Assuming a background of high school mathematics plus Chapter 1, the remaining chapters are virtually independent and can be taken in any combination and any order. The principal exception to this is that, although the elementary discussion of linear programming is an independent unit, the interesting parts of that chapter depend on the chapter on linear algebra.

There is sufficient material for a two-semester course, but with the flexibility allowed by the independence of the chapters, the instructor can organize a number of meaningful one-semester courses from this material.

Gail Young and the editorial staff of Addison-Wesley made many helpful suggestions for revision of the manuscript. The manuscript typing was done by Susan Hoyt, Mary Anne MacIlvaine, and Carol Stewart. Rhonda Kootz alphabetized the index and typed the instructor's manual. L. V. Venkataraman prepared the answers to the exercises. I want to thank all these people for their help.

Durham, New Hampshire M. E. M.
January 1968

CONTENTS

Chapter 1 PRELIMINARIES

1–1	Sets	1
1–2	Binomial coefficients	4
1–3	Summation	7
1–4	Functions	10
1–5	Composite functions	18
1–6	Variables and loci	22
1–7	Slopes and lines	27

Chapter 2 LOGIC

2–1	Logical possibilities	31
2–2	Basic connectives	34
2–3	Truth tables	37
2–4	Conditionals	42
2–5	Further applications of conditionals	46
2–6	Venn diagrams	49
2–7	Boolean functions	51
2–8	Valid arguments	55
2–9	Postulates	58

Chapter 3 CALCULUS

3–1	Introduction	60
3–2	Integrals	61
3–3	Derivatives	66
3–4	The fundamental theorem	69
3–5	Prospectus	74
3–6	Derivatives of variables	75
3–7	The chain rule	77
3–8	Differentials	82
3–9	Integration by substitution	83
3–10	Curve sketching	88
3–11	Area	90
3–12	Volume	93
3–13	Max-min problems	97

Chapter 4 PROBABILITY

4-1	Sample spaces	101
4-2	Probability measures	104
4-3	Conditional probability	108
4-4	Random variables	112
4-5	Expectation	115
4-6	Variance	118
4-7	Bernoullian trials	120
4-8	Poisson distributions	122
4-9	Limit theorems	127

Chapter 5 LINEAR ALGEBRA

5-1	Matrices	131
5-2	Matrix inversion	135
5-3	Vector spaces	138
5-4	Bases	141
5-5	Linear transformations; plane vectors	148
5-6	Linear transformations; other spaces	154
5-7	Duality	161

Chapter 6 LINEAR PROGRAMMING

6-1	Convex sets	165
6-2	Linear max-min problems	170
6-3	Matrix representation	174
6-4	Duality	177
6-5	The simplex method	179

Chapter 7 ABSTRACT ALGEBRAIC SYSTEMS

7-1	Symmetries	185
7-2	Groups	188
7-3	Isomorphisms	192
7-4	Subgroups	196
7-5	Homomorphisms	200
7-6	Rings	202
7-7	Polynomials	204
7-8	Fields	208

Chapter 8 COMPUTERS

8–1	Artificial languages	212
8–2	I–O and arithmetic statements	215
8–3	Library functions	219
8–4	Control statements	220
8–5	Do loops	224
8–6	Format	232
8–7	Functions	236
	ANSWERS TO SELECTED EXERCISES	245
	INDEX	263

PRELIMINARIES 1

1-1 SETS

The word *set* is used in mathematics to mean a collection or aggregate of things. The things that go to make up a set are called its *elements*. Thus "is an element of" is a basic relation in set theory. This relation is denoted by $\in$. That is,

$$a \in A$$

means that a is an element of A. To indicate that a is not an element of B, we write

$$a \notin B.$$

If every element of A is also an element of B, we say that A is a *subset* of B and write

$$A \subset B.$$

The subset relation may also be written the other way. That is,

$$B \supset A$$

means the same thing as $A \subset B$. The relation $A \subset B$ does not preclude the possibility that $A = B$, that A and B consist of exactly the same elements. If $A \subset B$ and $A \neq B$, we say that A is a proper subset of B. The symbol $\subset$ means "is a subset of," and there is no standard symbol for "is a proper subset of."

Often it is convenient to describe a set by specifying conditions characterizing its elements. For example, we might want to talk about the set of all real numbers definitely between 0 and 1. A commonly used notation for specifying this set is

$$\{x | 0 < x < 1\}.$$

Similarly,

$$\{x | x^2 \leq 2\}$$

denotes the set of all numbers whose squares are less than or equal to 2. In general, if $P(x)$ is a statement concerning x, then

$$\{x | P(x)\}$$

stands for the set of all x's for which $P(x)$ is true.

A careful distinction must be made between the relations $\in$ and $\subset$. The relation $\in$ is between an element and a set to which it belongs; the relation $\subset$ is between two sets. This comment becomes particularly important when we consider singleton sets. Let

$$a \in A;$$

we denote by

$$\{a\}$$

the set consisting of the single element a. Note that in terms of set-theoretic relations a and $\{a\}$ are quite different things. We have

$$a \in A, \quad a \in \{a\}, \quad \text{and} \quad \{a\} \subset A.$$

However, the statements

$$a \subset A \quad \text{and} \quad \{a\} \in A$$

are *not* correct.

Another very special sort of set is the vacuous or *empty* set. This is the set that has no elements. The usual symbol for the vacuous set is

$$\emptyset.$$

No matter what a may be,

$$a \notin \emptyset.$$

Furthermore, if A is any set, then every element of $\emptyset$ (of which there are none) is an element of A; so

$$\emptyset \subset A.$$

The vacuous set is a subset of every set.

The vacuous set is not just a mathematical abstraction. It is a very realistic consideration in many investigations. To look at a simple example, suppose we stop a man on the street and classify the coins in his pocket by denomination. We have five sets of coins: P, pennies, N, nickels, D, dimes, Q, quarters, H, half-dollars. Clearly, one or more of these sets may be vacuous.

If A and B are two sets, the *union* of A and B, written

$$A \cup B,$$

is the set of all things that are elements of A or B (or both). The *intersection* of A and B, written

$$A \cap B,$$

is the set of all things that are elements of both A and B. These ideas are illustrated in Fig. 1–1. There $A \cup B$ is the entire shaded area and $A \cap B$ is the region with the double crosshatching.

1-1 SETS

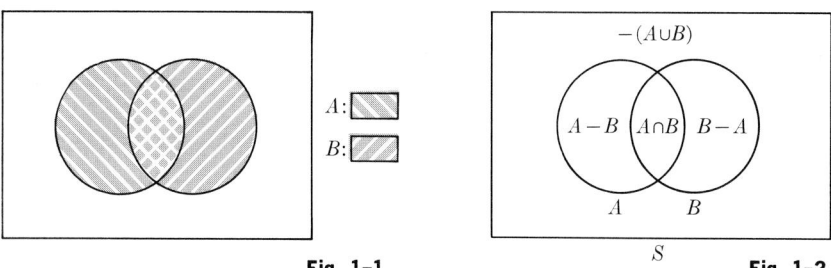

Fig. 1-1 **Fig. 1-2**

In Fig. 1-1 everything is enclosed in a rectangle. This is suggestive of the fact that in any discussion of sets there must be a *space* or *universe*, the set of all things to be considered in the problem at hand. This is necessary because the concept "set of all things" leads to logical contradictions. Given a space S the allowable sets are the subsets of S. (Others could be introduced, but the subsets of our space will suffice for our purposes.)

Suppose that S is the space and $A \subset S$. The set of all elements of S which are not elements of A is denoted by

$$-A$$

and called the *complement* of A. (Learn to spell this word; it comes from the same item as the word complete. The word meaning flattery is spelled compliment.) Given two sets A and B, the complement of B relative to A is written

$$A - B$$

and is the set of all things that are elements of A but not elements of B.

Figure 1-2 shows various sets generated by two subsets of a space and Fig. 1-3 shows various sets generated by three.

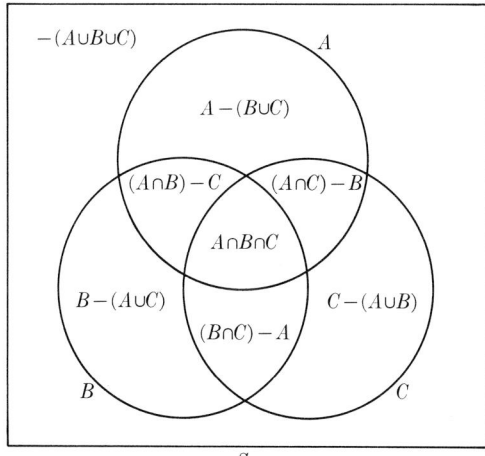

Fig. 1-3

EXERCISES

1. Let the space be the set of integers 1 through 10. Let A be the set of odd integers and let B be the set of integers less than or equal to 5. List the elements of each of the following sets.
   a) $A \cup B$ b) $A \cap B$ c) $A - B$ d) $B - A$
   e) $-A$ f) $-B$ g) $-(A \cup B)$ h) $-(A \cap B)$

2. From a diagram similar to Fig. 1-2, verify each of the following relations.
   a) $A \cap B \subset A \subset A \cup B$
   b) $-(A \cup B) = (-A) \cap (-B)$
   c) $-(A \cap B) = (-A) \cup (-B)$
   d) $A - B = A - (A \cap B) = (A \cup B) - B$

3. From a diagram similar to Fig. 1-3, verify each of the following relations.
   a) $A \cap (B \cup C) = (A \cap B) \cup (A \cap C)$
   b) $A \cup (B \cap C) = (A \cup B) \cap (A \cup C)$
   c) $A \cap (B - C) = (A \cap B) - (A \cap C)$
   d) $(A - B) - C = A - (B \cup C)$
   e) $A - (B - C) = (A - B) \cup (A \cap C)$

4. Let S be the space and $A \subset S$. Identify each of the following sets by a single letter.
   a) $A \cap S$ b) $A \cup S$ c) $A \cup \emptyset$ d) $A - \emptyset$
   e) $A \cap \emptyset$ f) $-\emptyset$ g) $-S$ h) $A - S$

1-2 BINOMIAL COEFFICIENTS

The following array of numbers is the beginning of what is called *Pascal's triangle*.

$$\begin{array}{c}
1 \\
1 \quad 1 \\
1 \quad 2 \quad 1 \\
1 \quad 3 \quad 3 \quad 1 \\
1 \quad 4 \quad 6 \quad 4 \quad 1 \\
1 \quad 5 \quad 10 \quad 10 \quad 5 \quad 1 \\
1 \quad 6 \quad 15 \quad 20 \quad 15 \quad 6 \quad 1 \\
1 \quad 7 \quad 21 \quad 35 \quad 35 \quad 21 \quad 7 \quad 1 \\
1 \quad 8 \quad 28 \quad 56 \quad 70 \quad 56 \quad 28 \quad 8 \quad 1
\end{array}$$

It is easy to continue this listing once we note the system to this array. Each row begins and ends with 1 and otherwise each entry is the sum of the two entries diagonally above it.

The symbol
$$\binom{n}{r}$$
is used to denote the $(r + 1)$st entry in the $(n + 1)$st row because each index starts from 0 rather than 1. In this notation the various positions in

the triangle have labels as follows.

$$\binom{0}{0}$$

$$\binom{1}{0} \quad \binom{1}{1}$$

$$\binom{2}{0} \quad \binom{2}{1} \quad \binom{2}{2}$$

$$\binom{3}{0} \quad \binom{3}{1} \quad \binom{3}{2} \quad \binom{3}{3}$$

The rules for forming the triangle can now be expressed in formulas:

$$\binom{n}{0} = \binom{n}{n} = 1, \tag{1}$$

$$\binom{n}{r} = \binom{n-1}{r-1} + \binom{n-1}{r}. \tag{2}$$

The numbers $\binom{n}{r}$ are called *binomial coefficients* because they appear as coefficients in the expansion of a power of a binomial. Specifically,

$$(1+x)^n = \binom{n}{0} + \binom{n}{1}x + \binom{n}{2}x^2 + \cdots + \binom{n}{r}x^r + \cdots + \binom{n}{n}x^n.$$

To see why this is so, note the following pattern of multiplications:

$$
\begin{array}{r}
1+x \\
1+x \\
\hline
1+x \\
x+x^2 \\
\hline
1+2x+x^2 = (1+x)^2 \\
1+x \\
\hline
1+2x+x^2 \\
x+2x^2+x^3 \\
\hline
1+3x+3x^2+x^3 = (1+x)^3 \\
1+x \\
\hline
1+3x+3x^2+x^3 \\
x+3x^2+3x^3+x^4 \\
\hline
1+4x+6x^2+4x^3+x^4 = (1+x)^4
\end{array}
$$

It should be clear from this sample that formula (2) is the key to building up higher powers of $1 + x$. The general formula for $(1 + x)^n$ is known as the *binomial theorem*.

Binomial coefficients also play an important role in set theory. If S_n is a space with n elements, then the number of r-element subsets of S_n is $\binom{n}{r}$. The following illustration shows how this result is obtained from formula (2).

$S_4 = \{1, 2, 3, 4\}$ $\qquad\qquad$ $S_5 = \{1, 2, 3, 4, 5\}$

2-element subsets: $\qquad\qquad$ 3-element subsets:

Count: $\binom{4}{2}$ $\quad\begin{array}{l}\{1, 2\}\\ \{1, 3\}\\ \{1, 4\}\\ \{2, 3\}\\ \{2, 4\}\\ \{3, 4\}\end{array}$ $\quad\begin{array}{l}\{1, 2, 5\}\\ \{1, 3, 5\}\\ \{1, 4, 5\}\\ \{2, 3, 5\}\\ \{2, 4, 5\}\\ \{3, 4, 5\}\end{array}$ $\quad$ Count: $\binom{5}{3} = \binom{4}{2} + \binom{4}{3}$

3-element subsets:

Count: $\binom{4}{3}$ $\quad\begin{array}{l}\{1, 2, 3\}\\ \{1, 3, 4\}\\ \{1, 2, 4\}\\ \{2, 3, 4\}\end{array}$ $\quad\begin{array}{l}\{1, 2, 3\}\\ \{1, 3, 4\}\\ \{1, 2, 4\}\\ \{2, 3, 4\}\end{array}$

In general, we obtain an r-element subset of S_n by adding the extra element to an $(r - 1)$-element subset of S_{n-1} or by taking an r-element subset of S_{n-1}. Thus formula (2) shows that the binomial coefficients give the right count.

Finally, we note that there is a well-known formula for the binomial coefficients in terms of factorials. The symbol $n!$ (read n-factorial) is frequently defined as the product of all the positive integers up to and including n. The trouble with this definition is that it does not give us $0!$. More satisfactory is the following procedure:

$$0! = 1$$
$$1! = 1 \cdot 0! = 1$$
$$2! = 2 \cdot 1! = 2$$
$$3! = 3 \cdot 2! = 6$$
$$\vdots$$
$$n! = n \cdot (n - 1)!$$

In terms of this notion the formula for binomial coefficients is

$$\binom{n}{r} = \frac{n!}{r!(n - r)!}.$$

This formula is verified by showing that it satisfies (1) and (2). We omit the computational details.

EXERCISES

1. Show that a space with n elements has 2^n subsets. [*Hint:* Expand $(1+x)^n$ by the binomial theorem and set $x = 1$.]
2. In how many ways can one write down a sequence of 10 digits, each either 0 or 1, with exactly six 1's and four 0's in the list? [*Hint:* Think of a 10-element space with a subset indicated by putting a 1 in a space if that element is in the subset and a 0 if it is not.]
3. How many different sequences of results are there on 10 tosses of a coin with exactly 6 heads and 4 tails?
4. Generalize Exercise 3. An experiment has two possible results which we will label success and failure. How many different sequences of n repetitions of the experiment are there with exactly r successes?
5. Show by direct computation that

$$\frac{(n-1)!}{(r-1)!(n-r)!} + \frac{(n-1)!}{r!(n-r-1)!} = \frac{n!}{r!(n-r)!}.$$

What is the significance of this result?

1-3 SUMMATION

Let $a_1, a_2, \ldots, a_n$ be an ordered set of n numbers. The sum of these,

$$a_1 + a_2 + \cdots + a_n,$$

is often denoted by

$$\sum_{i=1}^{n} a_i. \qquad (1)$$

The symbol $\sum$ is called a *summation sign*, and the symbol i in (1) is called the *summation index*. Given the same set of numbers as above, other sums may be formed; for example,

$$\sum_{i=3}^{k} a_i = a_3 + a_4 + a_5 + \cdots + a_k \qquad (3 \leq k \leq n),$$

$$\sum_{i=1}^{k} a_{2i} = a_2 + a_4 + a_6 + \cdots + a_{2k} \qquad \left(1 \leq k \leq \frac{n}{2}\right).$$

More generally, if m, n, j, k are integers with $m \leq j \leq k \leq n$ and if $a_m, a_{n+1}, \ldots, a_n$ is an ordered set of numbers, define

$$\sum_{i=j}^{k} a_i = a_j + a_{j+1} + a_{j+2} + \cdots + a_k.$$

Here j and k are called the *lower* and *upper limits of summation*, respectively. Informally, the summation sign means: "Assign to the summation index successive integer values from the lower to the upper limit of summation, inclusive. For each of these values of the summation index, evaluate the expression behind the summation sign, and compute the sum of all these results."

More precisely, the summation symbol may be defined inductively as follows:

$$\sum_{i=k}^{k} a_i = a_k, \qquad \sum_{i=k}^{n} a_i = a_n + \sum_{i=k}^{n-1} a_i.$$

Note that the result does not depend on the summation index; therefore the letter used for this index is immaterial; that is, each of

$$\sum_{m=1}^{n} a_m, \qquad \sum_{k=1}^{n} a_k, \qquad \sum_{j=1}^{n} a_j,$$

means the same thing as (1).

Similar notation is used for unions and intersections of a number of sets. That is,

$$\bigcup_{i=1}^{n} A_i$$

means

$$A_1 \cup A_2 \cup \cdots \cup A_n,$$

which is to say that it stands for the set of things that are elements of at least one of the sets $A_1, A_2, \ldots, A_n$. We do the same thing with intersections. That is,

$$\bigcap_{i=1}^{n} A_i$$

means the set of all things that are elements of all the sets $A_1, A_2, \ldots, A_n$.

EXERCISES

1. Evaluate each of the following:

a) $\sum_{i=3}^{7} 2i$

b) $\sum_{i=3}^{7} i^2$

c) $\sum_{i=1}^{4} \frac{1}{i}$

d) $\sum_{i=2}^{4} \frac{1}{i^2}$

e) $\sum_{i=1}^{5} (2i+3)$

f) $\sum_{i=1}^{4} (i^2 - 1)$

g) $\sum_{i=5}^{8} (2i+1)^2$

h) $\sum_{i=2}^{5} \frac{1+i}{1-i}$

i) $\sum_{i=3}^{7} \frac{2i}{2i+1}$

j) $\sum_{i=3}^{6} \frac{i}{1+i^2}$

2. Write each of the following with a summation sign.
   a) $1 + 3 + 5 + 7 + 9 + 11$
   b) $1 + 4 + 9 + 16 + 25 + 36 + 49 + 64$
   c) $1 + 9 + 25 + 49 + 81 + 121 + 169$
   d) $1 + 3 + 5 + \cdots + (2n + 1)$
   e) $2 + 4 + 6 + \cdots + (2n + 2)$
   f) $1 \cdot 2 + 2 \cdot 3 + 3 \cdot 4 + \cdots + n(n+1)$
   g) $\sqrt{2} + \sqrt{5} + \sqrt{10} + \cdots + \sqrt{1 + n^2}$
   h) $c_1^2(c_1 - c_0) + c_2^2(c_2 - c_1) + \cdots + c_n^2(c_n - c_{n-1})$
   i) $\sqrt{1 - c_1}\,(c_1 - c_0) + \sqrt{1 - c_2}\,(c_2 - c_1) + \cdots + \sqrt{1 - c_n}\,(c_n - c_{n-1})$

3. a) Compute
$$\sum_{i=3}^{7} (i^2 + 2i).$$

Compare Exercises 1(a) and 1(b) above.

b) Prove that
$$\sum_{i=k}^{n} (a_i + b_i) = \sum_{i=k}^{n} a_i + \sum_{i=k}^{n} b_i.$$

What properties of the operation of addition are needed in this proof?

c) Apply the result of part (b) to Exercise 1(e). What does
$$\sum_{i=1}^{5} 3$$
mean?

d) If c is a number, what is the value of
$$\sum_{i=k}^{n} c?$$

4. a) Show that
$$\sum_{i=3}^{n} a_i = \sum_{i=2}^{n-1} a_{i+1} = \sum_{i=4}^{n+1} a_{i-1} = \sum_{i=0}^{n-3} a_{n-i}.$$

b) Write three other forms yielding the same sum.

5. Write the binomial theorem with a summation sign.

6. For each positive integer n, let A_n be the set of integers
$$\{n, n+1, n+2, \ldots, n+10\}.$$
That is, A_1 is 1–11; A_2 is 2–12; etc. Describe each of the following sets.

a) $\bigcup_{n=1}^{10} A_n$ b) $\bigcup_{n=5}^{15} A_n$ c) $\bigcup_{n=1}^{5} A_{2n}$

d) $\bigcup_{n=2}^{5} A_{20n}$ e) $\bigcup_{n=1}^{4} A_{15n-1}$ f) $\bigcap_{n=1}^{5} A_n$

g) $\bigcap_{n=3}^{6} A_{2n}$ h) $\bigcap_{n=1}^{11} A_n$ i) $\bigcap_{n=1}^{12} A_n$

1-4 FUNCTIONS

In many different connections one sees tabulations of numbers in two parallel columns. A simple example:

$$\begin{array}{rr} 2 & -1 \\ -1 & 4 \\ 0 & 5 \\ 3 & -2 \\ -5 & -1 \end{array} \qquad (1)$$

As a general rule, the columns are labeled to indicate that the entries represent measurements of some sort. Essentially, this introduces additional concepts (see Section 1-6); so the labels have been omitted here in an effort to distill out one basic idea for discussion in the present section.

If one reads across rather than down, the table (1) appears to consist of five ordered pairs of numbers. For example, the first row in (1) reads

$$2 \quad -1.$$

To say that this is an ordered pair of numbers is to distinguish it from

$$-1 \quad 2,$$

which consists of the same two numbers in the reverse order. The notation (a, b) is commonly used for the ordered pair whose first entry is a and whose second entry is b. In this notation (1) would be written

$$(2, -1), (-1, 4), (0, 5), (3, -2), (-5, -1).$$

Now a *function* is defined as *a set of ordered pairs of numbers no two of which have the same first entry*.

Note that (1) is an example of a function. The first and last pairs in (1) have the same second entry, but this is immaterial. It is only duplications among the first entries that are ruled out in the definition of a function.

To turn to other familiar examples, note that for purposes of numerical computation, logarithmic and trigonometric functions are finite sets of ordered pairs displayed in a book of tables.

The *domain* of a function is the set of all first entries in its ordered pairs; the *range* of a function is the set of all its second entries. For the function (1), the domain is displayed in the first column, and the range in the second column.

The order in which the ordered pairs of a function are listed is of no significance. That is, by definition,

$$\begin{array}{rr} -5 & -1 \\ -1 & 4 \\ 0 & 5 \\ 2 & -1 \\ 3 & -2 \end{array} \tag{1'}$$

is the same function as (1). Often it is convenient to arrange a function as in (1'): put the numbers of the domain in increasing order. However, sometimes another arrangement is more convenient; and if this is the case, the rearrangement is quite permissible.

Frequently, a single letter is used to denote a particular function. The ones in most common use are f, g, F, G, ϕ, ψ; though occasionally others are introduced as needed. If f is a function and a is a number in its domain, then the symbol

$$f(a)$$

is used to denote the entry in the range corresponding to a. The symbol $f(a)$ is read "f of a," and is called the *value of f at a*. Given a, the operation of getting $f(a)$ is called *application* of f to a. If, for example, f denotes the function displayed in (1), then

$$f(2) = -1,$$
$$f(-1) = 4, \quad \text{etc.}$$

If a, b, and c are numbers, then $a(b + c)$ means, "a times the number $b + c$." Parentheses will still be used in this way, but the function value symbol introduces a new use for parentheses that generally has nothing to do with multiplication. This creates no confusion, provided it is borne in mind that parentheses signal application of a function, if and only if two conditions prevail:

(1) The symbol before the parentheses stands for a function.
(2) The symbol inside the parentheses stands for a number in the domain of this function.

The next step is to define the sum of two functions. Note that if f and g are functions, $f + g$ is not intrinsically defined. Other definitions could be devised, but the following has proved to be useful and is generally adopted. If f and g are functions, $f + g$ is the function consisting of all ordered pairs of numbers $(a, b + c)$, where (a, b) is in f and (a, c) is in g. Informally, pair off (as far as possible) equal entries in the two domains, and add corresponding entries in the ranges. Example:

f		g		$f+g$	
−5	−1	−5	−1	−5	−2
−1	4	−1	3	−1	7
0	5	0	−2	0	3
2	−1				
3	−2	3	0	3	−2
		4	4		

Subtraction, multiplication, and division are defined in a similar manner. The student should formulate precise definitions. Examples:

f		g		$f-g$		fg		f/g	
−5	−1	−5	−1	−5	0	−5	1	−5	1
−1	4	−1	3	−1	1	−1	12	−1	$\frac{4}{3}$
0	5	0	−2	0	7	0	−10	0	$-\frac{5}{2}$
2	−1								
3	−2	3	0	3	−2	3	0		
		4	4						

Note that division by zero is not defined; and where it is indicated, that ordered pair is deleted from f/g.

Multiplication of functions introduces in a natural way the positive integer powers of a function. That is, $f^2 = ff$; $f^3 = fff$. In general,

$$f^n = f^{n-1}f.$$

The notion of a fractional exponent requires a more elaborate discussion for a careful definition. We shall not give a complete discussion of the matter, but by way of expanding the list of examples, we shall talk about fractional exponents in this chapter. Briefly,

$$f^{1/n}$$

is a function whose nth power is f. Often $f^{1/n}$ is referred to as the nth root of f.

For any function f it is natural to write $f+f$ as $2f$, $f+f+f$ as $3f$, etc. More generally, it is useful to define the function

$$cf$$

(where c is a number and f is a function) as the set of all ordered pairs (a, cb) for which (a, b) is in f.

This "mixed multiplication" of numbers and functions is a highly useful idea, but it is a little treacherous because it is not completely reversible by division. It is all right to divide the number out; if

$$g = cf, \tag{2}$$

then

$$f = \frac{1}{c} g.$$

However, to divide (2) by f would seem to yield "$g/f = c$." Something is wrong here because g/f is a function and c is a number. What can be derived from (2) is that

$$\frac{g}{f} = c \frac{f}{f}.$$

Now the function f/f is what might be called a "unit constant function." For every a in its domain, $(f/f)(a) = 1$. However, there is deleted from the domain of f/f every a in the domain of f for which $f(a) = 0$. When we define a unit constant function, it is desirable to put these back in. Thus, for any function f,

$$f^0$$

(f to the zero power) is defined as the set of all ordered pairs $(a, 1)$ where (a, b) is in f.

For example, if f is as shown below, then, strictly speaking, f/f and f^0 are different:

f		f/f		f^0	
1	−1	1	1	1	1
2	0			2	1
3	1	3	1	3	1
4	2	4	1	4	1

It makes things go more smoothly if it is agreed that whenever a quotient f/g is a constant function, it be extended to have for its domain the entire common part of the domains of f and g. This is *not* a "definition" of division by zero. It is merely a convention for the automatic extension of a certain special type of function. With this convention established, one now derives from (2) that

$$g/f = cf^0.$$

The functions considered so far have been very small sets of ordered pairs. In such cases it is convenient to display the entire function. However, the functions in most common use cannot be so displayed. An alternative to listing all the ordered pairs in a function is to describe a process for manufacturing ordered pairs and say that the function being defined consists of all the ordered pairs that can be manufactured by this process. This is to say that a specific function may be *defined* by giving a rule for the computation of its values. Furthermore, it is frequently practical to state such a rule in the form of a formula. Example: "Let f be defined by

$$f(a) = a^2 - 2a + 3 \qquad (3)$$

for all real numbers a." Note carefully the wording of the sentence in quotes. The formula (3) is part of the definition of the function; it cannot be said to be the function. Furthermore, (3) is not the entire definition; the domain must also be specified. For example,

$$\text{"}g(a) = a^2 - 2a + 3 \qquad \text{for } 0 \leq a \leq 1\text{"}$$

defines a smaller set of ordered pairs, though the formula is the same as (3).

To simplify matters in this respect, let us adopt the following convention with regard to the domains of functions defined by formulas. *Unless otherwise specified, the domain of a function will be the set of all real numbers for which the formula for function values yields real numbers.* For example,

$$f(a) = a^2 - 2a + 3$$

with no further explanation will be interpreted as defining a function whose domain is the entire real number system. On the other hand,

$$f(a) = (1 - a^2)^{1/2},$$

if not further qualified, will define a function whose domain is the set of numbers a for which

$$-1 \leq a \leq 1.$$

Often the word "on" is used to relate a function and its domain. That is, the sentence "f is a function whose domain is the set A" is often rendered "f is a function on A."

While algebraic formulas such as the above may be used to describe many functions in common use, the notions of function and formula must not be confused. There are many sets of ordered pairs that cannot be described by anything as systematic as a simple algebraic formula.

For example, the values of a function might be given by two different formulas, each applying over part of the domain. Functions of this type appear frequently, and the standard form for describing them is illustrated by the following example:

$$f(a) = \begin{cases} a^2 - 1 & \text{for } a < 1, \\ 2a - 3 & \text{for } a \geq 1. \end{cases}$$

In this particular example, the domain of f is the entire real number system.

For an intelligible discussion of calculus one almost has to have self-explanatory notation for the most commonly encountered functions. In some cases this is easy. For example, the symbol sin stands for a well-known rule for pairing numbers. The chief practical difficulty is that mathematics has no standard symbols for the polynomial functions. These are easily manufactured if only one has a symbol for the *identity function*—the function that pairs each real number with itself. The symbol I will be used for the identity function here. That is, throughout this book (and without repetition of the definition) I will be the function consisting of all ordered pairs (a, a), where a is a real number. In terms of a defining formula, I is defined by

$$I(a) = a$$

for all real numbers a. A typical finite subset of I:

-3	-3
-2	-2
-1	-1
0	0
1	1
2	2
3	3
4	4

Note that I^0 is the unit constant function on the entire real number system and the general constant function is cI^0. A *polynomial function* is one of the form

$$\sum_{i=0}^{n} c_i I^i.$$

In particular, the polynomial function defined by (3) is

$$I^2 - 2I + 3I^0.$$

Since, by definition, $I(a) = a$, and since powers and multiplication by numbers are defined as they are, it follows that

$$\left(\sum_{i=0}^{n} c_i I^i \right)(a) = \sum_{i=0}^{n} c_i a^i.$$

Rule of thumb: If a function is described in terms of I, to apply it to a, substitute a for I.

By way of example, let $f = I^2$ and $g = I^3 + I^0$. Let us find $f(0)$, $f(-1)$, $g(0)$, $g(-1)$. As noted above, this is done by substitution:

$$f(0) = 0^2 = 0, \quad f(-1) = (-1)^2 = 1;$$
$$g(0) = 0^3 + 1 = 1, \quad g(-1) = (-1)^3 + 1 = 0.$$

As another example, let $f = I^2 - I^{1/2}$; in terms of an arbitrary positive number a, let us find $f(a^2)$, $f(a^{1/2})$, $[f(a)]^{1/2}$, $[f(a)]^2$. Again, substitution is called for:

$$f(a^2) = (a^2)^2 - (a^2)^{1/2} = a^4 - a;$$
$$f(a^{1/2}) = (a^{1/2})^2 - (a^{1/2})^{1/2} = a - a^{1/4};$$
$$[f(a)]^{1/2} = [a^2 - a^{1/2}]^{1/2} \quad (a \geq 1);$$
$$[f(a)]^2 = [a^2 - a^{1/2}]^2 = a^4 - 2a^{5/2} + a.$$

EXERCISES

1. Let f and g be as follows:

f		g	
2	−1	4	−3
0	4	1	2
−3	2	0	0
4	0	−1	2
1	−3	2	1

Find each of the following:

a) $f + g$ b) $f - g$ c) fg d) $\dfrac{f}{g}$

e) $\dfrac{g}{f}$ f) $f(0)$ g) $g(0)$ h) $\dfrac{f}{f}$

i) $\dfrac{g}{g}$ j) f^0 k) g^0

2. In each of the following, what is the domain of f?

a) $f(a) = a^2 - 1$ b) $f(a) = \dfrac{1}{a^2 - 1}$ c) $f(a) = (a^2 - 1)^{1/2}$

d) $f(a) = (1 - a^2)^{1/2}$ e) $f(a) = (3 - a^2)^{1/2}$ f) $f(a) = (1 - a)^{1/2}$

g) $f(a) = (a - 1)^{1/2}$ h) $f(a) = (a + 1)^{1/2}$ i) $f(a) = \dfrac{1}{a + 1}$

j) $f(a) = \left(\dfrac{1}{a + 1}\right)^{1/2}$

3. In each of the following, take the function described and find the function values listed.
   a) $f(a) = a^2 - 3a$; find $f(1), f(-2), f(\frac{1}{2}), f(-\frac{2}{3})$.
   b) $f(a) = \dfrac{1}{a^2 - 1}$; find $f(-2), f(-\frac{1}{2}), f(0), f(100)$.
   c) $f = I^3 + 3I^0$; find $f(2), f(-3), f(-\frac{1}{2}), f(0)$.
   d) $f = \dfrac{-I^0}{I_0 + I^2}$; find $f(1), f(-2), f(\frac{1}{3}), f(-\frac{2}{5})$.
   e) $f(a) = 1 - a^3$; find $f(a^3), [f(a)]^3, f\left(\dfrac{1}{a}\right), \dfrac{1}{f(a)}$.
   f) $f(a) = a + \left(\dfrac{1}{a}\right)$; find $f(-a), f\left(\dfrac{1}{a}\right), \dfrac{I}{f(a)}, -f(a)$.
   g) $f = 4I^0 - I^0$; find $f(a^2), [f(a)]^2, f\left(\dfrac{1}{a}\right), 4 - f(a)$.
   h) $f = 2I - \dfrac{I_0}{2I}$; find $f(2a), f(-a), f\left(\dfrac{1}{a}\right), \dfrac{1}{f(a)}$.

4. For each of the functions listed in Exercise 3, state in words the rule for computing function values.

5. For each of the following verbal descriptions of an operation, describe the indicated function in symbols and give the domain.
   a) Square a number, and add 1 to the result.
   b) Add 1 to a number, and square the result.
   c) Square a number, and add 1; then cube the given number and subtract 1; finally, divide the first of these results by the second.
   d) Square a number, add 1, and take the square root of the result.
   e) Add 1 to a number; take the square root of the result; add 1 to this; finally, square this last result.
   f) Add 1 to the reciprocal of a number.
   g) Add a number and its reciprocal.
   h) Add 1 to a number, and take the reciprocal of the result.
   i) Add 1 to the square root of a number, and take the reciprocal of the result.
   j) Add 1 to the reciprocal of a number, and take the square root of the result.

6. Many of the definitions of this section may be given in terms of application of functions. For example, $f + g$ may be defined by saying that

$$(f + g)(a) = f(a) + g(a)$$

for all a in the domains of both f and g. Give a similar definition for each of the following. Be careful to specify the domain in each case.

   a) fg b) $f - g$ c) $\dfrac{f}{g}$ d) cf e) f^0

18 PRELIMINARIES

7. Let
$$f = \sum_{k=1}^{3} kI^k, \quad g = \sum_{k=0}^{2} (k+1)^2 I^k.$$

Write as polynomial functions:
a) $f + g$ b) $f - g$ c) fg

1-5 COMPOSITE FUNCTIONS

If f and g are functions such that the domain of f overlaps the range of g, then the *composite function*
$$f \circ g,$$
read, "f circle g," is defined as the set of all ordered pairs (a, c) such that for some b, (a, b) is in g and (b, c) is in f.

To put it another way, one frequently says that a function *maps* one number into another. That is, if (a, b) is in g, one says that g maps a into b. In these terms, $f \circ g$ maps numbers in two stages. First, there is a mapping by g; then the result is mapped by f. The following diagram shows this idea schematically.

$$a \xrightarrow{g} b \xrightarrow{f} c$$

(with $f \circ g$ spanning from a to c)

In terms of application, $f \circ g$ may be defined by saying that
$$(f \circ g)(a) = f[g(a)]$$
for each a in the domain of g such that $g(a)$ is in the domain of f.

For example, let $f = I^{1/2} - I^0$, $g = I^2 + I$; we then have
$$f[g(a)] = (a^2 - a)^{1/2} - 1;$$
$$g[f(a)] = (a^{1/2} - 1)^2 + a^{1/2} - 1 = a - a^{1/2}.$$

Note that each of these is obtained by a simple succession of substitutions.

For still another description of the idea, note the following example of two finite sets of ordered pairs:

g		f		$f \circ g$	
3	−2	−5	−1		
−5	−1			−5	3
2	−1	−1	3	2	3
		0	−2		
		3	0		
−1	4	4	4	−1	4
0	5				

1-5 COMPOSITE FUNCTIONS

Informally, pair off second entries of g with equal first entries of f; then take the corresponding first entries of g and second entries of f to form the composite function.

In order to work with composites, the student must learn how composition combines with the operations on functions discussed in Section 1–4. The following formulas give the principal results:

$$(f \pm g) \circ \phi = (f \circ \phi) \pm (g \circ \phi), \tag{1}$$

$$(fg) \circ \phi = (f \circ \phi)(g \circ \phi), \tag{2}$$

$$(f/g) \circ \phi = (f \circ \phi)/(g \circ \phi), \tag{3}$$

$$(cf) \circ \phi = c(f \circ \phi), \tag{4}$$

$$I^n \circ \phi = \phi^n, \tag{5}$$

$$f \circ I = f. \tag{6}$$

Sample proof:

$$[(f + g) \circ \phi](a) = (f + g)[\phi(a)] \text{ by the definition of } \circ$$
$$= f[\phi(a)] + g[\phi(a)] \text{ by the definition of } +$$
$$= (f \circ \phi)(a) + (g \circ \phi)(a) \text{ by the definition of } \circ$$
$$= [(f \circ \phi) + (g \circ \phi)](a) \text{ by the definition of } +.$$

Thus the functions equated in (1) have equal values for each a; so they are equal if they have the same domain. Now a is in the domain of $(f + g) \circ \phi$, provided $\phi(a)$ is in the domain of $f + g$; it is in the domain of $(f \circ \phi) + (g \circ \phi)$, provided $\phi(a)$ is in the domain of f and also in that of g. By the definition of $f + g$ these conditions are equivalent; so (1) is proved. The other formulas may be checked in a similar manner.

It is also important to note that

$$(f \circ g) \circ \phi = f \circ (g \circ \phi) \tag{7}$$

because when either of these is applied to a, the result is $f\{g[\phi(a)]\}$. Since (7) holds, multiple composition may be written without parentheses; that is, $f \circ g \circ \phi$ is unambiguous.

Along with these manipulative formulas, there are a few "don'ts" that should be noted. In general,

$$f \circ g \neq g \circ f,$$
$$f \circ (g + \phi) \neq (f \circ g) \pm (f \circ \phi),$$
$$f \circ (g\phi) \neq (f \circ g)(f \circ \phi),$$
$$f \circ (g/\phi) \neq (f \circ g)/(f \circ \phi),$$
$$f \circ (c\phi) \neq c(f \circ \phi),$$
$$f \circ I^n \neq f^n \quad \text{for } n \neq 1.$$

The circle notation displays with great clarity the structure of a composite function. However, the circle is a fairly recent innovation in mathematical notation, and for the functions commonly encountered there are many ways of indicating composition. Unfortunately, the notation for composite differs from one function to another.

This begins to show up in formula (5) above. According to that,

$$I^3 \circ (I^0 + I^2)$$

could be written

$$(I^0 + I^2)^3.$$

The latter form is the more common one, though the former gives a clearer analysis of the function.

For example, if we were to write $[I + (I - 2I^0)^3]^{1/2}$ using $\circ$ to denote composition, we would have

$$I^{1/2} \circ \{I + [I^3 \circ (I - 2I^0)]\}.$$

Going the other way, if we were to write

$$I^5 \circ \left[\frac{I^{1/2} \circ (I + I^2)}{I^2 \circ (I - I^{1/2})} \right]$$

in a form without the $\circ$ symbol, we would have

$$\left[\frac{(I + I^2)^{1/2}}{(I - I^{1/2})^2} \right]^5.$$

Let $f = I^{1/2} - I^0$, $g = I^2 + I$; find $f[g(a)]$ and $g[f(a)]$.

Answers:

$$f[g(a)] = (a^2 - a)^{1/2} - 1;$$
$$g[f(a)] = (a^{1/2} - 1)^2 + a^{1/2} - 1 = a - a^{1/2}.$$

Note that each of these is obtained by a simple succession of substitutions.

EXERCISES

1. Given functions f and g as follows:

f		g	
2	−1	4	−3
0	4	1	2
−3	2	0	0
4	0	−1	2
1	−3	2	1

Find:
a) $f \circ g$ b) $g \circ f$ c) $f \circ g \circ f$ d) $g \circ f \circ g$
e) $f \circ f$ f) $g \circ g$ g) $(f \circ g)(0)$ h) $(g \circ f)(0)$
i) $f[g(0)]$ j) $g[f(0)]$

2. In each of the following, take the functions described and find the function values listed.

a) $f(a) = 1 + a,\ g(a) = 3a^2$; find $f[g(a)],\ g[f(a)]$.

b) $f(a) = \dfrac{1-a}{1+a},\ g(a) = a^{1/2}$; find $f[g(a)],\ g[f(a)]$.

c) $f = (I^0 + I)^{1/2};\ g = (I^0 - I)^{1/2}$; find $f[g(a)],\ g[f(a)]$.

d) $f = I^0 + I^2,\ g = I^0 + I^{1/2}$; find $f[g(a)],\ g[f(a)]$.

e) $f(a) = 1 + 2a^3,\ g(a) = a^{1/2}$; find $f\left[\dfrac{1}{g(a)}\right],\ g\left[\dfrac{1}{f(a)}\right]$.

f) $f(a) = (1+a)^2,\ g(a) = 1 + a^2$; find $f\left[g\left(\dfrac{1}{a}\right)\right],\ \dfrac{1}{f[g(a)]}$.

g) $f = \dfrac{I^0}{I},\ g = I^0 + I$; find $g[g(a)],\ f[f(a)]$.

h) $f = I^{1/2},\ g = I^0 - I$; find $f\{g[f(a)]\},\ g\{f[g(a)]\}$.

3. Write each of the following without the $\circ$ symbol.

a) $I^{1/2} \circ (I^2 - I^0)$ b) $I^3 \circ (I + I^{1/2})$
c) $I^2 \circ (I^0 + I^{1/2}) \circ (I^2 + I^0)$ d) $I^4 \circ (I^0 - I) \circ (3I^0 + I^{1/2})$
e) $I^5 \circ (I^2 - 2I)$ f) $I^{1/2} \circ (I^3 + 3I^2)$
g) $I^{1/2} \circ (I^0 - I) \circ I^{1/2} \circ (I^0 - I)$ h) $I^3 \circ (I^0 - 2I^{1/2}) \circ (3I^0 + I)$

4. Rewrite each of the following, using $\circ$ to denote composition:

a) $(I + I^2)^5$ b) $(I - I^{1/2})^3$
c) $(I - I^3)^{1/2}$ d) $[(I - I^0)^{1/2} - (I + I^0)^{1/2}]^3$
e) $[I^0 + (I^0 + I)^2]^2$ f) $[I + (I - I^0)^{1/2}]^{1/2}$
g) $\left(I^0 + \dfrac{I^0}{I^0 - I^2}\right)^3$ h) $\{I + [I + (I = I^0)^{1/2}]^{1/2}\}^{1/2}$

5. For each of the following functions f, write $f \circ f$ in a form without the $\circ$ symbol.

a) $f = I^2 + I^0$ b) $f = (I + I^0)^2$

c) $f = \dfrac{I^2 + I^0}{I^3 - I^0}$ d) $f = (I^2 + I^0)^{1/2}$

e) $f = [(I + I^0)^{1/2} + I^0]^2$ f) $f = I^0 + \dfrac{I^0}{I}$

g) $f = I + \dfrac{I^0}{I}$ h) $f = \dfrac{I^0}{I^0 + I}$

i) $f = \dfrac{I^0}{I^0 + I^{1/2}}$ j) $f = \left(I^0 + \dfrac{I^0}{I}\right)^{1/2}$

6. Functions are often informally described as "machines." That is, one takes a set of numbers, feeds it into the machine, and gets another set of numbers out at the other end. In their simplest uses, modern computers are just such machines. One gives such a machine "instructions" for processing data, then feeds in numbers and gets others out. For the computing-machine model, use the words "input," "instructions," and "output" to describe each of the following: (a) function, as defined in this section, (b) rule for computing function values, (c) domain, (d) range, (e) composition of functions.

7. In general $f \circ g$ and $g \circ f$ are quite different functions; so the phrase "composite of f and g" is ambiguous. Commonly used terminology is as follows: $f \circ g$ is referred to as "the composite function consisting of g followed by f." Discuss terminology in the light of (a) the definition, (b) the notation.

8. Let f be a function whose domain is the entire real number system. Discuss the relations among
$$I^0, \quad I^0 \circ f, \quad f^0.$$

9. A standard book of numerical tables will contain tables entitled Logarithms, Logarithms of Trigonometric Functions, and Natural Trigonometric Functions. These tables display functions f, g, and ϕ such that
$$\phi = f \circ g.$$

Which function comes from which table? Obtain a book of tables and check your answer numerically.

1-6 VARIABLES AND LOCI

The idea of a set of ordered pairs need not be restricted to that of ordered pairs of numbers. For example, students seated in a classroom exhibit a set of ordered pairs of the form (student, chair). To say that one is acquainted with everyone in the room means that one has in mind a set of ordered pairs (person, name).

Quite generally, then, a *mapping* is defined as a set of ordered pairs no two of which have the same first entry. The words domain (set of first entries) and range (set of second entries) apply to mappings in general as to the special case of functions. A map such as one finds in an atlas is the range of a mapping. Here points on the earth's surface are paired with points on a sheet of paper.

If two mappings have overlapping domains and if their ranges are sets of numbers, then their sum, difference, product, and quotient are defined as in the case of functions. If f and g are two mappings such that the domain of g overlaps the range of f, then the composite mapping $g \circ f$ is defined in the usual way.

For many purposes a *variable* is defined as a mapping whose domain is a set of geometric or physical entities and whose range is a set of numbers.

Examples: (1) Geometry. To introduce a scale of measurement on a line is to pair each point on the line with a number. (2) Physics. The "time variable" associates a number with each instant of time. (3) Economics. "Let p be the price of corn in a changing market." Here p associates a number with each of a set of market situations. (4) Probability. "Let r be the number of heads that turn up in n tosses of a coin." Here r associates a number with each possible sequence of results of the coin-tossing experiment.

The foundations of analytic geometry involve two variables, each of which maps points of the plane into numbers. These are defined as follows. First, a frame of reference is determined by drawing two perpendicular lines in the plane. These lines are called the *coordinate* axes. For reasons shortly to appear, the horizontal one is called the x-axis and the vertical one the y-axis. On each coordinate axis a scale of measurement is agreed upon, usually—but not necessarily— the same scale on each axis. This stage of development is shown in Fig. 1–4. It should be noted that the measuring scales measure *directed distances*. This is, counting from the *origin* (the point of intersection of the coordinate axes), distances up or to the right are given positive measurements, while distances down or to the left are given negative measurements. The coordinate axes divide the plane into four *quadrants*, which are customarily numbered as indicated by the roman numerals in Fig. 1–4.

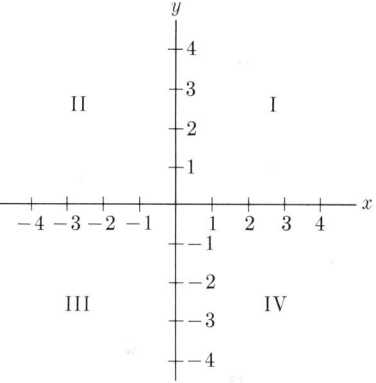

Fig. 1–4

This structure associates with each point in the plane two directed distance measurements, one horizontal, the other vertical. The horizontal measurement is called the *abscissa* of the point, and the vertical measurement is called the *ordinate*. These two numbers are called the *coordinates* of the point.

Now the set of all ordered pairs (p, a), where p is a point of the plane and a is its abscissa, is called the *abscissa variable*. The standard symbol for this variable is x. The set of all pairs (point, ordinate) is called the *ordinate variable*, and is denoted by y. The phrase *coordinate variable* refers to either x or y.

The basic idea of analytic geometry is that of a *locus*. Specifically, let x and y be the coordinate variables and let f be a function. One speaks of

$$\text{"the locus of } y = f \circ x\text{."}$$

This is defined as the set of all points p in the plane for which

$$y(p) = (f \circ x)(p).$$

The word "locus" is pure Latin. A literal translation is "place." Now, in general, y and $f \circ x$ are quite different mappings; so as a simple statement of fact, "$y = f \circ x$" is not true. However, the locus of the equation means "the place where y does equal $f \circ x$."

As is often the case with Latin words brought directly into English, the Latin plural form, *loci*, is retained in English usage.

Though locus is the more traditional word for this idea, a synonym in frequent use today is the phrase *truth set.*

By way of example, let us look first at some finite variables. Let x and y be abscissa and ordinate variables, respectively, each having for its domain only the five points shown in Fig. 1–5. Specifically:

x		y	
p_1	-4	p_1	-2
p_2	-3	p_2	4
p_3	-1	p_3	1
p_4	2	p_4	4
p_5	3	p_5	-2

Fig. 1–5

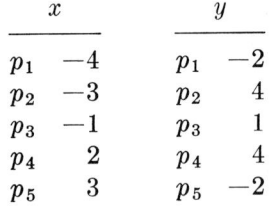

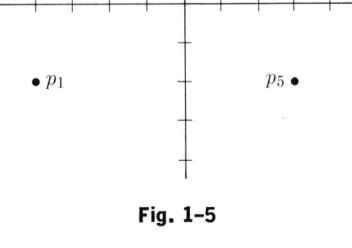

Let $f = I^2$, and compare y and $f \circ x$:

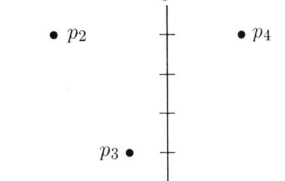

y		$I^2 \circ x$	
p_1	-2	p_1	16
p_2	4	p_2	9
p_3	1	p_3	1
p_4	4	p_4	4
p_5	-2	p_5	9

These variables have two ordered pairs in common; therefore the locus of $y = x^2$ is the set consisting of p_3 and p_4.

For a more standard example, let x and y be the coordinate variables on the entire plane. Sketch the locus of

$$y = x^2 - 2x - 3.$$

Mechanically, one substitutes some values for x and finds the corresponding values for y. For example:

x	-3	-2	-1	0	1	2	3	4	5
y	12	5	0	-3	-4	-3	0	5	12

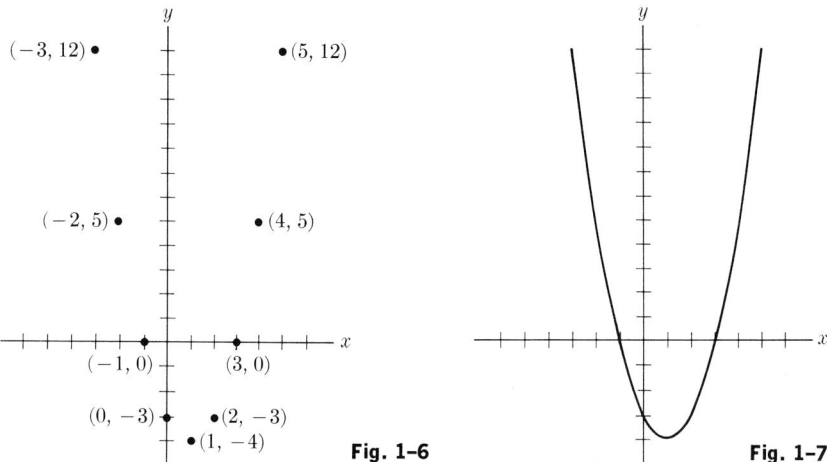

Fig. 1-6   Fig. 1-7

More precisely, what this amounts to is the following. Take the first pair here, $(-3, 12)$. Consider all the points in the plane having abscissa -3; which of these has an ordinate so that the equation is satisfied?

Since values of x and y determine points in the plane uniquely, the number pairs in the chart above may be transferred to a graph, as shown in Fig. 1-6. Presumably, then a smooth curve should be filled in Fig. 1-7 for the completed sketch.

This is a pedestrian way of sketching a locus, but it will suffice for the present. The idea of plotting a few points and filling in is quite sound, but the secret of successful curve-sketching is to know beforehand which points give the framework. Techniques for finding key points (rather than just points) will be presented in Chapter 3.

Functional notation based on the ∘ symbol for composition yields a very precise analysis of function structure. Such an analysis is needed in many connections, but it is usually not displayed very graphically by the notation commonly used in mathematics. For example,

$$\sqrt{1 + x^2}$$

means

$$I^{1/2} \circ (I^0 + I^2) \circ x,$$

and

$$I^3 \circ (I^0 + I^{1/2}) \circ (I^0 + I) \circ x$$

is commonly written

$$(1 + \sqrt{1 + x})^3.$$

The student must learn to read "colloquial" mathematics, so we shall use it here. However, to give some practice in analyzing what this imprecise notation means we have given below (Exercises 5 and 6) some drill in translating from the vernacular to consistent notation, and vice versa.

EXERCISES

1. Draw a set of coordinate axes and locate on it each of the following points:
   a) $(0, 1)$ b) $(1, 0)$ c) $(-1, 1)$ d) $(-1, -1)$
   e) $(-3, -5)$ f) $(-2, 3)$ g) $(3, -5)$ h) $(-5, 3)$
   i) $(\frac{1}{2}, \frac{5}{2})$ j) $(2, -\frac{1}{2})$ k) $(-\frac{3}{2}, \frac{2}{3})$ l) $(\frac{2}{3}, -\frac{3}{2})$

2. From each of the following equations relating coordinate variables, make a table of number pairs by substituting for x the values 0, $\pm\frac{1}{2}$, ± 1, ± 2 (whenever possible). On one set of coordinate axes plot the corresponding points and make rough sketches of the loci of all these equations.
   a) $y = x$ b) $y = x^2$ c) $y = x^3$
   d) $y = x^{1/2}$ e) $y = x^{1/3}$ f) $y = x^{2/3}$

3. Each of the following lists a pair of variables (with explanations of the symbols following). In each case name a function that maps the first variable into the second. Note that the three answers are the same. One function may appear in many different connections.
   a) s, A; s measures the length of a side and A the area, both applied to squares.
   b) r, A/π; r measures the radius and A the area, both applied to circles.
   c) t, $2s/g$; t measures elapsed time and s distance traveled, both applied to freely falling bodies which start from rest; g is the acceleration-by-gravity constant.

4. Let x and y be the usual coordinate variables; let f and g be functions; let p and q be points of the plane; let a and b be numbers. Assume that each of the functions f and g has the entire real number system for both domain and range. Each of the following symbols falls in exactly one of four categories: a number, a function, a variable, meaningless. Classify each of them.
   a) $f \circ x$ b) $g[y(p)]$ c) $x \circ g$ d) $p \circ x$
   e) $f(a)$ f) $y \circ x$ g) $f[x(a)]$ h) $g[f(b)]$
   i) $a \circ b$ j) $f \circ g \circ x$ k) $y(b)$ l) $x[y(p)]$
   m) $f \circ g$ n) $p \circ g$ o) $x(q)$ p) $q(p)$
   q) $g \circ f \circ x$ r) $f \circ y$ s) $b(p)$ t) $f\{g[y(q)]\}$
   u) $g\{x[f(a)]\}$ v) $x\{g[y(p)]\}$ w) $g(b)$ x) $g \circ y$
   y) $g(q)$ z) $g \circ f$

5. Rewrite each of the following in a form that displays the structure of the mapping.
   a) $(1 + \sqrt{x})^2$ b) $\sqrt{1 - x^3}$
   c) $3 + (2 - x)^4$ d) $(3 + \sqrt{2 - x})^4$
   e) $[2 + (1 - \sqrt{x + 4})]^3$ f) $\sqrt{1 - (4 + x^2)^3}$
   g) $(2 - \sqrt{1 - x^3})^2$ h) $(1 - x\sqrt{1 - x^2})^2$
   i) $\sqrt{x - \sqrt{1 - x}}$ j) $x\sqrt{1 - 2\sqrt{x}}$

1-7   SLOPES AND LINES

6. Rewrite each of the following in standard notation. (See the last paragraph before these exercises for an illustration of "standard" notation.)
   a) $I^{1/2} \circ (I^0 + I) \circ x$ b) $I^3 \circ (I^{1/2} - I^2) \circ x$
   c) $I^2 \circ (2I - I^2) \circ (I^0 - I) \circ x$ d) $I^{1/2} \circ (I^0 + I^{1/2}) \circ x$
   e) $(I^0 - I^2) \circ (I - I^2) \circ x$ f) $(I - I^3) \circ (I - I^{1/2}) \circ x$
   g) $(I^{3/2}) \circ (I^0 - I) \circ x$ h) $\{I[I^{1/2} \circ (I^0 - I)]\} \circ x$
   i) $\{I^3 \circ (I^3 - I^2)](3I^2 - 2I)\} \circ x$ j) $I^{1/2} \circ (I^0 + I) \circ I^{1/2} \circ (I^0 + I) \circ x$

7. Write each of the following in symbols.
   a) The sum of the abscissa and ordinate variables.
   b) The product of the abscissa and ordinate variables applied to the point p.
   c) The product of the abscissa of p and the ordinate of p.
   d) The composite consisting of the abscissa variable followed by the cube of the identity function. [*Note:* See Exercise 7, Section 1–5.]
   e) The value at the number a of the sum of the cube of the identity function and the square of the identity function.
   f) The composite consisting of the sum of the abscissa and ordinate variables, followed by the square of the identity function.
   g) The sum of the two composites consisting of the abscissa and ordinate variables, each followed by the square of the identity function.
   h) The square root of the sum of the unit constant function and the identity function.
   i) The sum of the unit constant function and the square root of the identity function.

8. Let x and y be the abscissa and ordinate variables on the five points shown in Fig. 1–5. Find each of the following:
   a) $x(p_1)$ b) $y(p_2)$ c) $(x + y)(p_3)$
   d) $(xy)(p_4)$ e) the locus of $y = x + 2$

9. Sketch the locus of each of the following:
   a) $y = \begin{cases} x^2 & \text{for } 0 \leq x \leq 1 \\ x & \text{for } x > 1 \end{cases}$
   b) $y = \begin{cases} 1 & \text{for } -1 \leq x < 0 \\ -1 & \text{for } 0 < x \leq 1 \end{cases}$ c) $y = \begin{cases} x & \text{for } x < 0 \\ 0 & \text{for } x > 0 \end{cases}$
   d) $y = \begin{cases} -1 & \text{for } x < -1 \\ x & \text{for } -1 \leq x \leq 1 \\ 1 & \text{for } x > 1 \end{cases}$ e) $y = \begin{cases} 1 & \text{for } x < 1 \\ \frac{3}{2} & \text{for } x = 1 \\ 2 & \text{for } x > 1 \end{cases}$

1-7 SLOPES AND LINES

Figure 1–8 shows how two points on a line determine a right triangle. Figure 1–9 illustrates the fact that for a given line any two such triangles are similar. Thus the ratio

$$\frac{y(q) - y(p)}{x(q) - x(p)} \tag{1}$$

Fig. 1-8

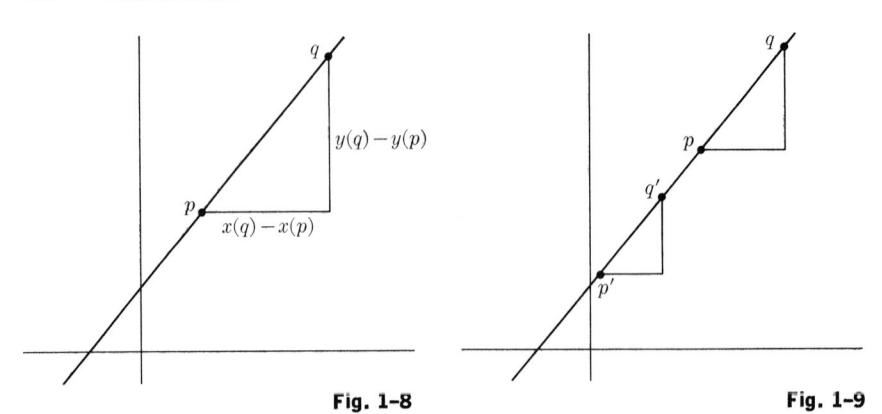

Fig. 1-9

depends only on the line chosen and not on the points p and q. This ratio is called the *slope* of the line. Note (Fig. 1-10) that slopes may be negative.

For a horizontal line the numerator in (1) is zero and for a vertical line the denominator is zero. Thus a horizontal line has 0 for a slope, while for a vertical line slope is not defined. Note carefully the distinction between "zero slope" and "no slope."

Now suppose we are given a number m and a point p_0 in the plane with coordinates (x_0, y_0). There is a unique line through p_0 with slope m. To find its equation we turn to Fig. 1-11. The point p lies on the line if and only if

$$\frac{y(p) - y_0}{x(p) - x_0} = m;$$

so the equation of the line is

$$y - y_0 = m(x - x_0) \tag{2}$$

This is known as the *point-slope form* of the straight-line equation. The

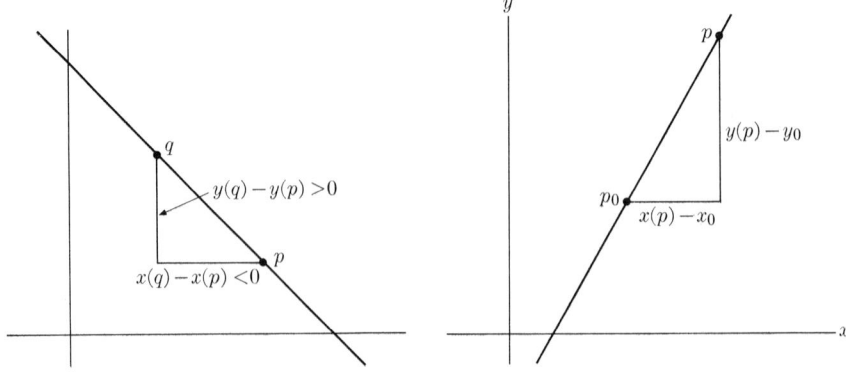

Fig. 1-10

Fig. 1-11

constants that appear in it are coordinates of a point on the line and the slope of the line.

The special case of (1) in which $x_0 = 0$ and $y_0 = b$ reads

$$y = mx + b. \tag{3}$$

This line passes through $(0, b)$ and has slope m. The number b—ordinate of the point in which the line intersects the y-axis—is called the *y-intercept* of the line. The form (2) is called the *slope-intercept form* of the straight-line equation.

Though the constants appear in different places and have different geometric significance, the forms (1) and (2) have in common the feature that each is an equation of the first degree in x and y. The general first-degree equation in x and y may be written

$$Ax + By + C = 0. \tag{4}$$

If $B \neq 0$, this may be reduced to

$$y = -\frac{A}{B}x - \frac{C}{B}, \tag{5}$$

which fits the form (2). If $B = 0$, (3) becomes

$$x = -C/A,$$

which is obviously the equation of a line parallel to the y-axis. Thus, in all cases, the graph of (4) is a straight line.

In algebra the phrase *linear equation* is used to mean an equation of the first degree. This terminology is obviously motivated by the fact just noted, that an equation of the first degree in the rectangular coordinate variables has a line for its graph. However, this coincidence between linear equations and straight lines depends on the geometric significance of the variables in the equation. In general, the notion of linearity is a strictly algebraic one—referring to the form of an equation—and the graph of a linear equation in arbitrary variables may be first one thing and then another, depending on what it is that the variables measure.

The point-slope form is useful for finding equations from geometric data. For example, let us find the equation of the line through the two points $(2, -3)$ and $(3, 4)$. The slope is

$$\frac{4 - (-3)}{3 - 2} = 7;$$

therefore the point-slope form of the required equation would read

$$y - 4 = 7(x - 3).$$

This reduces to

$$7x - y - 17 = 0.$$

Note that this could equally well have been set up with $(2, -3)$ as the point in the point-slope form:

$$y + 3 = 7(x - 2), \qquad 7x - y - 17 = 0.$$

The slope-intercept form can be used to find the slope from the equation. For example, let us find the slope of the line whose equation is $3x + 4y - 5 = 0$. Solve for y:

$$y = -\tfrac{3}{4}x + \tfrac{5}{4}.$$

This is the slope-intercept form, and in this form the slope is the coefficient of x; thus here $m = -\tfrac{3}{4}$.

EXERCISES

1. In each of the following, coordinates of two points in the plane are given. In each case plot the points and determine the slope (if any) of the line joining them.
   a) $(2, 3), (-1, 2)$
   b) $(-1, 4), (6, 7)$
   c) $(4, 1), (4, -2)$
   d) $(2, -1), (4, 0)$
   e) $(0, 0), (-2, 1)$
   f) $(3, 2), (-2, 2)$
   g) $(-2, -1), (4, -3)$
   h) $(3, -2), (4, 1)$
   i) $(2, -3), (3, -2)$
   j) $(1, 4), (-5, 2)$

2. On a clock face let h be the slope of the hour hand and m the slope of the minute hand. For each of the following times of day list, in increasing order, h, m, and zero.
   a) 8:20
   b) 7:10
   c) 1:25
   d) 4:05
   e) 9:10
   f) 2:05
   g) 1:55
   h) 3:25
   i) 11:10
   j) 10:05
   k) 12:25
   l) 12:35
   m) 4:20
   n) 4:25
   o) 7:40

3. Find the equation of the line through each of the following pairs of points.
   a) $(1, 1), (2, 3)$
   b) $(-1, -1), (-2, -3)$
   c) $(0, 0), (5, -1)$
   d) $(2, -10), (-5, 1)$
   e) $(7, -4), (-1, -4)$
   f) $(2, -1), (-4, -7)$
   g) $(-3, 5), (2, 4)$
   h) $(1, \sqrt{3}), (\sqrt{3}, 1)$
   i) $(3, 4), (3, -2)$
   j) $(x_1, y_1), (x_2, y_2)$

4. For the line defined by each of the following equations find the slope and the intercepts and draw a sketch.
   a) $2x - 3y + 5 = 0$
   b) $5x + 4y + 7 = 0$
   c) $4y - 5x + 8 = 0$
   d) $3y - 4 = 0$
   e) $2y + 3 = 0$
   f) $x + 5y - 10 = 0$
   g) $3x - 6y - 5 = 0$
   h) $2y - 3x - 9 = 0$
   i) $3x + 4y = 0$
   j) $5x - 7y = 0$

LOGIC 2

2-1 LOGICAL POSSIBILITIES

"Christmas is on Sunday." Is this true or false? Obviously, it depends on what year we are talking about. For the 16-year period 1951–66 the day of the week for Christmas is as follows.

1951 Tue.	1955 Sun.	1959 Fri.	1963 Wed.
1952 Thur.	1956 Tue.	1960 Sun.	1964 Fri.
1953 Fri.	1957 Wed.	1961 Mon.	1965 Sat.
1954 Sat.	1958 Thur.	1962 Tue.	1966 Sun.

Thus our opening assertion is true for 1955, 1960, and 1966 and false for the other years of this period.

The first point to be noted in this introduction to elementary logic is that statements such as "Christmas is on Sunday" are not to be regarded as assertions of fact but as the objects of mathematical study. The first step in studying such statements is to list the logical possibilities for background and determine for each possible background situation the truth or falsity of each statement to be studied.

There are various factors involved in this process of listing logical possibilities that are best pointed out by means of further examples. Let us continue to consider the years 1951–66. This is an artificial restriction that must be regarded simply as part of the statement of the problem. Thus, while 1492 was a very real year, it is not to be regarded as a logical possibility in this problem. As suggested above, we could list 16 possible cases and find that "Christmas is on Sunday" is true in 3 of them and false in the other 13. This suggests that, for an analysis of "Christmas is on Sunday," a greatly simplified listing would suffice.

Year	C. on Sun.
1955, 1960, 1966	T
Other years	F

Now, let us look at some *unsatisfactory* listings. Note first of all that we do not say here that 1955, 1960, and 1966 are the only logically possible cases. They are the only cases for which our statement is true, but in the study of logic the cases of falsity are just as important as those of truth. For another illustration, note that the dates in our list that are divisible by 3 are 1953, 1956, 1959, 1962, 1965. Suppose we try

Year	C. on Sun.
1955, 1960, 1966	T
Divisible by 3	F

Even though it displays both true and false cases for our statement, this is *not* a proper listing because it does not cover all possibilities. The listing

Year	C. on Sun.
1951–1954	F
Divisible by 3	F
1955, 1960, 1966	T
Other years	F

is also unacceptable because the first two cases have 1953 in common. Note, finally, the following abortive attempt at a listing.

Year	C. on Sun.
1951–1959	?
1960–1966	?

This is obviously unsatisfactory because the cases listed do not distinguish between truth and falsity of our statement.

A pattern begins to emerge here. A listing of logical possibilities in conjunction with a given statement should have the following properties.

1. It should list all possibilities.

2. The cases listed should be mutually exclusive.

3. For each case listed the given statement should be either definitely true or definitely false.

Usually we shall be concerned with more than one statement in connection with a given possibility listing. The point to be noted here is that the division into cases must be fine enough to distinguish between truth and falsity for each statement separately.

For example, continuing our discussion of the years 1951–66, let us consider the two statements "Christmas is on Sunday" and "It is leap year." A little experimentation shows that the following is a minimal acceptable listing.

Year	C. on Sun.	Leap year
1960	T	T
1955, 1966	T	F
1952, 1958, 1964	F	T
Other years	F	F

It should be apparent from these examples that an appropriate listing of two cases will suffice to analyze a simple statement, that four cases can be made to do for two statements, and in general that n statements can be analyzed with the right 2^n cases. It is important to note, however, that in some problems not all these cases actually materialize. For example (still referring to 1951–1966), consider the statements "Christmas is on Sunday" and "The date is divisible by 19." The only date in our list that is divisible by 19 is 1957; so we have the following three-case listing.

Year	C. on Sun.	Div. by 19
1955, 1960, 1966	T	F
1957	F	T
Other years	F	F

EXERCISES

1. Because of the way most classes are scheduled, the students at a certain university think of the days of the week as coming in three groups:

> Lecture days — Monday, Wednesday, Friday
> Lab days — Tuesday, Thursday
> Weekend days — Saturday, Sunday

Still referring to the years 1951–66, give a list of logical possibilities for the analysis of each of the following sets of statements.

a) Christmas is on a weekend day; it is an even-numbered year.
b) Christmas is on a lab day; it is a leap year.
c) It is a leap year; the date is divisible by 3.
d) Christmas is on a lecture day; it is an even-numbered year; it is a leap year.
e) Christmas is on a lab day; it is an even-numbered year; the date is divisible by 3.
f) Christmas is on a weekend day; it is an odd-numbered year; it is in the 1960's.
g) Christmas is on a lab day; it is an even-numbered year; it is in the 1950's.
h) Christmas is on a weekend day; the date is divisible by 5; it is an even-numbered year.

2. If two dice are thrown, an appropriate list of logical possibilities is the set of all ordered pairs (a, b) [$a = 1, 2, \ldots, 6$; $b = 1, 2, \ldots, 6$]. The physical significance is that the first die shows a and the second shows b. Give an appropriate grouping of these possibilities to analyze each of the following sets of statements.
   a) The total is 6.
   b) The total is 7; the first die shows 4.
   c) The total is 4; the first die shows 4.
   d) One die shows 3; the total is 7.
   e) The first die shows an odd number; the two dice show the same; the total is 6.
   f) The first die shows 2; the second die shows 5; the total is 6.
   g) One die shows 3; one die shows 4; the total is 7.

3. In the game of craps, if the player with the dice throws a 6 (total) on his first throw, he continues to throw the dice until he repeats his 6 or throws a 7. If he throws the second 6 first, he wins; if he throws a 7 first, he loses. Assume that the player with the dice has thrown a 6 on his first throw. Which of the 36 ordered pairs from Exercise 2 constitute logical possibilities for finishing the game? On how many of these does the player with the dice win?

4. List logical possibilities for analysis of the two statements, "Sarah and Mary are sisters" and "Susie is older than Sally," given restrictions as follows.
   a) No restrictions; the four names can refer to any four girls.
   b) Mary and Susie are sisters.
   c) Sarah and Sally are the same person; Sally is a nickname.
   d) Both (b) and (c) hold.

2–2 BASIC CONNECTIVES

"It is leap year and Christmas is on Sunday." Reference to the table at the beginning of Section 2–1 shows that for the period 1951–66 this statement is true for 1960 and false for all other years. Note two things about the opening sentence here.

1. It is a statement sometimes true, sometimes false, just like the statements considered in Section 2–1.

2. It is a *compound statement* consisting of two statements taken from Section 2–1 connected by the conjunction "and."

The brief introduction to logic in this chapter consists primarily of showing how the study of compound statements can be put in a mathematical framework. One of the first points to note is (item 1 above) that a compound statement is itself a statement; so we shall often discuss the compounding of compound statements. Indeed (see Exercise 1 below) it is not a good idea to try to distinguish between "simple" (noncompound) and compound statements. Rather, a *statement* is something that *has truth values* (is either true or false for each logical possibility) and the mathematical problem is to find truth values for compounds, given truth values for the component parts.

The basic logical connectives are "and," "or," and "not." The first step in the mathematical study of logic is to put compound statements in symbolic form. The symbols for the connectives are as follows:

$$\text{and}: \land$$
$$\text{or}: \lor$$
$$\text{not}: \sim$$

Now we put a compound statement in symbolic form by using a single letter to denote each component part and joining the letters by these connective symbols. For example, let p and q stand for statements as follows:

p: It is leap year.

q: Christmas is on Sunday.

We then have these symbolic representations for certain compound statements.

$p \land q$: It is leap year and Christmas is on Sunday.

$p \lor \sim q$: Either it is leap year or Christmas is not on Sunday.

$\sim(p \land q)$: It is not true that it is leap year and that Christmas is on Sunday.

The connective $\land$ is called *conjunction*. That is, $p \land q$ is called the conjunction of p and q. The compound $p \lor q$ is called the *disjunction* of p and q. Sometimes $\lor$ is called inclusive disjunction because the interpretation of $p \lor q$ is "p or q or both." By contrast, exclusive disjunction (which we shall not use here) would mean "one or the other but not both." If we want the exclusive disjunction of p and q we shall write it $(p \lor q) \land \sim(p \land q)$. The connective $\sim$ is called *negation;* $\sim p$ is the negation of p.

We begin the systematic study of connectives in Section 2-3. Before doing that we should note some of the contrasts between the rigid forms of symbolic logic and the vagaries of colloquial English. Negation often is rendered into English without the use of the word "not." Example:

p: I will pass this course.

$\sim p$: I will fail this course.

36 LOGIC

Mathematical symbols can also suppress the word "not." Example:

$$p: x < y.$$
$$\sim p: x \geq y.$$

The connective $\wedge$ may not appear as "and" in English. A common substitute is "but." Example:

$$p: \text{It is warm.}$$
$$q: \text{It is raining.}$$
$$p \wedge q: \text{It is warm but raining.}$$

"Either ... or ..." and "Neither ... nor ..." are also tricky. Note that "Either p or q" means

$$p \vee q,$$

whereas "Neither p nor q" means

$$\sim p \wedge \sim q.$$

EXERCISES

1. Referring to the years 1951–66, let p_n be the statement "It is the year n." Let q be "Christmas is on Sunday." Compare q with the statement

$$p_{1955} \vee p_{1960} \vee p_{1966}.$$

   Is q a simple or a compound statement?

2. In each part of Exercise 1, Section 2–1, either two or three statements are given. Where there are two, call them p and q; where there are three, call them p, q, and r. For each part below refer to the corresponding part of Exercise 1, Section 2–1, and translate the given compound statement into English. In each case list the years for which the compound statement is true.
    a) $p \wedge q$ [*Answer:* Christmas is on a weekend day and it is an even-numbered year. True in 1954, 1960, 1966.]
    b) $p \wedge \sim q$ c) $\sim p \vee q$
    d) $p \wedge q \wedge \sim r$ e) $\sim p \wedge (q \vee r)$
    f) $p \vee (\sim q \wedge r)$ g) $p \wedge \sim(q \vee r)$
    h) $(\sim p \wedge \sim q) \vee r$

3. Write each of the following compound statements in symbolic form. In each case define precisely what your letters stand for.
    a) John is older than Mary but younger than Jim.

b) I will either pass this course or have to go to summer school.
c) He can neither read nor write.
d) It is not raining but snowing.
e) John is older than both Jim and Mary.
f) John is older than neither Jim nor Mary.
g) The weather is not both hot and humid.
h) The weather is either cool or dry.

4. Let p be "John will pass this course" and let q be "Jim will pass this course."
   a) Compare for meaning the two statements, "John will pass this course" and "John will not fail this course."
   b) Write the two statements of part (a) in symbolic form.
   c) Compare for meaning the two statements, "John or Jim will pass this course" and "John and Jim will not both fail this course."
   d) Write the two statements of part (c) in symbolic form.
   e) Compare for meaning the two statements, "John and Jim will both pass this course" and "It is not true that either John or Jim will fail this course."
   f) Write the two statements of part (e) in symbolic form.

2-3 TRUTH TABLES

In Section 2-1 we listed logical possibilities in terms of the content of specific statements. We now want to study some general procedures for determining truth values. So let p be a statement (any statement); what are the logical possibilities for its analysis? With no more information than this, all we can list is

$$\begin{array}{c} p \\ T \\ F \end{array} \qquad (1)$$

Let p and q be statements; the obvious list now is

$$\begin{array}{cc} p & q \\ T & T \\ T & F \\ F & T \\ F & F \end{array} \qquad (2)$$

If all four of the possibilities listed in (2) can actually materialize, we say that p and q are *logically independent*. To study compound statements in general, we always assume that the component parts are logically independent. In a specific application, if a certain case is impossible we merely delete a row from the table. If we have three logically independent

38 LOGIC

statements p, q, and r, the list of possibilities is

p	q	r
T	T	T
T	T	F
T	F	T
T	F	F
F	T	T
F	T	F
F	F	T
F	F	F

(3)

Now a *truth table* for a compound statement is a listing of logical possibilities such as (1), (2), or (3), followed by another column giving the corresponding truth values for the compound statement. Thus the truth tables for the three basic compounds are

p	q	$p \wedge q$		p	q	$p \vee q$		p	$\sim p$
T	T	T		T	T	T		T	F
T	F	F		T	F	T		F	T
F	T	F		F	T	T			
F	F	F		F	F	F			

(4)

Note that the row T T T in the table for $p \vee q$ makes $\vee$ the inclusive disjunction connective. For the exclusive disjunction, this row would read T T F.

Using the truth tables in (4) as references, we can find a truth table for any compound statement. The following examples will serve to explain the method.

Suppose we want a truth table for $\sim p \vee q$. We write the statement out across the top of our work sheet, leaving space between symbols because each symbol is to be the head of a column.

$$\sim \quad p \quad \vee \quad q$$

Under p and q we fill in the logical possibilities, always following the format in (2). At the second stage our work sheet looks like this.

$\sim$	p	$\vee$	q
	T		T
	T		F
	F		T
	F		F

2-3 TRUTH TABLES

Now we consider the connectives in the order indicated by parentheses or understood parentheses. In this problem the understanding is $(\sim p) \vee q$; apply $\sim$ to p first, then combine the result with q by $\vee$. So in the column labeled $\sim$, we fill in what the last table in (4) gives us for each entry in the p column.

$\sim$	p	$\vee$	q
F	~~T~~		T
F	~~T~~		F
T	~~F~~		T
T	~~F~~		F

Here we have drawn a line through the p column to remind us not to use it again. This device is hardly needed here, but is quite helpful in longer problems. Finally, now, we fill in under $\vee$ the results obtained by applying the second table in (4) to the two working columns ($\sim$ and q).

$\sim$	p	$\vee$	q
~~F~~	~~T~~	T	~~T~~
~~F~~	~~T~~	F	~~F~~
~~T~~	~~F~~	T	~~T~~
~~T~~	~~F~~	T	~~F~~

We scratch out the used columns and the one that remains is our "answer." That is, we take the standard possibility list (2) and put this answer column with it to get a truth table.

p	q	$\sim p \vee q$
T	T	T
T	F	F
F	T	T
F	F	T

Let us consider another example.

$\sim$ ($\sim$	p	$\wedge$	$\sim$	q)
	T			T
	T			F
	F			T
	F			F

40 LOGIC

[Note: The parentheses will not be column heads; they merely indicate the order of procedure.] Next stage for this work sheet:

$$\sim(\sim p \land \sim q)$$

	~	p	∧	~	q
	F	T		F	T
	F	T		T	F
	T	F		F	T
	T	F		T	F

Third stage:

	~	p	∧	~	q
	F T	F	F T
	F T	F	T F
	T F	F	F T
	T F	T	T F

Final stage:

	~	(~	p	∧	~	q)
	T	F T	F	F T
	T	F T	F	T F
	T	T F	F	F T
	F	T F	T	T F

Answer:

p	q	~(~p ∧ ~q)
T	T	T
T	F	T
F	T	T
F	F	F

Note that this result is exactly the same as the table for $p \lor q$ given in (4). If two compound statements have identical truth tables, we say that they are *logically equivalent*. Thus we have just seen that $p \lor q$ is logically equivalent to $\sim(\sim p \land \sim q)$. This points up a fact that should be noted. We said in Section 2-2 that there were three basic logical connectives. Now it appears that there are really only two, because $\lor$ could be defined in terms of $\sim$ and $\land$. However, as a practical matter, it is just as well to regard all three of the truth tables in (4) as basic working tools.

2-3 TRUTH TABLES

Finally, let us look at an example with three independent statements.

(p	∧	q)	∨	(~	q	∧	r)
T		T		F	T		T
T		T		F	T		F
T		F		T	F		T
T		F		T	F		F
F		T		F	T		T
F		T		F	T		F
F		F		T	F		T
F		F		T	F		F

(p	∧	q)	∨	(~	q	∧	r)
T	T	T		F	T	F	T
T	T	T		F	T	F	F
T	F	F		T	F	T	T
T	F	F		T	F	F	F
F	F	T		F	T	F	T
F	F	T		F	T	F	F
F	F	F		T	F	T	T
F	F	F		T	F	F	F

(p	∧	q)	∨	(~	q	∧	r)
T	T	T	T	F	T	F	T
T	T	T	T	F	T	F	F
T	F	F	T	T	F	T	T
T	F	F	F	T	F	F	F
F	F	T	F	F	T	F	T
F	F	T	F	F	T	F	F
F	F	F	T	T	F	T	T
F	F	F	F	T	F	F	F

p	q	r	$(p \wedge q) \vee (\sim q \wedge r)$
T	T	T	T
T	T	F	T
T	F	T	T
T	F	F	F
F	T	T	F
F	T	F	F
F	F	T	T
F	F	F	F

EXERCISES

1. Find the truth table for each of the following compound statements.
   - a) $p \vee \sim q$
   - b) $p \wedge \sim q$
   - c) $(\sim p \vee q) \wedge (p \vee \sim q)$
   - d) $(p \wedge q) \vee (\sim p \wedge \sim q)$
   - e) $(p \wedge q) \vee \sim q$
   - f) $(p \vee q) \wedge \sim q$
   - g) $(p \wedge \sim q) \vee (\sim p \wedge q)$
   - h) $(p \vee q) \wedge (\sim p \vee \sim q)$
   - i) $p \wedge q \vee \sim r$
   - j) $p \vee \sim(q \wedge r)$
   - k) $(p \wedge \sim r) \vee \sim(q \vee r)$
   - l) $\sim(p \vee \sim q \wedge r)$

2. Show how conjunction could be defined in terms of negation and disjunction and show that your definition is logically equivalent to that already given.

3. In the comments immediately following the list (4) of basic truth tables, a truth table for exclusive disjunction was described. Show that the statement with such a truth table is logically equivalent to $(p \vee q) \wedge \sim(p \wedge q)$.

4. Show that there are exactly 16 logically different compounds of two logically independent statements. When one uses three statements, how many compounds are there?

2-4 CONDITIONALS

"If Jim fails this course, then he will go on scholastic probation." Let us examine the possible grade reports and actions of the Scholastic Standing Committee and determine the cases of truth and falsity for this statement.

1. Suppose Jim fails and is put on probation. Our opening statement is then certainly true.

2. Suppose Jim fails but the committee is feeling lenient and does not put him on probation. This is exactly what we asserted would not happen; so in this case our opening statement is false.

3. Suppose Jim passes his course. He might go on probation for failing another course or he might not. In either case our assertion is not contradicted, so we shall say it is true.

This example introduces another connective called the *conditional*. It is denoted by $\rightarrow$, and we read $p \rightarrow q$ as "If p, then q" or as "p implies q." In items 1–3 above we agreed that the truth table will be:

p	q	$p \rightarrow q$
T	T	T
T	F	F
F	T	T
F	F	T

(1)

Conditionals are sufficiently important that (1) should be added to the list of basic truth tables.

In the conditional statement $p \to q$, it is common to refer to p as the hypothesis and q as the conclusion. In adopting the truth table (1), we are agreeing that whenever the hypothesis is false the conditional is true. This is the interpretation of the conditional that is commonly used in logic and mathematics.

Suppose the dean is going to warn Jim that failure in this course will result in probation. He might well word the warning, "Either you pass this course or you go on scholastic probation." Here the dean is still saying

$$p \to q$$

but he is putting it in the form

$$\sim p \lor q.$$

Comparison of (1) in this section with (5) in Section 2–3 shows that these are indeed logically equivalent statements. Thus $\to$ is not a new basic connective; it is merely a much-used combination of $\sim$ and $\lor$.

Look at the following examples of truth-table problems.

(p	$\lor$	q)	$\to$	(p	$\land$	q)
T	T	T	T	T	T	T
T	T	F	F	T	F	F
F	T	T	F	F	F	T
F	F	F	T	F	F	F

(p	$\land$	q)	$\to$	(p	$\lor$	q)
T	T	T	T	T	T	T
T	F	F	T	T	T	F
F	F	T	T	F	T	T
F	F	F	T	F	F	F

Now "p or q implies p and q" is a perfectly respectable compound statement. We find that it is true in two of the four logically possible cases and false in the other two. On the other hand, "p and q implies p or q" is true in all logically possible cases. This does not give $(p \land q) \to (p \lor q)$ any special status among conditional statements, but it does lead to a new idea. We say that p *logically implies* q (and write this symbolically $p \Rightarrow q$), provided the conditional $p \to q$ is true in all logically possible cases. Thus the second truth table above shows that

$$(p \land q) \Rightarrow (p \lor q).$$

We have introduced the following symbols and terminology.

44 LOGIC

The conditional statement:

$$p \to q;$$
$$\text{if } p, \text{ then } q;$$
$$p \text{ implies } q.$$

The logical implication relation:

$$p \Rightarrow q;$$
$$p \text{ logically implies } q.$$

It is essential to distinguish between $p \to q$ and $p \Rightarrow q$. Note that in a discussion of logic these appear in quite different connections. The conditional, $p \to q$, is merely something we talk about. It has a truth table with some T's and an F in it. The conditional is not a statement of fact; it is an object of study. By contrast, the logical implication, $p \Rightarrow q$, is not something to be studied; it is an announcement of the result of such a study. Thus $p \to q$ is merely something we talk about; $p \Rightarrow q$ is a statement we make with the idea of conveying a message.

As we continue this discussion of logic, we must be careful to distinguish between $\to$ and $\Rightarrow$. However, $\Rightarrow$ is the only one of these notions to appear extensively in mathematics outside formal logic, and there logical implication is most commonly described by a simple "if ... then ..." Thus our five distinctions in language are valid for the rest of this chapter, but not outside it.

The *biconditional* is a connective denoted by $\leftrightarrow$ and read "if and only if" or "is equivalent to." It is defined by the following truth table.

p	q	$p \leftrightarrow q$
T	T	T
T	F	F
F	T	F
F	F	T

This says that $p \leftrightarrow q$ is true whenever p and q have the same truth values and false whenever they have different truth values. From this we can easily see that the notion of logical equivalence introduced in Section 2–3 bears the same relation to the biconditional that logical implication does to the conditional. That is, p and q are logically equivalent (symbolically, $p \Leftrightarrow q$), provided the biconditional $p \leftrightarrow q$ is true in all logically possible cases.

Again we have a list of symbols and terminology.

The biconditional statement:

$$p \leftrightarrow q;$$
$$p \text{ if and only if } q;$$
$$p \text{ is equivalent to } q.$$

The logical equivalence relation:

$$p \Leftrightarrow q;$$
$$p \text{ is logically equivalent to } q.$$

EXERCISES

1. Find the truth table for each of the following compound statements.
   a) $p \to {\sim}q$
   b) ${\sim}p \to q$
   c) ${\sim}(p \leftrightarrow {\sim}q)$
   d) $(p \to q) \to (p \leftrightarrow q)$
   e) $(p \to q) \to (q \to p)$
   f) $(p \to q) \leftrightarrow (q \to p)$
   g) $(p \land q) \to r$
   h) $(p \lor q) \leftrightarrow r$
   i) $(q \land {\sim}r) \to {\sim}p$

2. Prove each of the following logical implications by finding an "all true" truth table for the appropriate conditional.
   a) $p \Rightarrow (p \lor q)$
   b) $(p \land q) \Rightarrow q$
   c) $(p \leftrightarrow q) \Rightarrow (p \to q)$
   d) $(p \leftrightarrow {\sim}q) \Rightarrow (p \lor q)$
   e) $[(p \to q) \land (q \to r)] \Rightarrow (p \to r)$
   f) $[p \to (q \to r)] \Rightarrow [(p \to q) \to (p \to {}^\cdot r)]$

3. Prove that $(p \land {\sim}p) \Rightarrow q$. Let p be "Thanksgiving is on Thursday" and let q be "New York City is in Central Siberia."

4. Prove each of the following logical equivalences.
   a) ${\sim}(p \lor q) \Leftrightarrow ({\sim}p \land {\sim}q)$
   b) $({\sim}q \lor p) \Leftrightarrow (q \to p)$
   c) $[(p \land q) \to r] \Leftrightarrow [(q \land {\sim}r) \to {\sim}p]$

5. "p if and only if q" is logically equivalent to "if p then q and if q then p."
   a) Write this out in symbols and prove it.
   b) Of the two conditionals $p \to q$ and $q \to p$, one can be read "p if q" and the other "p only if q." Which is which?

6. "The refrigerator light is on only if the door is open."
   a) Write this statement in symbols.
   b) In a normally manufactured refrigerator, the light switch is forced off when you close the door. When you open the door the switch goes on (unless its spring is broken) and this turns on the light (unless the bulb is burned out or the house current is off). List the logical possibilities for the statement being considered here.

46 LOGIC

c) Show from part (b) that the opening statement in this exercise can actually be regarded as a statement of logical implication.

d) Discuss the distinction between causality and logical implication as illustrated in this example. (Do you turn on the light by opening the door or open the door by turning on the light?)

2-5 FURTHER APPLICATIONS OF CONDITIONALS

Suppose we are asked to prove that if n^2 is an odd integer, then n is an odd integer. The simple way is to assume that n is even; that is, that $n = 2k$. Then $n^2 = 4k^2$ and is clearly even.

This proves it, but let us see exactly what we have proved. Put the problem into logical symbols:

$$p \text{ --- } n^2 \text{ is odd};$$
$$q \text{ --- } n \text{ is odd},$$
$$\sim p \text{ --- } n^2 \text{ is even},$$
$$\sim q \text{ --- } n \text{ is even}.$$

We were asked to prove
$$p \to q;$$
what we did was to prove
$$\sim q \to \sim p.$$

A little work with truth tables shows that this suffices.

$\sim$	q	$\to$	$\sim$	p
F	T	T	F	T
T	F	F	F	T
F	T	T	T	F
T	F	T	T	F

Now, T F T T is the truth table for $p \to q$; so

$$(p \to q) \Leftrightarrow (\sim q \to \sim p).$$

The statement $\sim q \to \sim p$ is called the *contrapositive* of $p \to q$. In our little number-theory problem we were asked to prove a conditional statement; instead we proved its contrapositive. Since contrapositives are logically equivalent, this solves the problem. This procedure is used quite often in mathematics. It is frequently referred to as *proof by contradiction*. We prove an implication by showing that the contradiction (which just means negation) of the conclusion implies the contradiction of the hypothesis. In the language of logic, this method of proof is summarized very succinctly: Prove the contrapositive instead.

The *converse* of the conditional statement $p \to q$ is the statement

$$q \to p.$$

Note that the contrapositive of the converse is

$$\sim p \to \sim q.$$

Contrapositives are logically equivalent, but converses bear no particular logical relation one to the other. Therefore, when one is organizing logical arguments, it is essential that the following four conditional statements be kept firmly separated into two groups.

$$\text{Group I:} \quad (p \to q) \Leftrightarrow (\sim q \to \sim p).$$
$$\text{Group II:} \quad (q \to p) \Leftrightarrow (\sim p \to \sim q).$$

This sounds simple, but mathematicians try to complicate the issue by introducing variant renderings of the conditional into English. The most common of these come from breaking down natural expressions for the biconditional. That is,

$$(p \leftrightarrow q) \Leftrightarrow [(p \to q) \wedge (q \to p)];$$

so an expression for $p \leftrightarrow q$ with an "and" in it yields expressions for $p \to q$ and $q \to p$. The problem is to keep them straight. There are two major examples of this.

1. $p \leftrightarrow q$: p if and only if q.
   $p \to q$: p only if q.
   $q \to p$: p if q.
2. $p \leftrightarrow q$: p is necessary and sufficient that q.
   $p \to q$: p is sufficient that q.
   $q \to p$: p is necessary that q.

Just to complicate matters a little more, "p is sufficient that q" is also written, "In order that q, it is sufficient that p."

EXERCISES

1. Let m and n be positive integers. Prove that if mn is odd, then m and n are both odd.
2. Let m and n be positive integers. Prove that if $m + n < 100$, then m and n are each less than 100.

3. The board of governors of the country club removed from club committees all members whose dues were in arrears. Which of the following statements about club member Jones reflect this action by the board?
   a) Jones is on a committee if his dues are paid up.
   b) In order for Jones to be on a committee, it is necessary that his dues be paid up.
   c) For Jones's dues to be in arrears, it is sufficient that he not be on a committee.
   d) If Jones is not on a committee, then his dues are in arrears.
   e) Jones is on a committee only if his dues are paid up.
   f) Jones's membership on a committee is a necessary condition that his dues be paid up.
   g) Jones is not on a committee only if his dues are in arrears.
   h) If Jones is on a committee, then his dues are paid up.
4. Let n be a positive integer. In the first paragraph of this section we proved half of each of the following statements. In each case identify the half proved in terms of the connecting words used in the statement.
   a) For n^2 to be odd it is necessary and sufficient that n be odd.
   b) n^2 is odd if and only if n is odd.
5. In Chapter 7 (no knowledge of which is assumed here), it will be pointed out that if an algebraic system S is an integral domain, then it is a ring, but not conversely. Which of the following statements is correct?
   a) For S to be an integral domain it is necessary that S be a ring.
   b) S being an integral domain is a sufficient condition that S be a ring.
   c) S is a ring only if it is an integral domain.
   d) If S is not an integral domain, then it is not a ring.
   e) For S not to be a ring, it is necessary that it not be an integral domain.
   f) S is a ring if it is an integral domain.
6. "To win the election the Republicans must carry New York."
   a) Write this in the form "If ..., then ..."
   b) Give the contrapositive of the statement in part (a).
   c) Give the converse of the statement in part (a).
   d) Give the contrapositive of this converse statement.
7. Show that, for a given conditional statement, the converse of its contrapositive is the contrapositive of its converse.
8. We have seen that $(p \to q) \Leftrightarrow (\sim p \lor q)$.
   a) Write the contrapositive of $p \to q$ in terms of $\sim$ and $\lor$.
   b) Write the converse of $p \to q$ in terms of $\sim$ and $\lor$.
9. Show that $\sim(p \to q) \Leftrightarrow (\sim q \land p)$.
10. Using Exercise 9, write the contrapositive of $p \to (q \to r)$.
11. Use Exercise 10 to prove the following: If $x > 0$, then $x^2 = 4$ implies $x = 2$.
12. Show that
$$[(p \to q) \to (r \to s)] \Leftrightarrow [(\sim r \lor s) \lor (p \land \sim q)].$$

13. This exercise refers to Section 2–1, in particular to Exercise 1 of that section. For the years 1951–66, show that "If it is a leap year, then it is in the 1950's" logically implies "If Christmas is on a lecture day, then it is an odd-numbered year."

2-6 VENN DIAGRAMS

When two dice are thrown, the logical possibilities may be listed as the set of all ordered pairs (m, n), where $m = 1, 2, \ldots, 6$ and $n = 1, 2, \ldots, 6$. The interpretation is that m gives the number appearing on the first die and n that on the second. (If the designations "first" and "second" seem strained for the usual method of throwing two dice, imagine that one die is red and the other green.) We can picture this set of logical possibilities as in Fig. 2–1.

Fig. 2–1

Now consider the statements

p: The number on the first die is 4 or greater.

q: The number on the second die is 2 or less.

On the 6 × 6 square introduced in Fig. 2–1, it is natural to "picture these statements" as in Fig. 2–2.

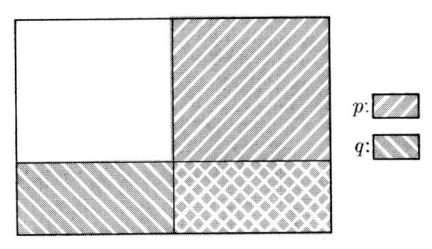

Fig. 2–2

50 LOGIC

Mathematically, this is what we are doing here. We are reverting to basic ideas of set theory and introducing as a space the set of all logical possibilities. We represent this space as a geometric point set. Any statement concerning these logical possibilities then has a *truth set*: the set of points in this space for which the statement is true. What we have done in Fig. 2–2 is to picture the truth sets for p and q.

Clearly, in Fig. 2–2 the double-cross-hatched area is the truth set for $p \wedge q$ and the entire shaded area is the truth set for $p \vee q$. In other words, we have the following pattern.

Statement	Truth set
p	P
q	Q
$p \vee q$	$P \cup Q$
$p \wedge q$	$P \cap Q$

Because of the way the words "or" and "and" appear in the definition of union and intersection, respectively, it is easily established that this is a completely general pattern.

A Venn diagram is a picture that exploits this correspondence between logical connectives and set-theoretic operations to introduce a geometric representation of compound statements. Figure 2–3 is a Venn diagram for two statements. The various areas there are labeled with the truth values as they would appear in a truth table. Figure 2–4 shows the same thing for three statements.

To get a geometric representation of $p \rightarrow q$, we write it as $\sim p \vee q$. Then it is clear that the representation is

$$p \rightarrow q: \quad -P \cup Q.$$

This is shown as the shaded area in Fig. 2–5. Now $p \Rightarrow q$ means that the

Fig. 2–3

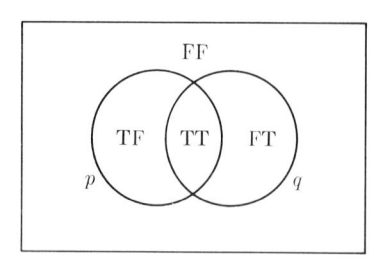

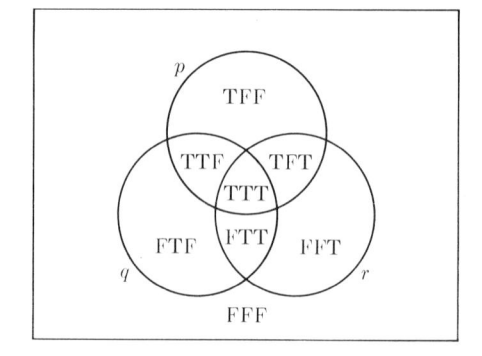

Fig. 2–4

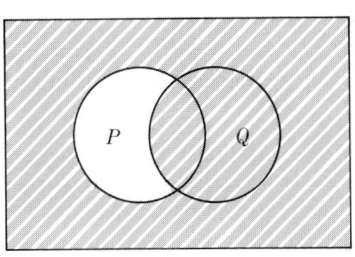

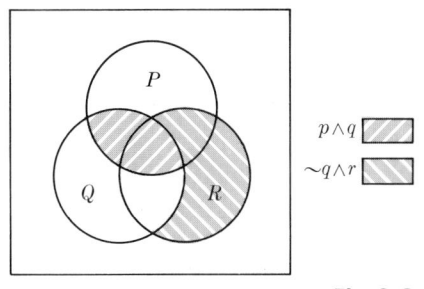

Fig. 2-5

Fig. 2-6

set for $p \to q$ is the entire space. In Fig. 2-5 the white area disappears if and only if there is a "total eclipse," with P covered by Q. So, geometrically,

$$p \Rightarrow q \quad \text{means} \quad P \subset Q.$$

Venn diagrams furnish another method for doing many of the things we do with truth tables. For example, our final illustration in Section 2-3 was to find the truth table for $(p \wedge q) \vee (\sim q \wedge r)$. The Venn diagram for this compound may be found by cross-hatching as shown in Fig. 2-6. The truth set for $(p \wedge q) \vee (\sim q \wedge r)$ is the entire shaded region. By identifying the regions in Fig. 2-6 with their labels in Fig. 2-4, we can easily check that this result is equivalent to the truth table at the end of Section 2-3.

EXERCISES

1. Repeat Exercise 1, Section 2-3, using Venn diagrams rather than truth tables. Compare results.
2. Find the Venn diagram for $p \leftrightarrow q$ and use it to show that $p \Leftrightarrow q$ means $P = Q$.
3. Repeat Exercise 1, Section 2-4, using Venn diagrams rather than truth tables. Compare results.
4. Repeat Exercise 2, Section 2-4, using Venn diagrams rather than truth tables. [*Note:* Instead of looking for an all-true table for a conditional, we are now looking for a subset relation.]
5. Repeat Exercise 4, Section 2-4, using Venn diagrams rather than truth tables. (See Exercise 2 above.)

2-7 BOOLEAN FUNCTIONS

In a sense, formal logic introduces "methods for reasoning without thinking." That is, devices like truth tables and Venn diagrams enable us to analyze compound statements purely on the basis of their form, without

52 LOGIC

regard for their content. We introduce here a third such device that accomplishes very much the same thing in a slightly different way.

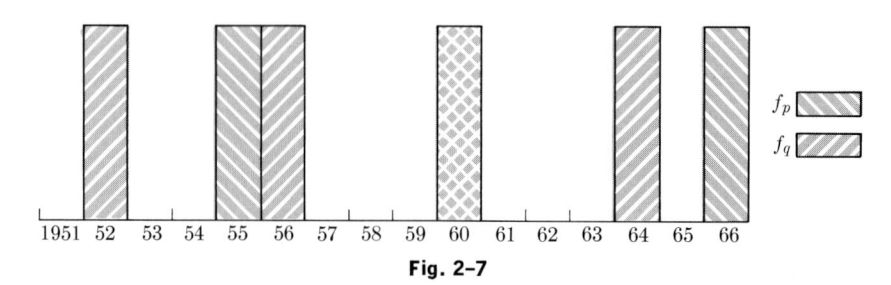

Fig. 2-7

Let S be a set of logical possibilities pertinent to a set of statements. If p is one of these statements, we define a function f_p on S as follows:

$$f_p(x) = \begin{cases} 1 & \text{if } p \text{ is true at } x, \\ 0 & \text{if } p \text{ is false at } x. \end{cases}$$

The range of f_p here looks like a pair of real numbers, but even though we use the familiar symbols 0 and 1, we want to regard this range as a different sort of structure, known as a *Boolean lattice*. We introduce an order relation by specifying that

$$0 < 1.$$

The unusual item is that we introduce an operation $\sim$, called negation, (quite different from taking a negative) by setting

$$\left.\begin{aligned}\sim 0 &= 1, \\ \sim 1 &= 0.\end{aligned}\right\} \tag{1}$$

Let us look at an example. We refer back to the example at the beginning of Section 2-1 concerning the years 1951-66. Let p be "Christmas is on Sunday" and let q be "It is a leap year." We then have the following truth sets.

$$\begin{aligned}p: &\quad 1955, 1960, 1966 \\ q: &\quad 1952, 1956, 1960, 1964 \\ p \vee q: &\quad 1952, 1955, 1956, 1960, 1964, 1966 \\ p \wedge q: &\quad 1960\end{aligned}$$

This information is shown graphically in Fig. 2-7. Note that the graph of $f_{p \vee q}$ is given by the total shaded area, while that of $f_{p \wedge q}$ is the single bar with the double cross-hatching. That is,

$$f_{p \vee q} = \max(f_p, f_q), \tag{2}$$

$$f_{p \wedge q} = \min(f_p, f_q). \tag{3}$$

Fig. 2-8 (a)

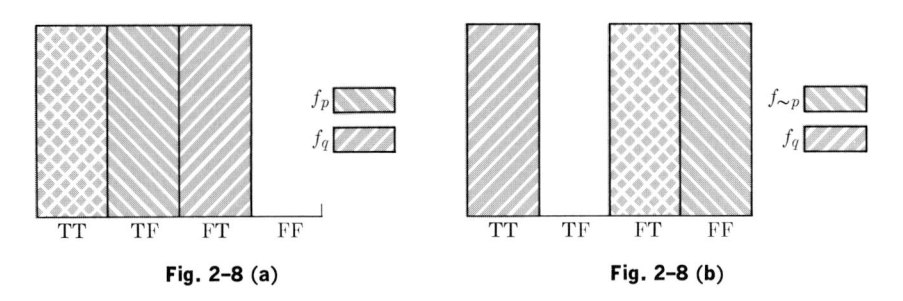

Fig. 2-8 (b)

It is further evident that the notion of negation in the Boolean lattice as defined by (1) is designated to reflect the notion of logical negation. That is,

$$f_{\sim p} = \sim f_p. \tag{4}$$

Equations (2), (3), and (4) are the basic working tools for representing compound statements by Boolean functions. Since the conditional plays such an important role, it would be helpful to have a formula for $f_{p \to q}$. To find this we recall that

$$p \to q \Leftrightarrow \sim p \vee q$$

and use (2) and (4) to find $f_{\sim p \vee q}$. The work is shown in Fig. 2-8. The logical possibilities are labeled as in a truth table. Figure 2-8(a) shows f_p and f_q, Fig. 2-8(b) shows $f_{\sim p}$ and f_q, and the maximum of these is the desired result. The bar that is blank in Fig. 2-8(b) is the one that in Fig. 2-8(a) has negative-slope cross-hatching only. Now negative-slope cross-hatching only at a point x of the domain means

$$f_p(x) > f_q(x);$$

so we have the following formula for $f_{p \to q}$:

$$f_{p \to q}(x) = \begin{cases} 1 & \text{if } f_p(x) \leq f_q(x), \\ 0 & \text{if } f_p(x) > f_q(x). \end{cases} \tag{5}$$

From this it follows that

$$p \Rightarrow q$$

if and only if

$$f_p \leq f_q$$

over the entire space of logical possibilities.

Often we find that it is easier, instead of using bar graphs, to work with Boolean functions just by tabulating their values. We turn to an example of this procedure. Suppose we want the Boolean function for $(p \wedge q) \vee (\sim q \wedge r)$ over the "natural" eight-point space of logical possibilities for three logically independent statements. We can arrange the work as follows.

I	II	III	IV	V	VI	VII
p	q	r	min (I, II)	$\sim$II	min (III, V)	max (IV, VI)
1	1	1	1	0	0	1
1	1	0	1	0	0	1
1	0	1				
1	0	0	0	1	0	0
0	1	1	0	0	0	0
0	1	0				
0	0	1	0	1	1	1
0	0	0				

The last column here is the "answer." We leave it to the reader to fill in the remaining rows and compare the result with the truth table for this same compound statement worked out at the end of Section 2–3. There is an obvious similarity between this procedure and that of working out a truth table. The principal distinction is that the mechanical step here is simply that of comparing 0's and 1's rather than referring to a "basic" truth table.

If there is a conditional in the compound, a slightly different procedure is needed. By (5) we see that this will call for comparing two columns, looking for an inequality, and recording 1 or 0 according as this inequality does or does not hold. The work sheet for $(p \to q) \to (p \wedge q)$ might look like this.

I	II	III	IV	V
p	q	I $\leq$ II?	min (I, II)	III $\leq$ IV?
1	1	1	1	1
1	0	0	0	1
0	1	1	0	0
0	0	1	0	0

EXERCISES

1. Repeat the following exercises, using Boolean functions rather than the truth tables. Compare results.
   a) Exercise 1, Section 2–3
   b) Exercise 1, Section 2–4
   c) Exercise 2, Section 2–4
   d) Exercise 4, Section 2–4

2. Let X be a space containing a single element. The subsets of X are then $\emptyset$ and X. Show that the set $\emptyset$, X forms a Boolean lattice just like the one used here if we define $\leq$ to mean $\subset$ and define negation to mean complementation.

2-8 VALID ARGUMENTS

The classical example of a logical argument (dating back to Aristotle) is

All men are mortal;

Socrates is a man.

∴ Socrates is mortal.

To analyze this in terms of symbolic logic, we must first recognize that the statement "All men are mortal" is a disguised conditional. It means, "If one is a man, then one is mortal." This is to be applied to Socrates; so we really have just two basic statements here.

p: Socrates is a man.

q: Socrates is mortal.

We then have the following combinations of these

$$\begin{array}{c} p \to q \\ p \\ \hline \therefore q \end{array} \qquad (1)$$

The argument about Socrates seems very plausible, but this might be because each of the individual statements appears to be true. Logic is concerned with form, not content, so a better question is whether or not the skeleton argument (1) is a "good" one whatever p and q might mean. We give an affirmative answer to this question on the grounds that

$$[(p \to q) \wedge p] \Rightarrow q. \qquad (2)$$

We leave it to the reader to use his favorite weapon (truth tables, Venn diagrams, Boolean functions) to check that (2) is correct.

What we have done here is the following. We have collected several statements (two in the above examples) which are called *premises*. Note that a premise may be a compound statement. We have listed these premises and drawn a line at the end of the list. Below this line we have put the "therefore" symbol (∴) followed by another statement (which, in general, may also be compound). This last statement is called the *conclusion.* The structure consisting of premises, ∴ , and conclusion is called an *argument.*

Definition. A *valid argument* is one in which the conjunction of the premises logically implies the conclusion.

Thus the argument (1) is valid because of the logical implication (2), and the opening argument about Socrates is valid because it fits the form (1) and not because of Socrates' lack of immortality.

Let us look at another example.

$$\begin{array}{r} \text{All men are mortal;} \\ \underline{\text{Socrates is mortal.}} \\ \therefore \text{Socrates is a man.} \end{array} \qquad (3)$$

This is *not* a valid argument even though both premises and the conclusion are true. This argument is in the form

$$\begin{array}{r} p \to q \\ \underline{q} \\ \therefore p \end{array} \qquad (4)$$

and this is not valid because

$$[(p \to q) \land q] \to p \qquad (5)$$

is false when p is false and q is true. We emphasize again that validity of an argument depends on form, not content. Note that if the observed truth values in (3) are assigned to the appropriate statements in (5), then (5) becomes a true statement. This is beside the point, however. The argument (3) is invalid because it is in the form (4) and (4) is invalid because (5) has a false case.

An invalid argument is also called a *fallacy.* There are two other basic outlines, one of a valid argument, the other of a fallacy.

$$\begin{array}{r} p \to q \\ \underline{\sim q} \\ \therefore \sim p \end{array} \quad \text{valid argument}$$

$$\begin{array}{r} p \to q \\ \underline{\sim p} \\ \therefore \sim q \end{array} \quad \text{fallacy}$$

Needless to say, arguments may be longer and more complex than the ones noted so far. For example:

> Monkeys can talk.
> Animals that can talk live in glass houses.
> Animals living in glass houses eat peanuts.
> ∴ Monkeys eat peanuts.

This is interesting in that it is a valid argument in which the conclusion is true and all the premises false.

EXERCISES

1. Test the validity of each of the following arguments.

    a) $p \leftrightarrow q$
    p
    ∴ q

    b) $p \lor q$
    $\sim p$
    ∴ q

    c) $p \land q$
    $\sim p \to q$
    ∴ $\sim q$

    d) $p \to q$
    $\sim q \to \sim r$
    ∴ $r \to p$

    e) $p \to q$
    $\sim r \to \sim q$
    ∴ $\sim r \to \sim p$

    f) $p \leftrightarrow q$
    $q \lor r$
    r
    ∴ $\sim p$

    g) $p \to q$
    $\sim p \to \sim q$
    $pr \sim r$
    ∴ s

    h) $\sim p \to q$
    $\sim r \to \sim q$
    ∴ $p \lor r$

2. Put each of the following arguments in symbolic form and test it for validity.

    a) I cannot pass this course without studying. If I go steady with that blonde I will not have time to study. I will not go steady with her unless I like her. I do not like blondes. Therefore I will pass this course.
    b) If I fail mathematics my allowance will be cut off. If I stop smoking my allowance will be continued. Therefore I will either pass mathematics or continue smoking.
    c) The candidate can win if he carries California. To carry California he must spend a month there campaigning. He will not campaign for a month in California. Therefore he will not win.
    d) I can pass this course only if I study. In order to graduate it is necessary that I pass this course. Therefore if I study I will graduate.
    e) To be popular I must do well in sports. If I do well in sports I cannot make good grades. If I make bad grades my father will be angry. Therefore I will be popular only if my father is angry.

2-9 POSTULATES

The following is easily seen to be a valid argument.

$$\begin{array}{l} \text{If } 1+1=2, \text{ then } 1+2=0; \\ \underline{1+1=2.} \\ \therefore 1+2=0. \end{array}$$

At first glance this looks like another of those examples of a valid argument having a false conclusion because it has a false premise. But is it? Actually, in Chapter 7 we shall see a perfectly respectable mathematical system in which $1+2=0$.

In this introduction to logic we have emphasized that false statements are just as important as true ones, and indeed in formal logic "true" and "false" do not mean very much except as labels for logically possible cases. Nevertheless, the beginner probably plays the game here with the unconscious reservation that in the "applications," things really are either true or false. Now pure mathematics is one of these "applications" of logic, but in twentieth-century mathematics "true" and "false" are not such clear-cut ideas as the novice might think.

The development of a mathematical theory is really just an elaborate and complicated example of drawing conclusions from premises via valid arguments. If little gems like the argument at the beginning of this section are good mathematics, then where does the mathematician get his premises?

The answer is an interesting story. In classical Greek mathematics (which was predominantly geometry), the premises were called *axioms*. This came from the Greek word *axioun* meaning "to deem worthy." Thus axioms were statements worthy of being believed, and it is from this source that we got the "self-evident truths" that plagued high school geometry books until quite recently. One of Euclid's axioms was that, given a line L and a point p not on L, there is one and only one line through p that does not intersect L. Non-Euclidean geometry appeared in the first part of the nineteenth century. Essentially this consisted of a model in which "line" and "point" were defined in such a way as to satisfy all the Euclidiean axioms except the one just mentioned, and in this model there were many lines through p that did not intersect L.

The details of non-Euclidean geometry are not nearly so important as the idea that there should be such a thing. Now the premises of mathematics are no longer thought of as axioms but as *postulates*, from the Latin word *postulare* meaning "to demand." Today one can demand anything of a mathematical system if it leads to an interesting and worthwhile theory. The demand that $1 + 2 = 0$ is not ridiculous; it can be quite useful.

If there is one feature that characterizes "modern" mathematics, it is the so-called postulational approach. Mathematics is not based on "true" statements but on valid arguments. So what are the mathematicians' premises? They are postulates.

EXERCISES

1. In terms of hours of the day, what is $8 + 5$?
2. The following argument is adapted from *Das Kapital* by Karl Marx. An asset has value only if it is the direct product of human labor. An asset should return a profit only if it has value. Invested capital is not the direct product of human labor. Therefore invested capital should not return a profit.
    a) Show that this is a valid argument.
    b) Most capitalists would disagree with the conclusion. On what basis can they refute it?
3. Bearing in mind that mathematics began its swing from the *axioun* to the *postulare* point of view in the early nineteenth century, comment on the following quotes from the Declaration of Independence and Lincoln's Gettysburg address.
    1776: We hold these truths to be self-evident: that all men are created equal . . .
    1863: Fourscore and seven years ago, our forefathers brought forth on this continent a new nation, conceived in liberty and dedicated to the proposition that all men are created equal.

CALCULUS 3

3-1 INTRODUCTION

Archimedes was killed in 212 B.C. during the Roman capture of Syracuse. He left instructions that his epitaph should consist of a drawing of a sphere and a cylinder. He felt that to have found formulas for the area and volume of these figures was the crowning achievement of his long scientific career. This was a strangely prophetic evaluation of Archimedes' accomplishments, for his work on areas and volumes was essentially integral calculus.

The reason calculus was not born in the third century B.C. was that Archimedes developed only one of the two basic ideas involved in the subject. For 1900 years after Archimedes, very little more was accomplished in the development of calculus. Then Newton (1642–1727) and Leibnitz (1646–1716), working independently, discovered that the study of velocities of moving particles is intimately connected with the study of areas and volumes. The study of velocities is an example of differential calculus, and the connection between this and integral calculus (the so-called fundamental theorem of calculus) is the thing that allowed the subject to flourish and blossom into the many-sided discipline that it has become since the days of Newton and Leibnitz.

It is, of course, an over-simplification to say that Newton and Leibnitz "invented" calculus. They depended heavily on their predecessors, and a great number of essential features have been added to the subject since their time. Roughly speaking, there have been two main lines of development in calculus since 1700: formal developments—the discovery of new formulas and techniques—and basic developments—the critical study of the underlying ideas and principles on which calculus is based. Though both these lines of development have proceeded (and still are proceeding) simultaneously, the eighteenth century is frequently thought of as the golden age of formal development in calculus, while the nineteenth century is regarded as the most important era of basic development. It should be noted, however, that the twentieth century has also seen a significant basic development in calculus.

An oversimplified, but suggestive, summary of this history would be to say that in the eighteenth century mathematicians got the answers, in the nineteenth a logical analysis of the intermediate steps, and in the twentieth a clear idea of the starting point. In terminology suggested by this generalization, we might characterize this chapter as an introduction to eighteenth-century calculus with twentieth-century improvements.

3-2 INTEGRALS

Figure 3-1 shows Archimedes' approach to the problem of finding the area of a circle. In terms of areas of triangles (formulas for which were known long before Archimedes' time), he found successive approximations to the area of a circle.

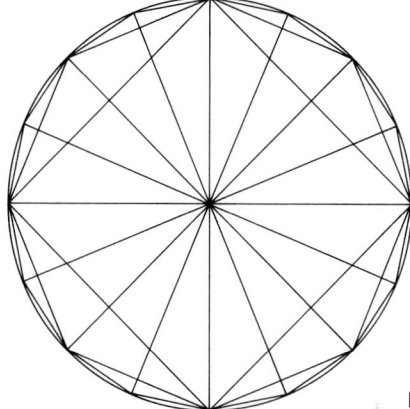

Fig. 3-1

Now no one of these approximating polygons actually gives the area of the circle. This approach to the problem can be described informally by saying that Archimedes observed a trend in the areas of the inscribed polygons as the number of sides was increased, and then discovered the end result of that trend, a result which is never actually reached. This unachieved end result is the answer to the problem.

In modern terminology Archimedes found the *limit* of the areas of the inscribed polygons. An understanding of the concept of a limit was the major nineteenth-century contribution to calculus. This is an aspect of the subject that we are omitting completely here; so we shall use the word limit with only the explanation given above: that it means the end result of a trend.

Let us look more specifically at another problem dealing with the area of a curved figure. Suppose we want the area of the shaded region shown in Fig. 3-2. An approximation method for this is suggested in Fig. 3-3.

Fig. 3-2

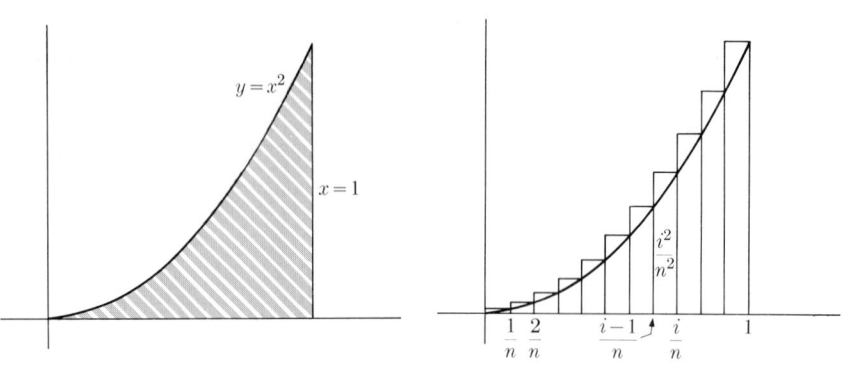

Fig. 3-3

The ith rectangle in Fig. 3–3 has base $1/n$ and altitude i^2/n^2; so the sum of the areas of the rectangles is

$$\sum_{i=1}^{n} \frac{i^2}{n^2} \cdot \frac{1}{n} = \frac{1}{n^3} \sum_{i=1}^{n} i^2.$$

Now there is a known formula for the summation involved here, specifically

$$\sum_{i=1}^{n} i^2 = \frac{n(n+1)(2n+1)}{6}.$$

Using this, we have, for the sum of the areas of the rectangles in Fig. 3–3,

$$\frac{1}{n^3} \sum_{i=1}^{n} i^2 = \frac{n(n+1)(2n+1)}{6n^3}$$

$$= \frac{1}{6} \cdot \frac{n}{n} \cdot \frac{n+1}{n} \cdot \frac{2n+1}{n} = \frac{1}{6}\left(1+\frac{1}{n}\right)\left(2+\frac{1}{n}\right).$$

From this last form (in which n appears only in denominators), the limit is reasonably apparent. Each fraction with an n in the denominator has the limit zero; so the entire expression has the limit $\frac{1}{3}$. We write this as follows:

$$\lim_{n \to \infty} \frac{1}{6}\left(1+\frac{1}{n}\right)\left(2+\frac{1}{n}\right) = \frac{1}{3}.$$

Thus the exact area under the parabola is $\frac{1}{3}$, though none of the approximating sums actually has this value.

More generally, suppose we want the area of the region bounded by three straight lines and a curve, as in Fig. 3–4. The method of attack is suggested in Fig. 3–5. Specifically, we introduce subdivision points with abscissas c_i such that

$$a = c_0 < c_1 < c_2 < \cdots < c_n = b. \tag{1}$$

Fig. 3-4

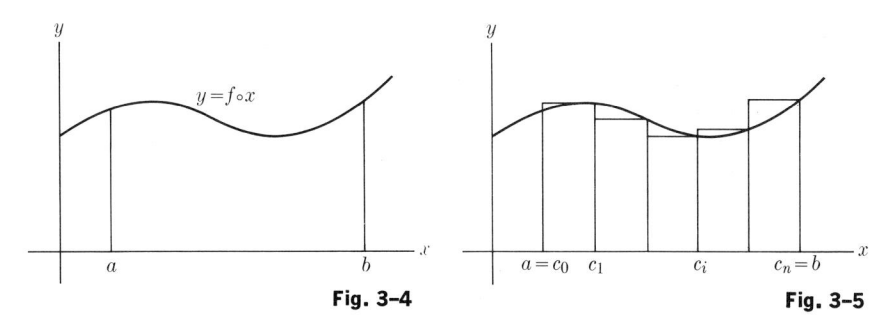

Fig. 3-5

Over each subinterval so determined, we erect a rectangle whose upper right-hand corner is on the curve. The height of the ith rectangle will be $f(c_i)$; so its area will be

$$f(c_i)(c_i - c_{i-1}).$$

Thus the total area contained in the rectangles of Fig. 3-5 will be

$$\sum_{i=1}^{n} f(c_i)(c_i - c_{i-1}). \tag{2}$$

Therefore

$$A = \lim_{n \to \infty} \sum_{i=1}^{n} f(c_i)(c_i - c_{i-1}). \tag{3}$$

The symbol A is used in (3) to suggest "area," but in general a function need not be thought of as generating an area. If the idea suggested by (3) is properly formulated and the function f has appropriate properties, then the right side of (3) denotes a *number*. The number obtained from f in this rather elaborate way is called the *integral of f from a to b*. This integral is denoted by

$$\int_a^b f.$$

It is more appropriate, then, to write

$$\int_a^b f = \lim_{n \to \infty} \sum_{i=1}^{n} f(c_i)(c_i - c_{i-1}), \tag{4}$$

and say that subject to proper interpretation of the right-hand side—details omitted—(4) serves as a definition of $\int_a^b f$.

The symbol $\int$ is called an *integral sign*. The numbers a and b appended to the integral sign are called the *limits of integration*. This terminology is unfortunate, but standard. Limits of integration must not be confused with the notion of limit as it is employed on the right-hand side of (4).

On the left-hand side of (4), there appear the limits of integration, and on the right the abscissas of the subdivision points. Note that these are related by (1). Given an appropriate sum, one sees what integral it approximates by noting what function is involved and what interval the indicated points subdivide.

For example, suppose we want to write as an integral

$$\lim_{n \to \infty} \sum_{i=1}^{n} \sqrt{1 + \left(\frac{2i}{n}\right)^2} \cdot \frac{2}{n}.$$

Set $c_i = 2i/n$; then

$$c_i - c_{i-1} = \frac{2}{n}, \qquad a = c_0 = \frac{0}{n} = 0, \qquad b = c_n = \frac{2n}{n} = 2.$$

Finally,

$$\sqrt{1 + \left(\frac{2i}{n}\right)^2} = (1 + c_i^2)^{1/2};$$

so the function must be $(I^0 + I^2)^{1/2}$. Thus the required integral is

$$\int_0^2 (I^0 + I^2)^{1/2}. \tag{5}$$

Note that the given limit of a sum could equally well be written

$$\lim_{n \to \infty} \sum_{i=1}^{n} 2\sqrt{1 + 4\left(\frac{i}{n}\right)^2} \cdot \frac{i}{n}.$$

The subdivision points could be given by

$$0, \frac{1}{n}, \frac{2}{n}, \ldots, \frac{i}{n}, \ldots, 1,$$

and the integral would be

$$\int_0^1 2(I^0 + 4I^2)^{1/2}. \tag{6}$$

Thus it appears directly from the definition that the integral in (5) is equal to that in (6). This illustrates with a simple example an important type of transformation on integrals. A more general picture of this idea will be introduced in Section 3–9.

In the initial discussion of the integral based on Fig. 3–4, we assumed that $a < b$ and that $f > 0$. Neither of these assumptions is essential to the notion of integral. The sums

$$\sum_{i=1}^{n} f(c_i)(c_i - c_{i-1})$$

are to be generated just as indicated, regardless of the signs of the numbers $f(c_i)$. If some of these are negative, the integral will not represent an area. For example, in Fig. 3-6, $\int_a^b f$ will give the area of B minus that of A.

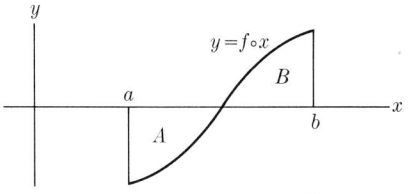

Fig. 3-6

EXERCISES

1. Write each of the following as an integral. [*Note:* Answers are not unique; see example of this type worked out in the text.]

   a) $\lim\limits_{n\to\infty} \sum\limits_{i=1}^{n} \left(\dfrac{2i}{n} - \dfrac{3i^2}{n^2}\right) \dfrac{1}{n}$

   b) $\lim\limits_{n\to\infty} \sum\limits_{i=1}^{n} \sqrt{\dfrac{i}{n}} \dfrac{1}{n}$

   c) $\lim\limits_{n\to\infty} \sum\limits_{i=1}^{n} \sqrt{3 + \dfrac{2i}{n}} \dfrac{2}{n}$

   d) $\lim\limits_{n\to\infty} \sum\limits_{i=1}^{n} \dfrac{1}{1 + \dfrac{2i}{n}} \dfrac{2}{n}$

   e) $\lim\limits_{n\to\infty} \sum\limits_{i=1}^{n} \sqrt{10i/n} \, \dfrac{10}{n}$

   f) $\lim\limits_{n\to\infty} \sum\limits_{i=1}^{n} \left(5 + \dfrac{4i}{n}\right)^3 \dfrac{4}{n}$

   g) $\lim\limits_{n\to\infty} \sum\limits_{i=1}^{n} \left(5 + \dfrac{4i}{n}\right)^3 \dfrac{2}{n}$

   h) $\lim\limits_{n\to\infty} \sum\limits_{i=1}^{n} 2^{i/n}(2^{i/n} - 2^{(i-1)/n})$

   i) $\lim\limits_{n\to\infty} \sum\limits_{i=1}^{n} 2^{3i/n}(2^{i/n} - 2^{(i-1)/n})$

   j) $\lim\limits_{n\to\infty} \sum\limits_{i=1}^{n} b^{i\alpha/n}(b^{i/n} - b^{(i-1)/n})$

2. Compute each of the following integrals. The following list gives the summation formulas that will be needed.

$$\sum_{i=1}^{n} i = \frac{n(n+1)}{2}, \quad \sum_{i=1}^{n} i^2 = \frac{n(n+1)(2n+1)}{6},$$

$$\sum_{i=1}^{n} i^3 = \frac{n^2(n+1)^2}{4}, \quad \sum_{i=1}^{n} r^i = \frac{1 - r^{n+1}}{1 - r}.$$

   a) $\int_0^1 I^2$
   b) $\int_0^1 I^3$
   c) $\int_2^3 I$
   d) $\int_2^3 I^3$

   e) $\int_a^b I^3$
   f) $\int_a^b I^0$
   g) $\int_1^3 (2I^2 - 3I)$
   h) $\int_2^3 (I^3 - I^0)$

   i) $\int_1^b I^k$, where k is a positive integer. [*Hint:* try the subdivision points 1, $b^{1/n}, b^{2/n}, \ldots, b^{i/n}, \ldots, b$.]

   j) $\int_a^b I^k$, where k is a positive integer.

3. In each of the following determine, without computing the integral, whether it is positive or negative.

a) $\int_0^1 I^4$ b) $\int_1^2 (I^2 - 4I^0)$ c) $\int_0^{-1} I^2$ d) $\int_{-2}^{-1} I^3$ e) $\int_0^{-2} I$

f) $\int_2^1 I^3$ g) $\int_{-1}^2 I^4$ h) $\int_1^{-2} I^2$ i) $\int_1^{-1} (I - I^0)$ j) $\int_{-3}^{-2} I^2$

3-3 DERIVATIVES

A particle starts from the origin at time $t = 0$ and moves out the x-axis in such a way that at any time t, its abscissa is t^2. We want to determine the instantaneous speed of the particle at an arbitrary time t. It is this type of motion problem that led Newton and Leibnitz into calculus.

Since the particle is picking up speed as it goes, our simultaneous time–distance readings do not yield speed values directly. However, we can solve the problem in the following way. At time $t + h$ the particle has abscissa $(t + h)^2$ and at time t it has abscissa t^2; so over this time interval (elapsed time h), it travels a distance

$$(t + h)^2 - t^2.$$

Therefore its average speed over this time interval is

$$\frac{(t + h)^2 - t^2}{h}.$$

To find the instantaneous speed at time t, we take this expression for average speed and find its limit as the elapsed time h is taken to be smaller and smaller. The following simple algebra allows us to see this limit quite easily:

$$\frac{(t + h)^2 - t^2}{h} = \frac{t^2 + 2th + h^2 - t^2}{h} = \frac{2th + h^2}{h} = 2t + h.$$

Clearly, the speed at time t is $2t$.

Look at another problem. In Fig. 3–7 we want to know the slope of the tangent line T. It appears from the figure that the slope of the chord C is

$$\frac{(x + h)^2 - x^2}{h},$$

and the slope of T should be the limit of this as $h \to 0$. The computations are exactly the same as those used in finding speed, and the slope of T is $2x$.

3-3
DERIVATIVES

Although these two problems deal with quite different applications, they seem to be virtually the same problem. This is due to the fact that they are formulated in terms of the same function. In the moving-particle problem,

$$x = I^2 \circ t;$$

on the parabola in Fig. 3–7,

$$y = I^2 \circ x.$$

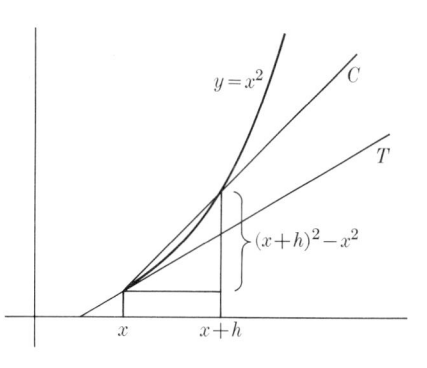

Fig. 3–7

The calculations given above involve doing something to I^2 and getting the answer $2I$.

This operation on a function is called *differentiation*, and $2I$ is called the *derivative* of I^2. In general, what we are doing is as follows. We take a function f and a number a in its domain; then we form the quotient

$$\frac{f(a+h) - f(a)}{h}.$$

If this quotient has a limit as $h \to 0$, we call this limit the derivative of f at a. The derivative of f is denoted by f'; so we have this formal definition. The derivative of f is the function f' defined by the formula

$$f'(a) = \lim_{h \to 0} \frac{f(a+h) - f(a)}{h}. \tag{1}$$

We can find the derivative of I^n by using the binomial theorem as follows. For any number a,

$$\lim_{h \to 0} \frac{I^n(a+h) - I^n(a)}{h} = \lim_{h \to 0} \frac{(a+h)^n - a^n}{h}$$

$$= \lim_{h \to 0} \frac{a^n + na^{n-1}h + \cdots + h^n - a^n}{h}$$

$$= \lim_{h \to 0} \frac{na^{n-1}h + \cdots + h^n}{h}$$

$$= \lim_{h \to 0} (na^{n-1} + \cdots + h^{n-1})$$

$$= na^{n-1},$$

because in the entry before the last one, each term after the first contains a positive power of h, and so tends to zero as h does.

Derivatives are ordinarily computed by using formulas, and the one just developed should be learned. That is,

$$(I^n)' = nI^{n-1}. \tag{2}$$

Though the above proof applies only to the cases in which n is a positive integer, the formula (2) is valid for all values of n—positive or negative, integral or fractional. It will be used here in this extended form, though derivation of the other cases will not be given. Note that, though the above derivation does not cover this case either, (2) also holds for $n = 0$. In this case it reads $(I^0)' = 0$. More generally (note next paragraph), the derivative of any constant function is identically zero. The student should check this directly from the definition of a derivative.

Let c be a constant and f and g be functions. Note that for any number a,

$$\frac{cf(a+h) - cf(a)}{h} = c\frac{f(a+h) - f(a)}{h},$$

$$\frac{f(a+h) + g(a+h) - f(a) - g(a)}{h} = \frac{f(a+h) - f(a)}{h} + \frac{g(a+h) - g(a)}{h}.$$

Thus, when one takes limits as h tends to zero, one has

$$(cf)' = c(f'); \qquad (f+g)' = f' + g'.$$

In words: The derivative of a constant times a function is the constant times the derivative of the function; the derivative of the sum of two functions is the sum of their derivatives. These two rules, together with formula (2) for the differentiation of power functions, suffice for the differentiation of any polynomial function.

The derivative of a function f is another function f'. This latter may have a derivative too, and this is called the *second derivative* of f, written f''. In general, the nth derivative of f, designated by $f^{(n)}$, is the function obtained by starting with f and applying the operation of differentiation n times. In this connection it is often convenient to agree that $f^{(0)}$ means f itself.

By way of example, let us compute by formula the first and second derivatives of each of the following functions:

$$3I^5 - 5I^4 + I^3 + 3I - 7I^0, \qquad I^3 + I^{1/3} - \frac{3I^0}{I}.$$

For the first function,

$$(3I^5 - 5I^4 + I^3 + 3I - 7I^0)' = 15I^4 - 20I^3 + 3I^2 + 3I^0;$$
$$(3I^5 - 5I^4 + I^3 + 3I - 7I^0)'' = (15I^4 - 20I^3 + 3I^2 + 3I^0)'$$
$$= 60I^3 - 60I^2 + 6I.$$

For the second function, rewrite $3I^0/I$ as $3I^{-1}$; then

$$(I^3 + I^{1/3} - 3I^{-1})' = 3I^2 + \tfrac{1}{3}I^{-2/3} + 3I^{-2};$$
$$(I^3 + I^{1/3} - 3I^{-1})'' = (3I^2 + \tfrac{1}{3}I^{-2/3} + 3I^{-2})'$$
$$= 6I - \tfrac{2}{9}I^{-5/3} - 6I^{-3}.$$

EXERCISES

1. Compute by formula the derivative of each of the following functions.

a) $3I^5 - 2I^3$
b) $6I^3 - 7I^2 + 9I^0$
c) $I^{15} - 15I$
d) $I^5 - 4I^3 - 8I^0$
e) $I - I^{1/4}$
f) $I^{1/2} + I^{1/3}$
g) $I^{3/4} + I^{4/3}$
h) $3I^{1/2} + 1/2I^3$
i) $I^2 + I^{1/2}$
j) $I^4 + I^{1/4}$
k) $8I^3 + (8I)^{1/3}$
l) $4I^{1/2} + 4^{1/2}I + (4I)^{1/2}$
m) $I^{1/2} - I^{-1/2}$
n) $3I^{-1/2} + 2I^{-4/3}$
o) $8I^{-1/3} + (8I)^{-1/3}$
p) $5I^{4/5} + 4I^{5/4}$
q) $I - \dfrac{I^0}{I}$
r) $\dfrac{I}{3} + \dfrac{3I^0}{I} + \dfrac{I^0}{3I}$
s) $\dfrac{I^0}{I^3} - \dfrac{I^0}{I^4}$
t) $\dfrac{I^3 - I^2 + 3I^0}{I}$
u) $\dfrac{I^3 - I^2 + 3I^0}{I^5}$
v) $I^{1/3} + \dfrac{I^0}{I^{1/3}}$
w) $(3I)^{1/2} + \dfrac{I^0}{\sqrt{3}\,I}$
x) $\dfrac{4I^0}{I^{1/2}} + \left(\dfrac{4I^0}{I}\right)^{1/2}$
y) $\dfrac{I^2 + 3I - 5I^0}{I^{3/2}}$
z) $\dfrac{I - I^{1/2} - 2I^0}{I^{1/3}}$

2. For each of the following functions use the definition (1) of a derivative to find $f'(a)$ for an arbitrary a in the domain.

a) I
b) I^3
c) I^7
d) $I^{1/2}$ Hint: $\dfrac{\sqrt{a+h} - \sqrt{a}}{h} \cdot \dfrac{\sqrt{a+h} + \sqrt{a}}{\sqrt{a+h} + \sqrt{a}} = \dfrac{a+h-a}{h(\sqrt{a+h} + \sqrt{a})}$
e) $I^{1/3}$
f) I^0/I
g) I^0/I^2
h) I^0/I^3
i) $I^0/I^{1/2}$
j) $I^0/I^{1/3}$

3-4 THE FUNDAMENTAL THEOREM

We begin by computing another integral:

$$\int_a^b I^2.$$

Consider the equally spaced subdivision numbers

$$a,\ a + \frac{(b-a)}{n},\ a + \frac{2(b-a)}{n},\ \ldots,\ a + \frac{i(b-a)}{n},\ \ldots,\ b.$$

Here we find that

$$f(c_i) = c_i^2 = \left[a + \frac{i(b-a)}{n}\right]^2 = a^2 + \frac{2a(b-a)}{n}i + \frac{(b-a)^2}{n^2}i^2$$

and

$$c_i - c_{i-1} = \frac{b-a}{n}.$$

Now (see formulas listed in Exercise 2, Section 3–2),

$$\sum_{i=1}^{n}\left[a^2 + \frac{2a(b-a)}{n}i + \frac{(b-a)^2}{n^2}i^2\right]\frac{(b-a)}{n}$$

$$= n\frac{a^2(b-a)}{n} + \frac{2a(b-a)^2}{n^2}\cdot\frac{n(n+1)}{2} + \frac{(b-a)^3}{n^3}\cdot\frac{n(n+1)(2n+1)}{6}$$

$$= a^2(b-a) + a(b-a)^2\left(1+\frac{1}{n}\right) + \frac{1}{6}(b-a)^3\left(1+\frac{1}{n}\right)\left(2+\frac{1}{n}\right).$$

In this last form, n appears only in denominators; so each function involved tends to zero as n tends to infinity, and

$$\int_a^b I^2 = a^2(b-a) + a(b-a)^2 + \tfrac{1}{3}(b-a)^3 = \tfrac{1}{3}(b^3 - a^3).$$

We get the idea of the fundamental theorem if we take this result, $(b^3 - a^3)/3$, write it in the form

$$(\tfrac{1}{3}I^3)(b) - (\tfrac{1}{3}I^3)(a),$$

and then note that

$$(\tfrac{1}{3}I^3)' = I^2.$$

The classical Greek mathematicians calculated areas by what they called the "method of exhaustions." By this they referred to the technique of adding in more and more simple figures whose areas were easily calculated, in an effort to exhaust the figure whose area was sought. This is closely akin to the methods used in Section 3–2 for the computation of integrals, and it may have occurred to the student that frequently it is the calculator that gets exhausted rather than the figure. However, Leibnitz and Newton eased the burden considerably by their discovery that many integrals may be evaluated by means of formulas obtained from derivative formulas. Specifically, they discovered what is suggested by the example above, that

$$\int_a^b f = F(b) - F(a), \qquad (1)$$

where

$$F' = f. \qquad (2)$$

The *fundamental theorem of calculus* states that (assuming all limits defining appropriate derivatives and integrals exist), given the relation (2), equation (1) gives a valid formula for evaluating an integral.

A function F whose derivative is f is called an *antiderivative* of f. It is common practice to use an integral sign without limits of integration to denote the operation of finding an antiderivative. That is,

$$\int f = F$$

is interpreted to mean

$$F' = f.$$

This is not very precise notation because any antiderivative plus a constant is another antiderivative. However, the notation $\int f$ is useful in listing formulas for use in the computation of integrals. It stands for the simplest antiderivative of f for use in the fundamental theorem.

For example, from the derivative formula

$$(I^n)' = nI^{n-1},$$

we can easily derive the antiderivative formula

$$\int I^n = \frac{I^{n+1}}{n+1}, \qquad n \neq -1. \tag{3}$$

Addition and multiplication by constants affect integrals just as they do derivatives; that is,

$$\int_a^b cf = c\int_a^b f; \qquad \int_a^b (f+g) = \int_a^b f + \int_a^b g.$$

Each of these results can be proved from the fundamental theorem and the corresponding result for derivatives.

Another important property of integrals is easily derived from the fundamental theorem. Let $F = \int f$; then

$$\int_a^b f + \int_b^c f = F(b) - F(a) + F(c) - F(b) = F(c) - F(a) = \int_a^c f. \tag{4}$$

This result is useful in many connections, but for the present note that if a function is defined by different formulas on different parts of its domain, it may be convenient to break an integral of the function into a sum of two integrals so that appropriate antiderivative formulas may be applied.

There is in common use a very helpful notation for systematizing the computations called for in the fundamental theorem. This consists

of writing
$$\int_a^b f = F\Big|_a^b = F(b) - F(a).$$

The function F is some antiderivative of f. The intermediate step lists the antiderivative function followed by a vertical bar with the limits of integration attached. This indicates that the operations of application and subtraction are yet to be performed.

By way of illustration let us evaluate
$$\int_{-1}^2 (I^3 - 3I^2 + I - 5I^0).$$

The antiderivative is computed term by term, using (3):
$$\int_{-1}^2 (I^3 - 3I^2 + I - 5I^0) = \tfrac{1}{4}I^4 - I^3 + \tfrac{1}{2}I^2 - 5I\Big|_{-1}^2$$
$$= 8 - 8 + 2 - 10 - (\tfrac{1}{4} + 1 + \tfrac{1}{2} + 5)$$
$$= -\tfrac{59}{4}.$$

As a second example, consider
$$\int_8^{27} \left(I^{1/3} + \frac{I^0}{I^{1/3}}\right).$$

Write $I^0/I^{1/3}$ as $I^{-1/3}$, and (3) still applies:
$$\int_8^{27} (I^{1/3} + I^{-1/3}) = \frac{I^{4/3}}{4/3} + \frac{I^{2/3}}{2/3}\Big|_8^{27} = \tfrac{243}{4} + \tfrac{27}{2} - 12 - 6 = \tfrac{225}{4}.$$

Finally, let us evaluate
$$\int_0^2 f,$$
where f is defined by
$$f(a) = \begin{cases} a & \text{for } 0 \le a < 1, \\ a^2 & \text{for } 1 \le a \le 2. \end{cases}$$

Break this into two integrals, and use (4):
$$\int_0^2 f = \int_0^1 f + \int_1^2 f = \int_0^1 I + \int_1^2 I^2$$
$$= \tfrac{1}{2}I^2\Big|_0^1 + \tfrac{1}{3}I^3\Big|_1^2 = \tfrac{1}{2} - 0 + \tfrac{8}{3} - \tfrac{1}{3} = \tfrac{17}{6}.$$

The fundamental theorem obviously represents quite a milestone in mathematics. Its proof is very simple if we accept some nineteenth-century results in calculus that are themselves not particularly simple to prove. First note (Fig. 3-8) that the tangent line at u_i is parallel to the chord, which is to say that

$$F'(u_i) = \frac{F(c_i) - F(c_{i-1})}{c_i - c_{i-1}}$$

or

$$F'(u_i)(c_i - c_{i-1}) = F(c_i) - F(c_{i-1}). \quad (5)$$

(It looks "obvious" from Fig. 3-8, but it is not trivial to prove that there always is a point u_i such that (5) will hold.) Now we suppose that $F' = f$, and we have

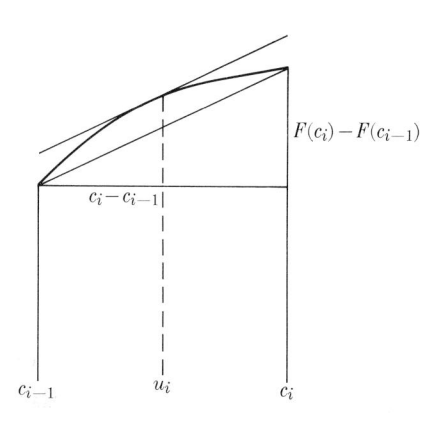

Fig. 3-8

$$\int_a^b f = \lim \sum_{i=1}^n f(c_i)(c_i - c_{i-1}) = \lim \sum_{i=1}^n F'(c_i)(c_i - c_{i-1}).$$

In this last sum the numbers $F'(c_i)$ may be replaced by the numbers $F'(u_i)$ in (5) without changing the limit. (This is the other nontrivial nineteenth-century result needed here.) Making this replacement and using (5), we have

$$\int_a^b f = \lim \sum_{i=1}^n F'(u_i)(c_i - c_{i-1}) = \lim \sum_{i=1}^n [F(c_i) - F(c_{i-1})],$$

but for every n,

$$\sum_{i=1}^n [F(c_i) - F(c_{i-1})] = F(c_n) - F(c_0) = F(b) - F(a),$$

because there is a systematic cancellation leaving only two terms.

At first glance the fundamental theorem seems rather startling. This rough sketch of a proof (omitting all the hard parts) should at least make the result seem plausible.

EXERCISES

1. Evaluate each of the following integrals.

a) $\int_0^1 (I^5 - 4I^3 + 5I - 3I^0)$ b) $\int_0^2 (3I^3 - 4I)$

c) $\int_1^3 (2I^3 - I + 6I^0)$

d) $\int_1^3 \left(\frac{I^0}{I^2} - \frac{I^0}{I^3}\right)$

e) $\int_{-2}^{-1} \left(\frac{I^0}{I^3} + \frac{I^0}{I^4}\right)$

f) $\int_0^1 (I^{1/2} + I^{1/3})$

g) $\int_{-8}^{-1} (I^{1/3} + I^{2/3})$

h) $\int_0^1 (\tfrac{1}{2}I^2 + 2I^{1/2})$

i) $\int_1^8 (I^{1/3} + I^{-1/3})$

j) $\int_1^2 \left(\frac{I^0}{I^{1/2}} - \frac{I^0}{I^{1/3}}\right)$

k) $\int_1^4 \left[\frac{2}{I^{1/2}} + \frac{I^0}{(2I)^{1/2}} + \left(\frac{2}{I}\right)^{1/2}\right]$

l) $\int_1^2 \frac{I^4 + 4I + 3I^0}{I^3}$

m) $\int_1^4 \frac{I^2 + 4I - 5I^0}{I^{3/2}}$

n) $\int_1^2 \frac{I^{3/2} + I^{1/2}}{I}$

2. Evaluate each of the following integrals.

a) $\int_0^2 f$ where $f(a) = \begin{cases} a^2 \text{ for } 0 \le a < 1, \\ a^3 \text{ for } 1 \le a \le 2. \end{cases}$

b) $\int_{-1}^2 f$ where $f(a) = \begin{cases} 1 \text{ for } a < 0. \\ a \text{ for } a \ge 0. \end{cases}$

c) $\int_2^3 f$ where $f(a) = \begin{cases} a^2 - 1 \text{ for } a < 1. \\ 2a - 3 \text{ for } a \ge 1. \end{cases}$

d) $\int_0^3 f$ where $f(a) = \begin{cases} 2a \text{ for } a < 1, \\ a^2 - 1 \text{ for } 1 \le a \le 2, \\ a^2 + 1 \text{ for } a > 2. \end{cases}$

3-5 PROSPECTUS

The formula
$$(I^n)' = nI^{n-1}$$
and the fundamental theorem enable us to compute
$$f' \quad \text{and} \quad \int_a^b f$$
for any polynomial function f.

How about other functions? A considerable portion of a normal first-year calculus course is devoted to the development of a set of derivative formulas adequate for most practical purposes, and to the development from these of reasonably comprehensive methods of antidifferentiation. Roughly, the situation is this. Derivative formulas are easily developed and quite systematic, though practical considerations require a sufficient number of them that considerable drill work is required for their mastery. Antiderivatives are not so simple. There are two reasons for this. First, the systematic pattern into which derivative formulas fall breaks down when they are reversed; so ingenuity is frequently required, as contrasted with the following of routine rules in differentiation. The second reason is more profound. Elementary functions (roughly those for which there are familiar formulas) all have elementary derivatives, but there are many elementary functions with nonelementary antiderivatives.

So, although the fundamental theorem is an essential part of calculus, it is not a complete panacea. As a result there were developed (as early as the eighteenth century) quite efficient methods for numerical integration. In essence, these are ingenious improvements on Archimedes' method of exhaustions. Until the advent of the digital computer, however, these methods were still too exhausting to be used indiscriminately. For the computer they pose no such problem. While at present it seems unlikely that the computer will replace the fundamental theorem of calculus, the development of computers has certainly increased the importance of numerical integration as a topic in calculus.

It is the aim of the preceding three sections to explain what calculus is about: integrals, derivatives, and the fundamental theorem connecting these two ideas. In the remainder of the chapter, we shall give some brief but representative samples of calculus methods and applications. Specifically, in Section 3–7, we shall present the formula that is the major item in systematizing the computation of derivatives. Then, in Section 3–9, we shall show how this fails to systematize the computation of antiderivatives to the same extent. The last sections of the chapter present some direct applications of integrals and derivatives. Numerical integration will be discussed in Chapter 8 in connection with computer programming.

3–6 DERIVATIVES OF VARIABLES

In Section 3–3 we introduced the notion of derivative through two examples. In the first we had

$$x = \text{distance}, \quad t = \text{time}, \quad x = t^2, \quad \text{speed} = 2t.$$

In the second we found

$$y = \text{ordinate}, \quad x = \text{abscissa}, \quad y = x^2, \quad \text{slope} = 2x.$$

Consideration of these two examples side by side was to point out that
$$(I^2)' = 2I$$
is the basic derivative formula involved and that this is quite independent of the applications.

Obviously, though, derivatives have applications, and in this section we shall introduce appropriate notation for talking about these.

Instantaneous speed is a limit of distance change divided by time change. We call it the *derivative of distance with respect to time*. If, as above, x is the distance variable and t the time variable, then the speed variable is denoted by
$$D_t x,$$
read "derivative of x with respect to t." Similarly, slope of tangent line is a limit of ordinate change divided by abscissa change, and is denoted by
$$D_x y.$$

Thus, for the specific examples mentioned above, we have
$$x = t^2, \qquad D_t x = 2t; \qquad y = x^2, \qquad D_x y = 2x.$$

The general situation is this. If
$$v = f \circ u,$$
then
$$D_u v = f' \circ u.$$

The variable $D_u v$ is called the derivative of v with respect to u.

The physical significance of the variable $D_u v$ depends, of course, on that of u and v. We have already mentioned speed and slope as examples of derivatives of variables. Another interesting example comes from economics. If c is a variable measuring manufacturing costs and v volume of production, then $D_v c$ is what the economist calls *marginal cost*.

The derivative of $D_u v$ with respect to u means
$$D_u(D_u v) = f'' \circ u;$$
this is written
$$D_u^2 v.$$

In general, if $v = f \circ u$, then
$$D_u^n v = f^{(n)} \circ u.$$

One of the most important illustrations of a second derivative of a variable is that of the second derivative of distance with respect to time. In the moving-particle problem, $D_t^2 x$ is called the *acceleration* of the particle.

EXERCISES

1. Compute by formula:

   a) $D_x(x^3 - 3x^2)$
   b) $D_u(5u^9 - 2u^4 + 6)$
   c) $D_t(t^{25} - 25t)$
   d) $D_x(x^4 - 3x + 7)$
   e) $D_y(y^2 + y^{1/2})$
   f) $D_t(t^{1/2} + t^{1/3})$
   g) $D_u(3u^{3/4} + 5u^{2/3})$
   h) $D_z(2z^{1/3} + \frac{1}{3}z^2)$
   i) $D_x(2x^2 + 3\sqrt{x})$
   j) $D_z(z^3 - \sqrt[3]{x})$
   k) $D_y(3y^2 + \sqrt{3y})$
   l) $D_t(t\sqrt{3} + 3\sqrt{t} + \sqrt{3t})$
   m) $D_v(v^{1/3} + v^{-1/3})$
   n) $D_u(u^{-1/3} - 2u^{-2/3})$
   o) $D_x[4x^{-1/2} - (4x)^{-1/2}]$
   p) $D_v(3v^{4/3} + 4v^{3/4})$
   q) $D_z\left(2z + \dfrac{2}{z}\right)$
   r) $D_z\left(\dfrac{2}{z} + \dfrac{z}{2} + \dfrac{1}{2z}\right)$
   s) $D_t\left(\dfrac{1}{t^2} + \dfrac{1}{t^3}\right)$
   t) $D_u \dfrac{u^2 + 2u - 3}{u}$
   u) $D_y \dfrac{2y^2 - 3y + 5}{y^3}$
   v) $D_x\left(\sqrt{x} + \dfrac{1}{\sqrt{x}}\right)$
   w) $D_u\left(\sqrt{2u} + \dfrac{1}{\sqrt{2u}}\right)$
   x) $D_v \dfrac{v^2 + 2v - 3}{v^{4/3}}$
   y) $D_x\left(\dfrac{2}{\sqrt{x}} + \sqrt{\dfrac{2}{x}}\right)$
   z) $D_y \dfrac{y + \sqrt{y} + 1}{\sqrt[3]{y}}$

2. If f is a function and y is a variable, one speaks of the "derivative of f," but of the "derivative of y with respect to x," where x and y are related variables. Let y map points onto numbers. Why cannot y' be defined by direct analogy with f'? Set up a "difference quotient" leading to y'; what part of this is meaningless?

3. With no reference to a connecting function, formulate a description of $D_u v$ as follows: Form a quotient of differences based on values of u and v at points p and q, and give the value of $D_u v$ at p as a limit of this quotient as $q \to p$ (this latter meaning that p is fixed and the distance between p and q tends to zero).

4. The variable $D_u v$ is usually described as meaning "the rate of change of v with respect to u." Discuss this in the light of Exercise 3.

5. Deduce from the introductory remarks in this section that on curves in the plane $D_x y$ measures slopes. What does $D_x^2 y$ measure? (See Exercise 4.)

3-7 THE CHAIN RULE

The process of differentiation by formula is easily systematized because, whenever a function is formed by putting two others together, we can get the derivative of the whole in terms of the derivatives of the pieces. For example, if f' and g' are known, then we immediately have $(f + g)'$ because it is just $f' + g'$.

It should be emphasized in passing that the derivative of a product is *not* the product of derivatives. For the record, the formula is $(fg)' = f'g + g'f$; the result comes out in terms of the factors and their derivatives. However, we shall neither develop nor use this formula in the brief sampling of calculus presented here.

In terms of productivity of new functions, the most potent operation for combining functions is composition. So we can get the flavor of derivative formula methods without beginning to study all the standard formulas by looking at the rule for differentiating a composite.

Let us do it in terms of derivatives of variables and begin with an example in which we already know how to differentiate the composite. Suppose that
$$y = x^2 \quad \text{and} \quad x = t^3;$$
then
$$y = t^6.$$

Applying familiar derivative formulas, we have
$$D_x y = 2x, \quad D_t x = 3t^2, \quad D_t y = 6t^5.$$

Now, how can $2x$ and $3t^2$ be put together to form $6t^5$? Once we note that $x = t^3$, the answer is obvious: multiply! This is, indeed, the general rule for differentiating composites:
$$D_t y = D_x y \, D_t x. \tag{1}$$

To get some idea of why this should hold in general, let p and q be points in the common domain of variables x, y, and t. Then
$$D_x y = \lim_{q \to p} \frac{y(q) - y(p)}{x(q) - x(p)}, \quad D_t x = \lim_{q \to p} \frac{x(q) - x(p)}{t(q) - t(p)};$$
however,
$$\frac{y(q) - y(p)}{x(q) - x(p)} \cdot \frac{x(q) - x(p)}{t(q) - t(p)} = \frac{y(q) - y(p)}{t(q) - t(p)},$$

and this last fraction has $D_t y$ for its limit. This must be regarded as a plausibility argument rather than a proof, because a rigorous analysis of the limit arguments (ignored here) would reveal that we might be dividing by zero. Nevertheless, the result is quite correct, provided the derivatives involved exist.

Formula (1) is usually referred to as the *chain rule*. It is also helpful to look at this rule purely in terms of functions. Suppose that
$$x = g \circ t \quad \text{and} \quad y = f \circ x$$
so that
$$y = f \circ g \circ t.$$

We can rewrite (1) in the form
$$(f \circ g)' \circ t = (f' \circ x)(g' \circ t) = (f' \circ g \circ t)(g' \circ t)$$
and it appears that
$$(f \circ g)' = (f' \circ g)g'. \tag{2}$$

This is the *function form of the chain rule*.

Suppose we want to find $D_x\sqrt{1+x^2}$. We can think of this as finding $D_x y$, where
$$y = \sqrt{u} \quad \text{and} \quad u = 1 + x^2;$$
then, by (1),
$$D_x y = D_u y D_x u = \frac{1}{2\sqrt{u}} \cdot 2x = \frac{x}{\sqrt{1+x^2}}.$$

It is recommended that the student practice until he can perform such calculations without explicit use of an intermediate variable such as u above. In this connection the function form (2) can be helpful in organizing the work.

The following (probably over-elaborate) analysis of this same problem may be helpful. What we are suggesting is that most of the analysis of the problem is usually not written down.

Thought processes	Written work
The function is $I^{1/2} \circ (I^0 + I^2)$. First I want the derivative of $I^{1/2}$, which is $\frac{1}{2} I^{-1/2}$.	$\dfrac{1}{2\sqrt{}}$
The remaining component forms $1 + x^2$; so to complete the first factor of the derivative I must substitute this into the form I have written down.	$\dfrac{1}{2\sqrt{1+x^2}}$
The derivative of $1 + x^2$ with respect to x is $2x$; so I multiply by this.	$\dfrac{1}{2\sqrt{1+x^2}} \cdot 2x$

Two applications of (2) yield an extended chain rule:
$$(f \circ g \circ \phi)' = (f' \circ g \circ \phi)(g \circ \phi)' = (f' \circ g \circ \phi)(g' \circ \phi)\phi' \tag{3}$$

The extension to a composite with any number of components follows the pattern indicated here.

Recall that $f \circ g$ is called "g followed by f" because to compute
$$(f \circ g)(a)$$

one applies g to a and then applies f to the result. Now a rule of thumb for composite functions is, "apply the components in one order and differentiate them in the reverse order." Thus, although the ∘ notation may seem backward when one considers application, it is just built for the chain rule.

To put the chain rule into words, agree that in the notation $f \circ g$, g will be said to "succeed" f. This avoids the word "follow," which has the reverse technical meaning. In this terminology the rule is very straightforward. Write the composite in the ∘ notation and number the components from left to right. If there are n components, the derivative consists of n factors. The first factor is the derivative of the first component succeeded by the successors of the first component. The second factor is the derivative of the second component succeeded by the successors of the second component, etc. Finally, the nth factor is merely the derivative of the nth component.

Let us use (3) to analyze the problem of computing

$$D_x(1 + \sqrt{1 + 2x^3})^4.$$

Note that in precise notation the connecting function is

$$I^4 \circ (I^0 + I^{1/2}) \circ (I^0 - 2I^3).$$

An outline of the work might run as follows. The first function is I^4; so the framework for the first factor in the derivative is

$$4(\quad)^3.$$

Succeeding components form $1 + \sqrt{1 - 2x^3}$; so this is substituted to complete the first factor:

$$4(1 + \sqrt{1 - 2x^3})^3. \tag{4}$$

The second component is $I^0 + I^{1/2}$; so the framework for the second factor of the derivative is

$$\frac{1}{2\sqrt{\quad}}.$$

Succeeding components form $1 - 2x^3$; so substitution completes the second factor:

$$\frac{1}{2\sqrt{1 - 2x^3}}. \tag{5}$$

The expression just substituted has the obvious derivative

$$-6x^2; \tag{6}$$

so this is the final factor. The desired result is now the product of (4), (5), and (6):

$$4(1+\sqrt{1-2x^3})^3 \cdot \frac{1}{2\sqrt{1-2x^3}} \cdot (-6x^2).$$

EXERCISES

1. For each of the following definitions of F, describe F as a composite function and write it in the ∘ notation.
   a) $F(a) = \sqrt{a^2 - 1}$
   b) $F(a) = (a + \sqrt{a})^3$
   c) $F(a) = (1 + \sqrt{a^2 + 1})^2$
   d) $F(a) = [1 - (3 + \sqrt{a})]^4$
   e) $F(a) = 3(a^2 - 2a)^5$
   f) $F(a) = \sqrt{a^3 + 3a^2}$
   g) $F(a) = \sqrt{1 - \sqrt{1-a}}$
   h) $F(a) = (1 - 2\sqrt{3+a})^3$

2. Compute each of the following derivatives.
   a) $D_x\sqrt{1+x^2}$
   b) $D_x\sqrt{1-x^2}$
   c) $D_x(1/\sqrt{1-x^2})$
   d) $D_x(1/\sqrt{1+x^2})$
   e) $D_x(x^3 - 3x^2 + 5)^4$
   f) $D_x(5x^4 - 2x^3)^7$
   g) $D_x\sqrt{3x^2 - 2x + 1}$
   h) $D_x(x^6 + 4x^3 - 5)^{1/3}$
   i) $D_x[1/(1 - x^{1/3})]$
   j) $D_x[1/(1 - x)^{1/3}]$
   k) $D_x\sqrt{x - (1-x)^3}$
   l) $D_x(x - \sqrt{1-x})^3$
   m) $D_x[(1/\sqrt{1+x}) + (1/\sqrt{1-x})]$
   n) $D_x[1/(\sqrt{1+x} + \sqrt{1-x})]$
   o) $D_x 1/\sqrt{x + [1/(1-x)]}$
   p) $D_x\sqrt{1 - (1-x)^2}$
   q) $D_x(x^{2/3} - x^{-2/3})^{1/3}$
   r) $D_x\sqrt{(1/\sqrt{x}) + (1/x^2)}$
   s) $D_x 1/[(1/x) - 1/(1-x)]$
   t) $D_x\sqrt{x + \sqrt{1-x}}$

3. From each of the following sets of relations compute $D_t y$.
   a) $y = x^2 - 2x + 1$, $x = 2t - \sqrt{t}$
   b) $y = 2x^2 + 3x$, $x = t^3 + \sqrt[3]{t}$
   c) $y = x^2 + 1$, $x = t^2 + 1$
   d) $y = \sqrt{1+x^2}$, $x = 3t^2 - 2$
   e) $y = \sqrt{x}$, $x = 4t^2 - 3t + 6$
   f) $y = 1 - x$, $x = t - \sqrt{t}$
   g) $y = \sqrt{1+x}$, $x = 3t^2 + 2$
   h) $y = 1/x$, $x = \sqrt{1-t^2}$
   i) $y = -2/x^3$, $x = \sqrt{1+4t^2}$
   j) $y = (1/x) - (1/\sqrt{x})$, $x = t + \sqrt{t}$
   k) $y = 1/(1-x)$, $x = t - t^2$
   l) $y = x^2 - 4x + 3$, $x = \sqrt{t}$
   m) $y = 1 - u$, $u = x^2 + 4$, $x = 2 - 3t$
   n) $y = \sqrt{1+u^2}$, $u = x - \sqrt{x}$, $x = 1/(1-t)$
   o) $y = \sqrt{u}$, $u = 1 + 2x$, $x = t^2 - 3$
   p) $y = 1/\sqrt{u}$, $u = \sqrt{x}$, $x = 1 - t^2$

82   CALCULUS   3-8

q) $y = 3u^2 - 2,\ u = \sqrt{x^3 + 4},\ x = 1/t$
r) $y = u^2 - 1,\ u = x^3 - 1,\ x = t^4 - 1$
s) $y = 1 - v,\ v = 2u^2,\ u = 2 - 3x,\ x = \sqrt{t}$
t) $y = \sqrt{1 - v},\ u = u^3 - 3u^2,\ u = \sqrt{x^2 + 4},\ x = 1/(1 - t)$

3-8 DIFFERENTIALS

For the derivative of a variable, which we have denoted by $D_x y$, Leibnitz used the notation

$$\frac{dy}{dx}. \tag{1}$$

This notational device has been the most useful and the most controversial in the history of calculus.

Suppose the form (1), which looks like a fraction, really is a fraction and is equal to $D_x y$. We then have $dy = D_x y\ dx$; and suppose that more generally for any variables u and v, du and dv mean something, and that

$$dv = D_u v\ du. \tag{2}$$

Actually, it can be shown that du and dv are variables. They are called the *differentials* of u and v, respectively.

Consider the following example. The equation

$$x^2 + y^2 = 2x \tag{3}$$

defines a locus (a circle, but that is immaterial), and we want to find an expression for the slope of the tangent line at an arbitrary point of this locus. From (2) we conclude that

$$d(x^2) = 2x\ dx,$$
$$d(y^2) = 2y\ dy,$$
$$d(2x) = 2\ dx;$$

so, given (3), we write

$$2x\ dx + 2y\ dy = 2\ dx.$$

It is now a very simple matter to solve this equation for dy/dx;

$$\frac{dy}{dx} = \frac{2 - 2x}{2y} = \frac{1 - x}{y}.$$

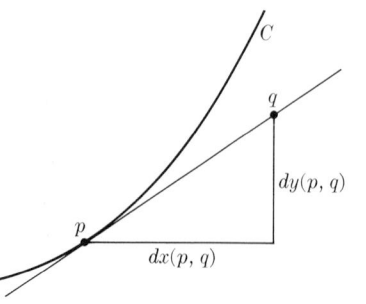

Fig. 3-9

The differential has many other uses in problem-solving; we present only this sample to illustrate the utility of the concept.

If a variable v is defined on a curve C, then dv is a variable whose domain is the family of tangent lines to C. That is, dv is defined on point pairs (p, q), where p is on C and q is on the tangent line to C at p. We can define a limited number of differentials geometrically. Figure 3–9 shows the usual geometric picture of dx and dy. Note, however, that in working with Eq. (3) above, we needed differentials for x^2 and y^2. In general, we need a differential for every pertinent variable.

There was developed during the first half of the twentieth century an extremely ingenious but rather highly sophisticated algebraic theory which accomplishes exactly this. We shall not attempt to summarize this theory here. Rather, let us say that some of the end results of it are as follows.

i) For each sufficiently well behaved variable v on a curve C, there is defined a variable dv on the family of tangent lines to C.

ii) For the rectangular coordinate variables x and y, the differentials have values as indicated in Fig. 3–9.

iii) For any two sufficiently well behaved variables u and v on C, the relation
$$dv = D_u v\, du$$
holds over the family of lines tangent to C.

EXERCISES

1. For each of the following equations, find an expression in x and y for the slope of the tangent line at an arbitrary point of the locus.

a) $x^2 + y^3 = 1$
b) $x^2 - y^2 = 1$
c) $2x^3 - 3y^2 = y$
d) $x^4 - 2x^2 + y^2 - y = 0$
e) $(1 + x^2)^3 = 3y^4 - 2y$
f) $3y^4 - 2x^2 = x^3 + \sqrt{y}$
g) $3x^2 + 4y^2 - 5x + 3y = 2$
h) $y - 2 = \sqrt{x^2 + y^2}$

3–9 INTEGRATION BY SUBSTITUTION

For reasons that we shall explain shortly, the integral that we have written
$$\int_0^1 I^2$$
is more often written
$$\int_0^1 x^2\, dx,$$
and we find that the fundamental-theorem calculations are carried out in

the following format:
$$\int_0^1 x^2\,dx = \tfrac{1}{3}x^3\Big|_0^1 = \tfrac{1}{3} - 0 = \tfrac{1}{3}.$$

In this notation, consider the problem
$$\int_0^1 2x\sqrt{1+x^2}\,dx. \tag{1}$$

We note that $d(1+x^2) = 2x\,dx$; so the integral (1) can be written as
$$\int_0^1 \sqrt{1+x^2}\,d(1+x^2).$$

With $1+x^2$ as the new base variable, this appears to be merely an integral of $I^{1/2}$; so we treat it that way and solve the problem as follows.
$$\int_0^1 2x\sqrt{1+x^2}\,dx = \int_0^1 \sqrt{1+x^2}\,d(1+x^2) = \tfrac{2}{3}(1+x^2)^{3/2}\Big|_0^1$$
$$= \tfrac{2}{3}(2)^{3/2} - \tfrac{2}{3}(1)^{3/2} = \tfrac{2}{3}(2\sqrt{2} - 1).$$

A slight variation on this procedure is illustrated in the following problem:
$$\int_0^1 x^2\sqrt{1-x^3}\,dx.$$

Now $d(1-x^3) = -3x^2\,dx$, and we do not have the factor -3. We can get it, however, by the following device:
$$\int_0^1 x^2\sqrt{1-x^3}\,dx = -\tfrac{1}{3}\int_0^1 -3x^2\sqrt{1-x^3}\,dx$$
$$= -\tfrac{1}{3}\int_0^1 \sqrt{1-x^3}\,d(1-x^3)$$
$$= -\tfrac{2}{9}(1-x^3)^{3/2}\Big|_0^1 = 0 - (-\tfrac{2}{9}) = \tfrac{2}{9}.$$

So far this is just sleight-of-hand. We have written an integral with something in it that looks like a differential and then treated this differential-like symbol as though it had all the properties developed in Section 3-8. We now turn to an outline of the justification of these procedures.

Let C be a curve and let u and v be variables defined on C. The form
$$\int_C u\,dv$$
stands for what is called a *line integral*. The following is a rough sketch of the definition. We partition the curve C by points $p_0, p_1, p_2, \ldots, p_n$. At each point p_i we draw the tangent line Tp_i. We then locate q_i on Tp_i

by "unrolling" the arc p_ip_{i+1} onto Tp_i (see Fig. 3-10). We then define

$$\int_C u \, dv = \lim \sum_{i=1}^{n} u(p_i) \, dv(p_i, q_i),$$

where, as more partition points are introduced, the limit is taken in such a way that the maximum distance between them tends to zero.

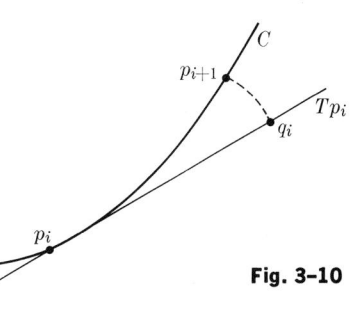

Fig. 3-10

The important thing about this integral definition is that the choice of the points q_i is completely independent of the variables u and v. Thus, if another variable w is introduced and dv is written as $D_w v \, dw$, the points q_i remain the same and

$$dv(p_i, q_i) = D_w v(p_i) \, dw(p_i, q_i).$$

Thus the approximating sums are not changed by this substitution, and it follows that

$$\int_C u \, dv = \int_C u D_w v \, dw. \tag{2}$$

In our first illustrative example above, we wrote

$$\int_0^1 2x\sqrt{1+x^2} \, dx = \int_0^1 \sqrt{1+x^2} \, d(1+x^2). \tag{3}$$

This is using formula (2) and reading it from right to left. Specifically, with

$$w = x, \qquad v = 1 + x^2, \qquad u = \sqrt{1+x^2},$$

(3) is just (2) in reverse order.

Formula (2) is the basic formula for *integration by substitution*. As just noted, the illustrations given so far involve reading it from right to left. It is also a useful tool when read from left to right, but in this case an additional mechanical feature enters into the manipulation. Consider the problem

$$\int_0^4 x^3 \sqrt{16 - x^2} \, dx.$$

This does not fit the pattern of the other examples in this section because $d(16 - x^2) = -2x \, dx$, and this is not a constant times $x^3 \, dx$. One way of solving this problem is to set

$$w = \sqrt{16 - x^2}; \tag{4}$$

then

$$x = \sqrt{16 - w^2}, \qquad dx = \frac{-w \, dw}{\sqrt{16 - w^2}}, \qquad x^3 = (16 - w^2)^{3/2}.$$

Making these substitutions, we have

$$\int_0^4 x^3 \sqrt{16-x^2}\, dx = \int_{x=0}^{x=4} (16-w^2)^{3/2} \cdot w \cdot \frac{-w\, dw}{\sqrt{16-w^2}}$$

$$= \int_{x=0}^{x=4} (w^4 - 16w^2)\, dw.$$

Now we introduced here without explanation the notation

$$\int_{x=0}^{x=4} . \tag{5}$$

This is to indicate that the integral of a variable is really an integral over a curve. The numerical "limits of integration" have the significance indicated in (5). Now, as indicated in (2), when we change variables through the substitution formula, the geometric domain of integration does not change. However, its representation by values of the variable in current use may well change. So, to complete the present illustrative example, we note from the substitution equation (4) that

$$w = 4 \quad \text{when } x = 0, \quad w = 0 \quad \text{when } x = 4;$$

thus

$$\int_0^4 x^3 \sqrt{16-x^2}\, dx = \int_{x=0}^{x=4} (w^4 - 16w^2)\, dw = \int_4^0 (w^4 - 16w^2)\, dw$$

$$= \left(\frac{w^5}{5} - \frac{16w^3}{3}\right)\Big|_4^0 = 0 - \left(\frac{1024}{5} - \frac{1024}{3}\right) = \frac{2048}{15}.$$

It is natural to ask how one discovers a substitution equation that will have the magical effect that (4) had on this problem. In this brief survey of calculus we cannot answer this question, except to say that a standard calculus course includes a study of the classification of problem types and effective substitutions.

In conclusion, then, we would refer back to the remarks in Section 3–5 to the effect that differentiation is more systematic than antidifferentiation. The chain rule will give us the derivative of any composite function for which we know the derivatives of the components. The substitution formula $dv = D_w v\, dw$ is just the differential form of the chain rule, so integration by substitution is the technique that the chain rule contributes to the list of antidifferentiation methods. As just noted, however, integration by substitution is not as systematic as the chain rule. The best quick description of its applicability is that it works when it works.

EXERCISES

1. Compute each of the following integrals.

a) $\displaystyle\int_0^1 x\sqrt{1+x^2}\,dx$

b) $\displaystyle\int_1^2 x\sqrt{4-x^2}\,dx$

c) $\displaystyle\int_0^1 \frac{x\,dx}{\sqrt[3]{2-x^2}}$

d) $\displaystyle\int_0^1 x^2\sqrt{1-x^3}\,dx$

e) $\displaystyle\int_0^1 x^4\sqrt{1-x^5}\,dx$

f) $\displaystyle\int_0^1 \frac{x^3\,dx}{(1+x^4)^{3/2}}$

g) $\displaystyle\int_0^1 \frac{3x\,dx}{(1+x^2)^{3/2}}$

h) $\displaystyle\int_0^2 \frac{4x^2\,dx}{(1+x^3)^{4/3}}$

i) $\displaystyle\int_0^1 2x^2(1-x^3)^{2/3}\,dx$

j) $\displaystyle\int_{-1}^1 5x\sqrt{1-x^2}\,dx$

k) $\displaystyle\int_{-1}^1 5x(1-x^2)^{2/3}\,dx$

l) $\displaystyle\int_{-1}^1 5x^2(1-x^3)^{2/3}\,dx$

m) $\displaystyle\int_{-1}^1 5x^2(1-x^3)^{1/3}\,dx$

2. In each of the following make the indicated substitution and evaluate the integral.

a) $\displaystyle\int_0^1 x\sqrt{1-x}\,dx,\ x=1-u^2$

b) $\displaystyle\int_0^{2/3} x^2\sqrt{2-3x}\,dx,\ x=\tfrac{1}{3}(2-u^2)$

c) $\displaystyle\int_0^{13} x(1+2x)^{2/3}\,dx,\ x=\tfrac{1}{2}(u^3-1)$

d) $\displaystyle\int_0^1 \frac{x\,dx}{(3-2x)^{1/3}},\ x=\tfrac{1}{2}(3-u^2)$

e) $\displaystyle\int_0^1 x^8(1-x^3)^{1/3}\,dx,\ x=\sqrt[3]{1-u^3}$

f) $\displaystyle\int_0^1 \frac{x^3\,dx}{(1+x^2)^{2/3}},\ x=\sqrt{u^3-1}$

g) $\displaystyle\int_1^2 \frac{\sqrt{4-x^2}\,dx}{x^4},\ x=\frac{1}{u}$

88 CALCULUS

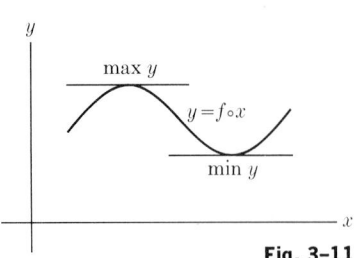

Fig. 3-11

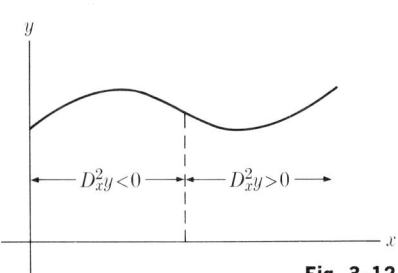

Fig. 3-12

3-10 CURVE SKETCHING

Let x and y be the coordinate variables, and let C be the locus of $y = f \circ x$. A local maximum point on C may be defined informally as one for which no nearby points of C are any higher. Similarly, a local minimum point is one for which no nearby points of C are any lower. Since y is the ordinate variable (measures height), local maximum and minimum points on C are also referred to as local maximum and minimum points for y.

Now (see Fig. 3-11) a smooth curve will have horizontal tangent lines, hence zero slope, at its maximum and minimum points. Since $D_x y$ measures slopes on C, it would seem that the local maxima and minima for y would occur at the points where

$$D_x y = 0.$$

To distinguish between maxima and minima, observe that the variable $D_x^2 y$ measures the rate of change of slope with respect to horizontal distance. Thus, if $D_x^2 y$ is positive, slope increases with a movement to the right; that is, the curve is concave upward. If $D_x^2 y$ is negative, the curve is concave downward (see Fig. 3-12). So the following characterizations are indicated:

$$D_x y = 0, \quad D_x^2 y > 0: \quad \text{minimum } y,$$
$$D_x y = 0, \quad D_x^2 y < 0: \quad \text{maximum } y.$$

Where $D_x^2 y = 0$, the issue remains in doubt. Wherever the above conditions hold, y will have a maximum or minimum as indicated. However, maxima and minima may occur under other circumstances, and the above is a considerable oversimplification of the problem, though it will suffice for many examples.

To see how this theory may be used in sketching curves, let us consider the problem of sketching the locus of

$$y = x^3 - 3x^2 - 9x + 1.$$

First we compute derivatives:

$$D_x y = 3x^2 - 6x - 9 = 3(x-3)(x+1); \qquad D_x^2 y = 6x - 6.$$

It appears from the factored form of $D_x y$ that $D_x y = 0$ when $x = -1$ or $x = 3$; so the pertinent information is given in the following chart.

x	y	$D_x y$	$D_x^2 y$	Remarks
-1	6	0	-12	max
3	-26	0	12	min

Figure 3–13 shows a sketch based on this information. The scale of measurement on the y-axis has been shortened in Fig. 3–13 in order to obtain an intelligible sketch of reasonable size. Note that because of this the signs, but not the magnitudes, of slopes are pictured correctly.

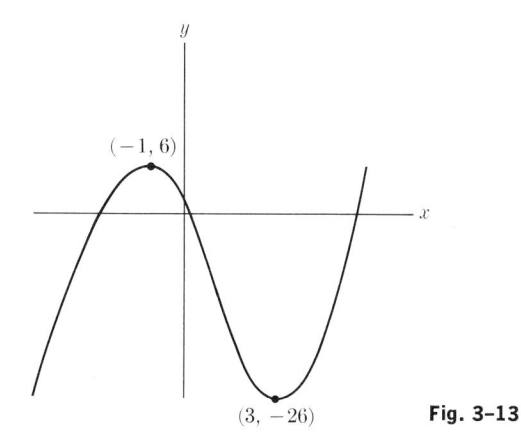

Fig. 3-13

Finally, it might be noted that $D_x^2 y = 0$ only if $x = 1$; so the direction of concavity can change only at that point.

EXERCISES

1. Sketch the graph of each of the following equations.

   a) $y = x^2$
   b) $y = x^2 + 1$
   c) $y = x^2 - 4$
   d) $y = x^2 + 2x + 1$
   e) $y = x^2 + 2x - 1$
   f) $y = x^2 + 2x + 2$
   g) $y = x^2 - 4x + 4$
   h) $y = x^2 - 4x + 5$
   i) $y = x^2 - 4x + 2$
   j) $y = 1 - x^2$
   k) $y = 1 + 2x - x^2$
   l) $y = 1 - 4x - x^2$
   m) $y = ax^2 + bx + c \, (a > 0)$
   n) $y = ax^2 + bx + c \, (a < 0)$
   o) $y = x^3 - 3x$
   p) $y = x^3 - x^2 - x + 1$
   q) $y = x^3 - 3x^2 + 1$
   r) $y = 6x - x^3$
   s) $y = 3x^2 - x^3$
   t) $y = 1 + 9x - 3x^2 - x^3$
   u) $y = x^4 - 3x^3 + x^2$
   v) $y = x^4 + 4x^3 - 8x^2$
   w) $y = x^4 - 4x^3 - 8x^2$
   x) $y = 1 - x^2 + 3x^3 - x^4$
   y) $y = 3 + 8x^2 - 4x^3 - x^4$
   z) $y = -2 + 8x^2 + 4x^3 - x^4$

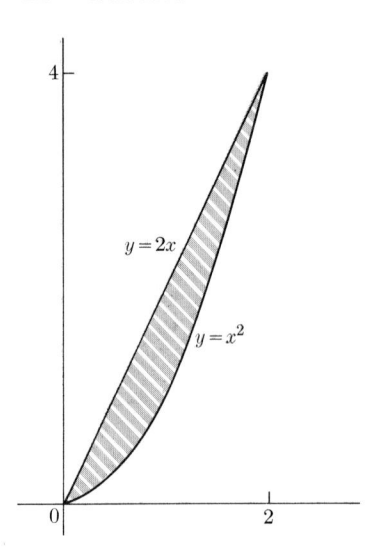

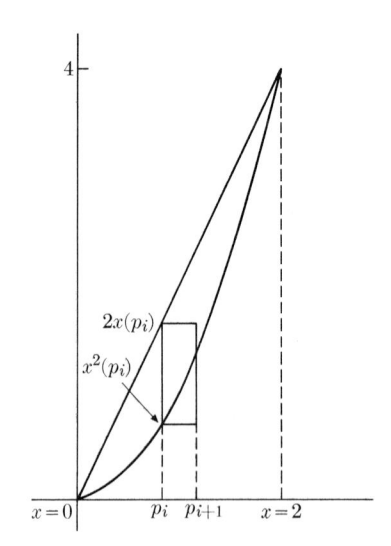

Fig. 3-14

Fig. 3-15

3-11 AREA

To find the area of the shaded region in Fig. 3-14, we may proceed as shown in Fig. 3-15. The base curve is the stretch of x-axis from 0 to 2. The "tangent" lines coincide with the curve itself; so the point p_{i+1} coincides with the point q_i in the definition of line integral (Section 3-9). Thus the area of the rectangle in Fig. 3-15 may be written

$$[2x(p_i) - x^2(p_i)]\, dx(p_i, p_{i+1})$$

and the limit of the sum of these terms is

$$\int_0^2 (2x - x^2)\, dx. \tag{1}$$

When one looks at geometric applications of integration, it is usually a good idea to draw a sketch for this problem, like the skeleton model shown in Fig. 3-16. We showed the more detailed sketch in Fig. 3-15 only to give a fuller explanation of the method. Note that Fig. 3-16 gives three items of information:

1. The height of a sample rectangle is measured by the variable $2x - x^2$.
2. It is the variable dx that measures widths of these rectangles.
3. The figure covers the x-axis from 0 to 2.

These are the three things we need to know to fill in the answer (1).

3-11
AREA

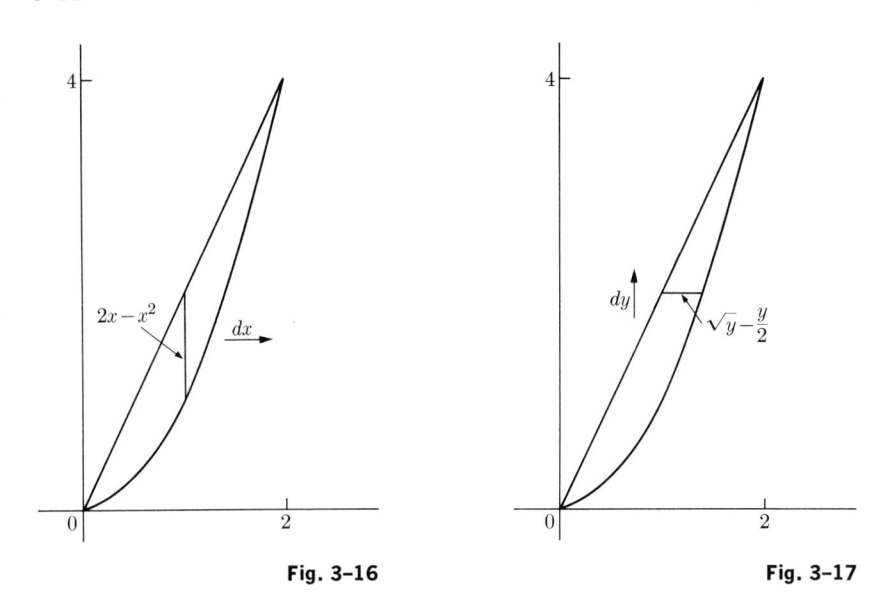

Fig. 3-16

Fig. 3-17

The same problem can be solved in another way, as indicated in Fig. 3-17. From this picture we get the answer

$$\int_0^4 \left(\sqrt{y} - \frac{y}{2}\right) dy.$$

Figure 3-18 shows another problem. The area of the enclosed region there is

$$\int_{-2}^1 [(1 - x^2) - (x - 1)] \, dx = \int_{-2}^1 (2 - x - x^2) \, dx.$$

This example illustrates the point that the formula for the height of a

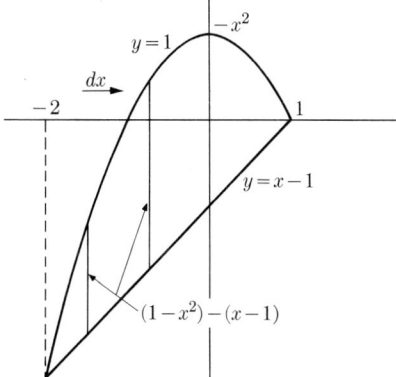

Fig. 3-18

Fig. 3-19

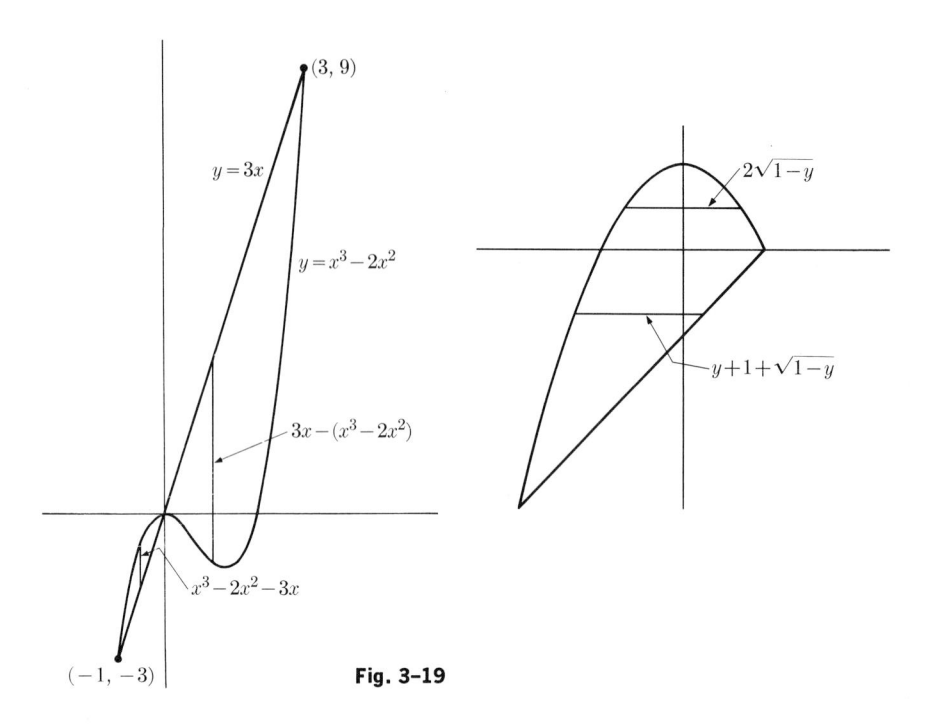

rectangle does not change when a curve crosses the axis. That is, the positive vertical distance between two curves is given by top ordinate minus bottom ordinate, regardless of the location of the axes.

By contrast, if the curves cross the formula changes. The total enclosed area in Fig. 3–19 is given by

$$\int_{-1}^{0} [3x - (x^3 - 2x^2)]\, dx + \int_{0}^{3} (x^3 - 2x^2 - 3x)\, dx.$$

As a final example, note (Fig. 3–20) that an attempt to solve the problem in Fig. 3–18 by horizontal rectangles runs into difficulties because the formula for the length of a rectangle changes at the "corner" point (1, 0).

EXERCISES

1. Figure 3–21 shows eleven portions of the plane, each labeled with a capital letter. Use an integral to find the area of each of these.
2. Figure 3–22 shows two portions of the plane, labeled A and B, respectively. By considering first horizontal, then vertical, rectangles, find the area of each of these in two different ways.

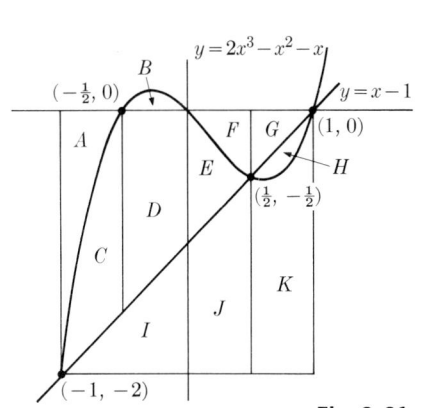

Fig. 3-21

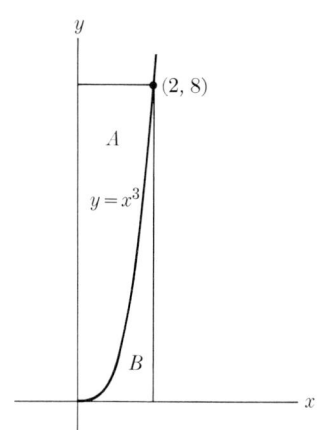

Fig. 3-22

3. In each of the following, find the area of the bounded region enclosed by the curves whose equations are given.

a) $y = x^4$, $y = 8x$
b) $y = x^4 - 1$, $y = 5x + 5$
c) $y = x^3$, $y = 4x$
d) $y = x(x - 2)(x - 3)$, $y = 0$
e) $y = x^4 - 4$, $y = 3x^2$
f) $y = x^3$, $y = 2 - x$, $y = 0$
g) $y = x^3 - x^2$, $y = 2x$
h) $x = y^2$, $x = y + 2$
i) $y = \sqrt{x - 1}$, $y = 5x - 5$
j) $y = x^3 + 1$, $y = 0$, $x = 0$
k) $y = x^3 - 1$, $y = 0$, $x = 0$
l) $y = x^2 - 5x + 6$, $y = 0$
m) $y = x^2$, $y = (x - 2)^2$, $y = 0$
n) $y = 6 + x - x^2$, $y = 0$
o) $y = 6 + x - x^2$, $y = 2x$
p) $xy^2 = 1$, $y = 3 - 2\sqrt{x}$
q) $y = 5 - x^2$, $y = 3 + x^2$
r) $x = y^2$, $5y = 6 - x^2$

3-12 VOLUME

The general pattern of an integral-calculus problem is that the solution assumes the form

$$\lim \sum u(p_i)\, dv(p_i, q_i).$$

We recognize that a limit of this sort is given by an integral and then use the fundamental theorem of calculus to get a numerical answer. In short, we set up an integral problem by recalling the definition of an integral; then we get the answer by using antiderivatives. There are many geometric and physical problems that fit this mold. Area is, of course, a good example, but there are many others. By way of emphasizing this, let us look at one other application of integration in this section.

The following procedure is frequently applicable to the problem of finding the volume of a solid. Place the solid on a set of coordinate axes, and choose one axis (for convenience, let the one chosen be called the

94 CALCULUS

x-axis). Partition that portion of the *x*-axis covered by the solid. At the partition point p_i let $A(p_i)$ be the area of the cross section of the solid cut off by the plane perpendicular to the *x*-axis (see Fig. 3–23). The volume of that portion of the solid that lies between the planes at p_{i-1} and p_i is approximately

$$A(p_i)\, dx(p_i, p_{i+1}),$$

so it would appear that

$$V = \lim_{n \to \infty} \sum_{i=1}^{n} A(p_i)\, dx(p_i, p_{i+1}) = \int_a^b A\, dx.$$

This procedure becomes practical whenever all the cross sections perpendicular to some axis are recognizable figures of the same type, so that A can be given in terms of x by a simple formula from plane geometry.

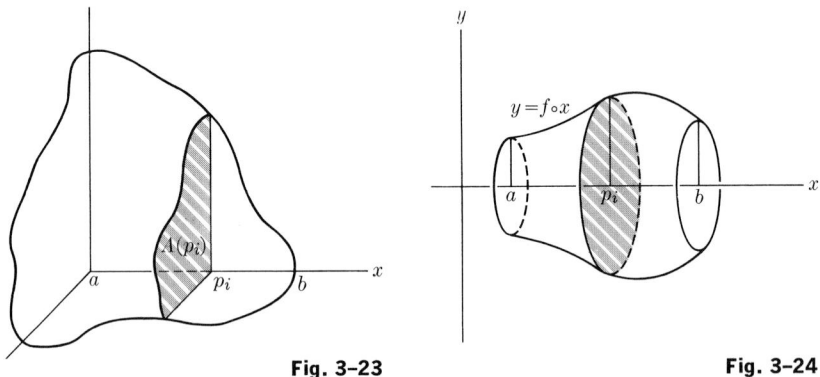

Fig. 3–23 **Fig. 3–24**

One type of figure that is particularly susceptible to this treatment is the *solid of revolution*. Figure 3–24 shows the plane figure bounded by the *x*-axis, a curve, and two vertical lines revolved about the *x*-axis to generate such a solid. The cross section at p_i is a circle with radius $y(p_i)$; so

$$A = \pi y^2,$$

and the volume of the solid of revolution is

$$\int_a^b \pi y^2\, dx.$$

The equation of the curve will give y in terms of x, and an appropriate substitution will yield an integral of the form

$$\int_a^b \pi (f \circ x)^2\, dx$$

that can be evaluated by the fundamental theorem.

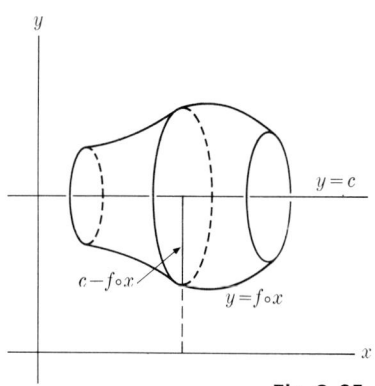

Fig. 3-25

Fig. 3-26

The general formula might be written

$$V = \int_a^b \pi r^2 \, dx,$$

where $r(p_i)$ is the radius of the figure at p_i. If the axis of revolution is the line on which $y = c$, then (Figs. 3-25 and 3-26) r is either

$$c - f \circ x \quad \text{or} \quad f \circ x - c,$$

depending on whether the locus of $y = f \circ x$ is below or above the line. One word of caution is in order here. A complete drawing of a solid of revolution shows both the locus of $y = f \circ x$ and the reflection of this curve through the axis of revolution. This reflection will have a different equation. In order to avoid confusion in deciding which way to subtract, label the curve whose equation is given.

For example, let us find the volume of a sphere of radius a. (Archimedes' crowning achievement was to do this the hard way.) By the Pythagorean theorem, $x^2 + y^2 = a^2$ on the circle with radius a and center at the origin. Therefore the locus of

$$y = \sqrt{a^2 - x^2}$$

is a semicircle which sweeps out the required sphere when it is revolved about the x-axis. The circular cross section (Fig. 3-27) has radius measured by y; so

$$V = \int_{-a}^{a} \pi y^2 \, dx.$$

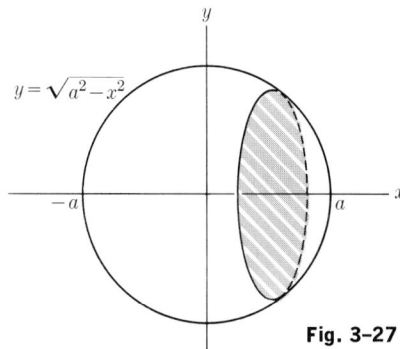

Fig. 3-27

96 CALCULUS

Since $y^2 = a^2 - x^2$ on the curve in question, then

$$V = \int_{-a}^{a} \pi(a^2 - x^2)\, dx$$

$$= \pi\left(a^2 x - \frac{x^3}{3}\right)\Big|_{-a}^{a} = \frac{4\pi a^3}{3}.$$

As another example, let us find the volume generated by revolving the bounded figure enclosed by the loci of

$$y = x^2,$$
$$y = 4,$$

and

$$x = 0$$

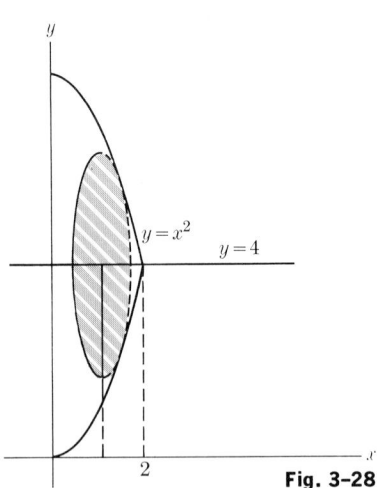

Fig. 3-28

about the line on which $y = 4$. It appears from Fig. 3-28 that the radius of the section is measured by $4 - y$; so

$$V = \int_{0}^{2} \pi(4 - y)^2\, dx.$$

Since $y = x^2$ on the curve to which these radii are measured,

$$V = \int_{0}^{2} \pi(4 - x^2)^2\, dx = \int_{0}^{2} \pi(16 - 8x^2 + x^4)\, dx$$

$$= \pi\left(16x - \frac{8x^3}{3} + \frac{x^5}{5}\right)\Big|_{0}^{2} = \frac{256\pi}{15}.$$

EXERCISES

1. Referring to Fig. 3-29, consider each of the following revolutions of a plane figure about an axis. In each case find the volume of the solid generated. It is suggested that answers be left in the form $F \circ x \big|_{a}^{b}$. The arithmetic involved in the remaining steps is not particularly enlightening and may be omitted.
   a) A about the x-axis
   b) B about the x-axis
   c) D about the x-axis
   d) $E + F + G$ about the x-axis
   e) F about the x-axis
   f) G and H about the x-axis
   g) $H + I + J + K$ about the line on which $y = -2$
   h) $B + C + D + I$ about the line on which $y = -2$
   i) $E + J$ about the line on which $y = -2$

j) $K + H$ about the line on which $y = -2$
k) K about the line on which $y = -2$

2. Each of the labeled plane figures in Fig. 3-30 is bounded by two straight lines. Revolve each of these plane figures about each of its bounding lines to generate four solids of revolution, and find the volume of each of these solids.

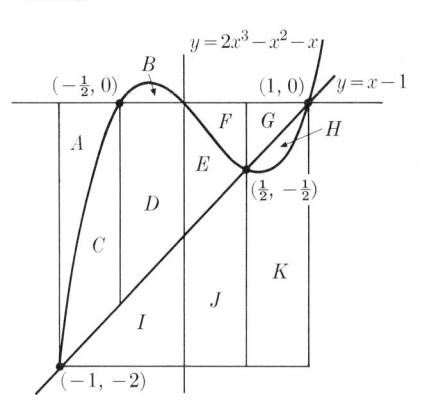

Fig. 3-29

Fig. 3-30

3-13 MAX-MIN PROBLEMS

In Section 3-10 we discussed the geometric theory of local maxima and minima. Actually, the ideas suggested there may be applied much more generally. Let u and v be two related variables (all sorts of physical and/or geometric interpretations are allowable.) If at some point of the common domain of u and v,

$$D_u v = 0 \quad \text{and} \quad D_u^2 v < 0,$$

then v has a local maximum at this point. If

$$D_u v = 0 \quad \text{and} \quad D_u^2 v > 0,$$

then v has a local minimum.

For example, let us find two numbers whose sum is 10 and whose product is a maximum. Let x and y be two variables such that

$$x + y = 10.$$

A geometric model for the domain of x and y could be supplied, but it would not contribute anything to the present discussion. The variable to be maximized is the product of x and y; so let

$$z = xy = x(10 - x).$$

Then
$$D_xz = 10 - 2x; \quad D_x^2 z = -2.$$

So z is a maximum when $x = 5$. The required numbers are 5 and 5.

Let us look at another example. A cylindrical tank with a bottom but no top is to have a volume of 10π cubic feet. Material for the bottom costs 15¢ a square foot, and that for the sides costs 12¢ a square foot. Find the dimensions for minimum cost. Let the variables r and h measure, respectively, radii and heights of cylinders, and let c measure costs. According to the conditions given,

$$c = 15\pi r^2 + 12 \cdot 2\pi rh.$$

Since the volume is to be 10π, then

$$\pi r^2 h = 10\pi, \quad \text{whence } h = 10/r^2;$$

therefore

$$c = 15\pi r^2 + \frac{240\pi}{r}; \quad D_r c = 30\pi r - \frac{240\pi}{r^2}; \quad D_r^2 c = 30\pi + \frac{480\pi}{r^3}.$$

Setting $D_r c = 0$ yields

$$30\pi r^3 - 240\pi = 0; \quad r = 2, \quad h = \tfrac{5}{2}.$$

Since $D_r^2 c > 0$ for $r = 2$, this is the desired minimum.

From these examples there emerges a definite pattern. The method of attack on such problems may be outlined as follows:

a) Introduce variables which measure quantities pertinent to the problem.

b) Write an equation giving the variable to be maximized or minimized in terms of other variables.

c) Use side conditions stated in the problem to eliminate all but one of the variables on the right-hand side of the equation in (b).

d) Differentiate and locate maxima and minima by setting the first derivative equal to zero and checking the sign of the second derivative.

EXERCISES

1. Find two numbers whose sum is 16 and the sum of whose squares is a minimum.

2. Find two numbers whose sum is 16 and the sum of whose cubes is a minimum.

3. Find two numbers whose sum is 16, such that the product of one number by the square of the other is a maximum.

4. Find two numbers whose sum is 16, such that the product of one number by the cube of the other is a maximum.

5. A man wants to fence off a rectangular garden plot, using his neighbor's stone wall for one side. He has 120 ft of fencing to use around the other three sides. Find the dimensions of the plot with maximum area.

6. A man wants to fence off a rectangular garden plot of 864 ft^2. He puts one side of it adjacent to his neighbor's property, and the neighbor agrees to pay half the cost of the fence down the property line. Find the dimensions of the plot for minimum cost to the owner.

7. A rectangular plot of perimeter 320 ft is to contain a rectangular swimming pool surrounded by a walk 4 ft wide along the sides and 6 ft wide along the ends. Find the dimensions of the plot for a pool of maximum area.

8. A poster is to contain 96 in^2 of printed matter with margins of 3 in. each at top and bottom and 2 in. at each side. Find the dimensions of printed matter for minimum total area.

9. An open storage bin with square base and vertical sides is to be constructed from 300 ft^2 of material. Assuming that no material is wasted, find the dimensions for maximum volume.

10. A box with square base and open top is to hold 32 in^3. Find the dimensions which require the least amount of material.

11. Right circular cylindrical tin cans are to be manufactured to contain 8 in^3 each. There is no waste in cutting the sides, but each end piece is cut from a square, and the remainder of the square is wasted. Find the dimensions of the cans to use the least material.

12. A box with square base is to be made from a square piece of cardboard 24 in. on a side by cutting out a square from each corner and turning up the sides. Find the dimensions if the box is to have maximum volume.

13. A box with a rectangular base is to be made from a rectangular piece of cardboard 24 by 12 in. by cutting out a square from each corner and turning up the sides. Find the dimensions if the box is to have maximum volume.

14. A box with a lid is to be made from a square piece of cardboard 24 in. on a side by cutting squares from two adjacent corners and then cutting from the other two corners rectangles so shaped that three of the resulting flaps will form sides and the fourth will form a side and the lid. Find the dimensions if the box is to have maximum volume.

15. A box with square base and top and vertical sides is to contain 625 ft^3. Material for the base costs 35¢ a square foot, for the top 15¢ a square foot, and for the sides 20¢ a square foot. Find the dimensions for minimum cost.

16. A silo in the form of a cylinder surmounted by a hemisphere is to have a capacity of 1000 $\pi/3$ ft^3. Construction costs per unit surface area are twice

as great for the hemisphere as for the cylinder, and it has a dirt floor. Find the dimensions for minimum cost.

17. A Norman window in the form of a rectangle surmounted by a semicircle is to have a perimeter of 24 ft. Find the dimensions for maximum area.

18. In the Norman window of Exercise 17, the rectangle is to have clear glass, while the semicircle is to have colored glass which admits only half as much light per square foot as the clear glass does. Find the dimensions that will admit the most light.

19. A paving contractor estimates that if he hires x men it will take $1 + 1200x^{-1}$ days to complete a certain job. He pays each man $10 a day, and he is to receive a bonus of $120 for each day less than 14 required for the job. Find the number of men he should hire for maximum profit.

20. A manufacturer's total costs in producing x articles per week are $ax^2 + bx + c$. There is a demand law $p = A - Bx$ relating his selling price and the number that he can expect to sell. Find the number that should be produced for maximum profit. [*Note:* a, b, c, A, and B are positive constants.]

21. The government imposes a tax of t dollars per item on the manufacturer. Add the tax to his costs, and redetermine the output for maximum profit. [*Note:* The answer here will depend on t.]

22. Assuming that the manufacturer proceeds as indicated in Exercise 21, find, in terms of the given constants, the value of t that will bring a maximum return to the government. Compute the price when this tax is imposed, and show that the increase in price is less than the tax.

23. Consider a particle moving back and forth on a straight line. Explain in terms of derivatives the intuitively evident fact that at the instant it turns around it has zero velocity.

24. According to Newton's second law of motion, the force on the particle in Exercise 23 is proportional to its acceleration. Explain in terms of derivatives the fact that the particle achieves its maximum speed at the instant the direction of the force is reversed.

25. Let c measure manufacturing costs, v volume of production, and r gross revenue to the manufacturer. An astute manufacturer will try to determine c and r in terms of v and adjust his volume of production so that the marginal cost ($D_v c$) is equal to the marginal revenue ($D_v r$). Why?

PROBABILITY 4

4-1 SAMPLE SPACES

It is the purpose of this chapter to describe briefly the basic ideas and techniques used in the mathematical formulation of probability problems. Roughly speaking, probability deals with the likelihood of experimental results. Now "likelihood" is essentially a psychological notion and "result" a physical one. (We class results as physical, though their significance may be sociological, economic, or what have you.) The basic question, then, is one of representing these physical and psychological notions by a mathematical model. We shall attack the physical problem in this section and the psychological one in Section 4-2. The remainder of the chapter will then present a few of the mathematical calculations that can be carried out once the proper model is set up.

The basic idea behind the representation of experimental results by a mathematical model is very simply described. We represent the set of all logically possible results of the given experiment by a space, each point of which represents uniquely an individual result. This space is called the *sample space* for the given problem.

$$\begin{matrix} \bullet & \bullet & \bullet & \bullet & \bullet & \bullet & \bullet & \bullet & \bullet & \bullet & \bullet \\ 2 & 3 & 4 & 5 & 6 & 7 & 8 & 9 & 10 & 11 & 12 \end{matrix}$$

Fig. 4-1

This is not quite as simple and clear-cut as it sounds at first because there may be some doubt as to what constitutes an "individual" result. Suppose, for example, that we want a sample space for the purpose of studying the result of throwing two dice. Often the only significant "result" is the total shown on the two dice. So an eleven-point sample space (Fig. 4-1) might suffice.

On the other hand, we might be interested in the various possible combinations of numbers on the individual dice. As dice are usually thrown, the two little cubes are indistinguishable one from the other; so we make

102 PROBABILITY 4-1

no distinction between the results (4, 3) and (3, 4), etc. This gives a 21-point sample space (Fig. 4–2).

Finally, we might want to distinguish between the two dice (perhaps, physically, by having them colored differently) and list as our sample space the set of all ordered pairs of numbers appearing, respectively, on the first and second dice. It would be natural to picture this space as in Fig. 4–3, with the abscissa of each point representing the result on the first die and the ordinate that on the second.

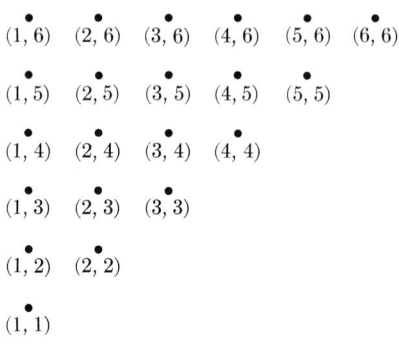

(1, 6) (2, 6) (3, 6) (4, 6) (5, 6) (6, 6)
(1, 5) (2, 5) (3, 5) (4, 5) (5, 5)
(1, 4) (2, 4) (3, 4) (4, 4)
(1, 3) (2, 3) (3, 3)
(1, 2) (2, 2)
(1, 1)

Fig. 4–2

Now in probability theory an *event* is defined as a subset of the sample space. For example, in Fig. 4–3 the physical event "total is six" is represented by the set outlined by the dashed lines. Another event is outlined by the solid lines in Fig. 4–3, but this one does not have as succinct a physical description. Note also that the phrase "throwing a double six" might naturally be referred to as describing either a result of the dice experiment or an event connected with the problem. In the technical

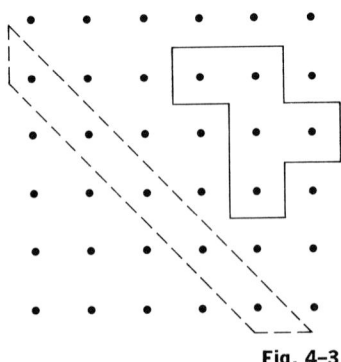

Fig. 4–3

terminology introduced here, this result is a point in the sample space of Fig. 4–3, while this event is a singleton set in that space.

Finally, note that the event "three on the first die" is the third column in Fig. 4–3, but is not representable in either Fig. 4–1 or 4–2. So, although our discussion of the dice example has shown that there may be more than one sample space to represent a given experiment, one factor in choosing a sample space is the type of event that is to be studied. In Section 4–2 we shall encounter other factors that serve to govern our choice of sample space.

EXERCISES

1. Assume that the 20 major-league baseball teams are located as follows. (This was correct for 1967 but may well change.)

    National League
    Atlanta
    Chicago
    Cincinnati
    Houston
    Los Angeles
    New York
    Philadelphia
    Pittsburgh
    San Francisco
    St. Louis

    American League
    Baltimore
    Boston
    Chicago
    Cleveland
    Detroit
    Kansas City
    Los Angeles
    Minneapolis-St. Paul
    New York
    Washington

    Construct a sample space to represent all logically possible World Series results. Here "result" means which teams played and who won; this space will have 200 points. On a sketch of this space identify each of the following events.
    a) The American League team won.
    b) The New York Yankees (AL) played but lost.
    c) The Yankees did not win the American League pennant.
    d) There was a Los Angeles team in the series.
    e) It was a "subway" series—both teams from the same city.
    f) The teams in the series were from the same state.
    g) The winning team was from east of the Mississippi River. (Call Minneapolis-St. Paul west of the river; the stadium is.)
    h) At least one of the country's five largest cities was represented in the series. [1960 census: New York, Los Angeles, Chicago, Philadelphia, Detroit.]

2. Return to the era 1920–1940, when each league had eight teams, as follows.

National League	American League
Boston	Boston
Brooklyn	Chicago
Chicago	Cleveland
Cincinnati	Detroit
New York	New York
Philadelphia	Philadelphia
Pittsburgh	St. Louis
St. Louis	Washington

Repeat the questions of Exercise 1.

3. There are 3 urns, each containing red, white, and blue balls. We conduct an experiment which involves choosing an urn by some device and then drawing a ball from it. Construct a sample space and identify each of the following events.
   a) Urn I was chosen.
   b) A white ball was drawn from Urn II.
   c) Either a red ball was drawn from Urn I or a white one from Urn II or a blue one from Urn III.
   d) The urn was either II or III and the ball drawn was either red or blue.
   e) The ball drawn was yellow.

4. If a coin is tossed 3 times in succession there are 8 possible results (sample result: H T H). List the 8 results and identify the following events.
   a) The first toss is heads.
   b) The first two tosses are the same.
   c) The first and last tosses are different.
   d) The last two tosses are the same.

5. Draw the 8-point sample space of Exercise 4 as the set of vertices of a cube. Place the cube in a 3-dimensional coordinate system so that each coordinate of a vertex indicates the result of one toss. Identify the four events of Exercise 4 on this sketch.

4–2 PROBABILITY MEASURES

The events connected with a probability problem are given a mathematical representation through the introduction of a sample space and its subsets. We now turn to the problem of introducing a numerical measure of the likelihood of these events. Now, in mathematical language, associating a numerical measure of something with each event means defining a real-valued function whose domain is the class of all subsets of the sample space.

Let S be a sample space. A real-valued function P on the class of all subsets of S is called a *probability measure* if it has the following properties.

1. $P(E) \geq 0$ for every $E \subset S$.
2. $P(S) = 1$.
3. If $A \cap B = \emptyset$, then $P(A \cup B) = P(A) + P(B)$.

4-2 PROBABILITY MEASURES

In technical terms we say that a probability measure is an additive (Postulate 3), nonnegative (Postulate 1) function on the subsets of the sample space which has the value 1 on the space itself (Postulate 2).

To keep the record straight, we should note in passing that in advanced probability theory a stronger additivity postulate than (3) above is needed, and that with this stronger postulate it is not always possible to define the measure on all subsets of the sample space. However, for the problems to be studied here, the more sophisticated postulate system will always reduce to that stated above.

To give a complete listing of a probability measure we would have to specify its value on each subset of the sample space. This gets rather cumbersome. For example, in an 8-point space there are $2^8 = 256$ subsets. Because of the additivity postulate, however, it suffices for finite spaces (which is all we shall consider here) to specify the measure of each singleton set. Then (see Exercise 5 below) the measure of any set is the sum of the measures of its singleton subsets. So the normal way of describing a probability measure is to assign a weight to each point in the sample space.

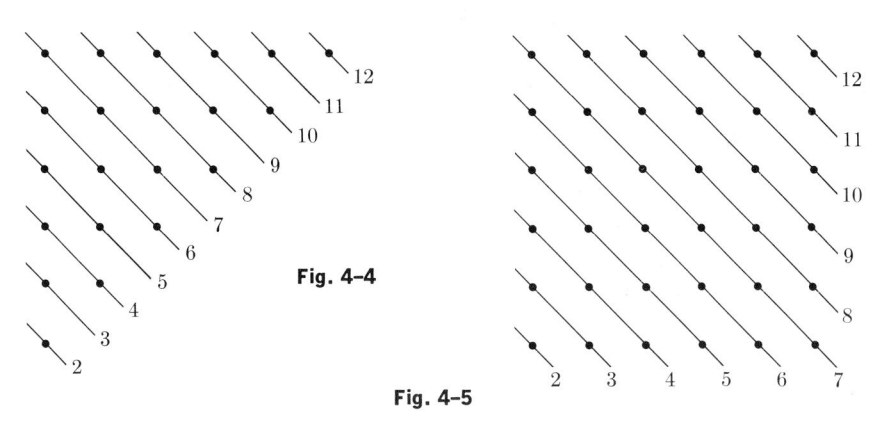

Fig. 4-4

Fig. 4-5

By way of example, let us return to the problem of two dice discussed in Section 4-1. There we suggested three different sample spaces for this problem. The last two of these are reproduced here (Figs. 4-4 and 4-5). The space of Fig. 4-4 contains 21 points. Suppose we assign a probability of $\frac{1}{21}$ to each of these singleton sets. The events "total equals so much" are indicated by the slanting lines; so it is a simple matter of counting to see that this assignment of probabilities for singleton sets yields the probabilities for totals as listed in Table 1.

Total	2	3	4	5	6	7	8	9	10	11	12
Probability	$\frac{1}{21}$	$\frac{1}{21}$	$\frac{2}{21}$	$\frac{2}{21}$	$\frac{1}{7}$	$\frac{1}{7}$	$\frac{1}{7}$	$\frac{2}{21}$	$\frac{2}{21}$	$\frac{1}{21}$	$\frac{1}{21}$

Table 1

Total	2	3	4	5	6	7	8	9	10	11	12
Probability	$\frac{1}{36}$	$\frac{1}{18}$	$\frac{1}{12}$	$\frac{1}{9}$	$\frac{5}{36}$	$\frac{1}{6}$	$\frac{5}{36}$	$\frac{1}{9}$	$\frac{1}{12}$	$\frac{1}{18}$	$\frac{1}{36}$

Table 2

Suppose, on the other hand, that each point in Fig. 4–5 is assigned a weight of $\frac{1}{36}$. The probabilities for totals then come out as in Table 2. Clearly, these two formulations of the problem are inconsistent, and experience shows that the latter is a better representation of the dice problem than the former.

Although the first analysis given above does not give a faithful representation of the dice problem, we mentioned it because it does constitute a perfectly good example of a sample space with probability measure. Primarily, probability theory is concerned with purely mathematical manipulations carried out *after the sample space and probability measure are given*. A simple example of this is the derivation of Tables 1 and 2 above from appropriate assumptions. Though Table 1 does not represent the usual situation with regard to dice, its derivation from the assignment of equal weights to the points in Fig. 4–4 is just as sound an exercise in probability theory as is the derivation of the more familiar Table 2 from a different set of assumptions.

Note that if the points in Fig. 4–4 were assigned weights as indicated in Fig. 4–6, then we would have a faithful representation of the dice problem and an analysis of probabilities of totals would yield Table 2. It is possible to arrive at this analysis of the problem directly, but for this particular problem the 36-point space with equal weights seems the simplest approach.

$$\begin{array}{cccccc}
\frac{1}{18} & \frac{1}{18} & \frac{1}{18} & \frac{1}{18} & \frac{1}{18} & \frac{1}{36} \\
\frac{1}{18} & \frac{1}{18} & \frac{1}{18} & \frac{1}{18} & \frac{1}{36} & \\
\frac{1}{18} & \frac{1}{18} & \frac{1}{18} & \frac{1}{36} & & \\
\frac{1}{18} & \frac{1}{18} & \frac{1}{36} & & & \\
\frac{1}{18} & \frac{1}{36} & & & & \\
\frac{1}{36} & & & & & \\
\end{array}$$

Fig. 4–6

In summary, let us note the following items concerning sample spaces and probability measures.

1. Often several different sample spaces suggest themselves in connection with a given problem. The choice of space is governed by at least two factors.

    a) The events to be discussed

    b) The complications involved in assigning a probability measure.

2. The sample space with probability measure is the structure *from* which probability theory works. It is not an end in itself.

3. *Any* function satisfying the postulates given in this section is a probability measure and is a legitimate object of study in probability theory. The process of finding one to fit a given physical situation must in the final analysis involve a subjective judgment and is not susceptible to a purely mathematical treatment.

4. If there are two spaces to represent a problem and one of them should have equally weighted points, then the subjective justification is probably easier there than in the space with unequally weighted points. This is the primary reason for the frequent appearance of equally weighted sample space points.

EXERCISES

1. In Exercise 4, Section 4–1, assume that each of the 8 possible results has probability $\frac{1}{8}$, and find the probability of each of the events listed there.
2. The following chart gives 9 numbers assumed to be probabilities of singleton sets in a 9-point space. The labels around the margins connect this space with the ball-and-urn scheme of Exercise 3, Section 4–1.

Red	0.025	0.25	0.075
White	0.05	0.25	0.1
Blue	0.025	0.1	0.125
	I	II	III

Find the probability of each event listed there.

3. Six tickets, numbered 1–6, are placed in a hat and two are drawn. The second drawing is made without replacing the first ticket drawn. Represent this by a 30-point sample space (6 by 6 with a diagonal missing) and give each singleton set probability $\frac{1}{30}$.
   a) The possible totals of the two numbers drawn range from 3 to 11. Find the probability for each of these totals.
   b) Find the probability that the first ticket drawn was number 4.
   c) Find the probability that the second ticket drawn was number 4.
   d) Find the probability that the larger of the two numbers drawn exceeded the smaller by an odd number.
4. A horse race has 4 entries: Man O'War, Whirlaway, Citation, and Beetlebaum. There are 24 possible orders of finishing and a soothsayer named Imabookie has assigned these probabilities as follows.

MWCB	0.05	WMCB	0.07	CMWB	0.05	BMWC	0.01
MWBC	0.04	WMBC	0.06	CMBW	0.05	BMCW	0.01
MCWB	0.04	WCMB	0.10	CWMB	0.08	BWMC	0.02
MCBW	0.03	WCBM	0.09	CWBM	0.07	BWCM	0.03
MBWC	0.02	WBMC	0.05	CBMW	0.02	BCMW	0.01
MBCW	0.02	WBCM	0.03	CBWM	0.03	BCWM	0.02

For each of the four horses, find the probability that he will win, will place (run first or second), will show (run first, second or third).

5. Prove that for any probability measure P and for any sets $E_1, E_2, \ldots, E_n$, with $E_i \cap E_j = \emptyset$ for $i \neq j$,

$$P\left(\bigcup_{i=1}^{n} E_i\right) = \sum_{i=1}^{n} P(E_i).$$

Hint: Use mathematical induction on the number of sets involved. Note that

$$\bigcup_{i=1}^{n} E_i = \left(\bigcup_{i=1}^{n-1} E_i\right) \cup E_n.$$

6. Prove that for any probability measure P, $P(\emptyset) = 0$.
7. Prove that if P is a probability measure and $A \subset B$, then $P(A) \leq P(B)$. Physically, we often say that one event implies another. Interpret this result in these terms.
8. Prove that if P is any probability measure, then $0 \leq P(A) \leq 1$ for every event A.
9. Let P be a probability measure and let A, B, and C be any events in its domain.
   a) Prove that $P(A \cup B) = P(A) + P(B) - P(A \cap B)$.
   b) Prove that $P(A \cup B \cup C) = P(A) + P(B) + P(C) - P(A \cap B) - P(A \cap C) - P(B \cap C) + P(A \cap B \cap C)$.

4-3 CONDITIONAL PROBABILITY

Let A and B be events. We introduce here the concept known in technical terms as the *probability of A, given B*. This is denoted by

$$P(A \mid B).$$

In terms of the physical and psychological background of probability theory, this is supposed to be the answer to the question, "Suppose B is known to have occurred, what then is the likelihood of the occurrence of A?"

Strictly speaking, this notion, known generally as conditional probability, is given a purely mathematical definition. To see why this definition was chosen, however, we turn to the physical-psychological interpretation. Suppose A and B are subsets of a sample space, as shown in Fig. 4–7. If B is assumed to have occurred, then the only possible manifestations of A are those represented by the points in $A \cap B$. So $P(A \mid B)$ should be the probability of $A \cap B$ adjusted to a scale in which B has probability 1. Thus we have the mathematical definition

$$P(A \mid B) = \frac{P(A \cap B)}{P(B)}. \tag{1}$$

This definition is often useful in the form

$$P(A \cap B) = P(B)P(A \mid B). \quad (2)$$

It may happen that

$$P(A \mid B) = P(A). \quad (3)$$

From the physical-psychological viewpoint, this says that the likelihood of A is the same no matter whether B is known to have occurred or whether nothing is known about B. In this case we say that A and B are independent. The usual definition of independence is obtained by substituting (1) into (3) and multiplying by $P(B)$. That is, A and B are *independent events* provided

$$P(A \cap B) = P(A)P(B). \quad (4)$$

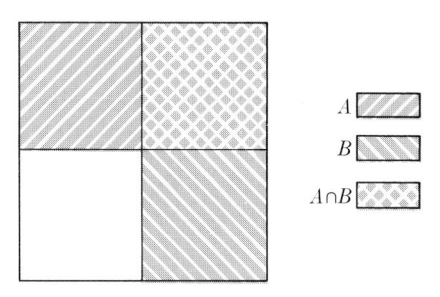

Fig. 4-7

It should be emphasized that in probability theory independence is a purely mathematical concept. Events A and B are independent if and only if (4) holds, no matter what causal relations may or may not seem to be present.

By way of example, let us consider a problem concerning three urns, each containing red, white, and blue balls. This was considered in Exercise 3, Section 4–1, and again in Exercise 2, Section 4–2. We are now in a position to obtain the probability measure from a physical description of the problem. Suppose there is a control urn containing ten tickets, one of them numbered I, six numbered II and three numbered III. Suppose, further, that the three numbered urns contain colored balls in the following quantities:

	Red	White	Blue
I	1	2	1
II	2	5	5
III	5	4	3

The procedure now is to draw a ticket from the control urn, choose the indicated numbered urn and draw a ball from it.

Clearly, the probability that we use Urn I is $\frac{1}{10}$. In obviously suggestive notation:

$$P(\text{I}) = 0.1.$$

Given that we are using Urn I, the probability of drawing a red ball is $\frac{1}{4}$. This we write

$$P(R \mid \text{I}) = 0.25.$$

Combining these results by Eq. (2) above, we have

$$P(R \cap \text{I}) = P(\text{I})P(R \mid \text{I}) = 0.025;$$

this is the top left entry in the table of Exercise 2, Section 4-2. We leave it to the reader to continue this procedure and show that the physical assumptions listed here lead precisely to the probabilities given in that exercise. We repeat that table for reference:

Red	0.025	0.25	0.075
White	0.05	0.25	0.1
Blue	0.025	0.1	0.125
	I	II	III

Adding across the rows in this table, we obtain the probabilities for the eventual appearance of the various colors:

$$P(R) = 0.35, \quad P(W) = 0.4, \quad P(B) = 0.25.$$

Adding down the columns, we recover the already assumed probabilities for the various urn choices:

$$P(\text{I}) = 0.1, \quad P(\text{II}) = 0.6, \quad P(\text{III}) = 0.3.$$

In this problem the conditional probabilities for colors, given urn number, were intuitively clear and were used in setting up the probability measure. Once the measure is obtained, however, all other conditional probabilities are available through the definition (1). For example, the probability that the urn used was II, given that a blue ball was drawn, is

$$P(\text{II} \mid B) = \frac{P(\text{II} \cap B)}{P(B)} = \frac{0.1}{0.25} = 0.4.$$

Finally, note that

$$P(\text{I} \cap B) = 0.025 = 0.1 \times 0.25 = P(\text{I})P(B);$$

so the events "Urn I was used" and "a blue ball was drawn" are independent. There is no obvious psychological basis for this, but in probability theory, independence is defined solely by Eq. (4) of this section.

EXERCISES

1. There are six tickets in an urn, numbered 1–6. A ticket is drawn and replaced; then a second ticket is drawn.
    a) Set up the sample space and probability measure.
    b) What is the probability that the second ticket drawn was No. 4?
    c) Find the probability that the second number drawn was exactly one more than the first, given that it was greater than the first.
    d) Are the following events independent or dependent?
       A: The second number drawn was exactly one more than the first.
       B: The first number drawn was 2 or 3 and the second was 4, 5, or 6.

2. From the urn of Exercise 1 the second ticket is drawn without replacing the first. Repeat the questions of Exercise 1 and compare results.

3. Still referring to the tickets in the urn, after the first draw, that ticket is held out; also all smaller numbers are removed before the second drawing. (Note that the effect of this procedure is to force the second draw to be larger than the first.) Set up the sample space and probability measure for this experiment and find the probability that the second number drawn is exactly one more than the first. Compare Exercises 1(c) and 2(c).

4. Refer to Exercise 4, Section 4–1, and justify the assignment of probabilities suggested in Exercise 1, Section 4–2. Show the following concerning the events listed in Exercise 4, Section 4–1.

   a) Events a, b, and c are *totally independent*. That is,
   $$P(a \cap b \cap c) = P(a)P(b)P(c).$$

   b) Events b, c, and d are independent by pairs but not totally independent.

5. Imabookie the soothsayer (Exercise 4, Section 4–2) also has a crystal baseball. He lists the following probabilities for the various major-league teams to win in their respective leagues.

   National League

Atlanta	0.15
Chicago	0.03
Cincinnati	0.15
Houston	0.005
Los Angeles	0.2
New York	0.005
Philadelphia	0.08
Pittsburgh	0.08
San Francisco	0.15
St. Louis	0.15

   American League

Baltimore	0.15
Boston	0.04
Chicago	0.1
Cleveland	0.1
Detroit	0.04
Kansas City	0.005
Los Angeles	0.01
Minneapolis-St. Paul	0.15
New York	0.4
Washington	0.005

   He further says that if teams A and B are in the World Series and A had a larger probability of winning in its league than did B, then the probability is 0.7 that A will win the Series. If they had equal probabilities of winning in their leagues, the Series is a toss-up. On the basis of these figures, find a probability measure for the sample space of Exercise 1, Section 4–1, and find the probability of each event listed there.

6. Make your own form chart for the teams of yesteryear (Exercise 2, Section 4–1), and repeat the questions of Exercise 5.

7. Suppose we describe the independence of A and B by saying that the probability of A is the same, given that B occurred, as it is when given that B did not occur. In symbols:
   $$P(A \mid B) = P(A \mid -B).$$

   Show that this is equivalent to definition (4) given above.

8. A system is in initial state I_1 or I_2 with probability a_1 and a_2, respectively. It shifts to final state F_1 or F_2, with b_{jk} denoting the probability of a shift from I_j to F_k. Set up a 4-point sample space, each point representing a possible combination of initial and final state. Find the probability measure and show that

$$P(I_1 \mid F_2) = \frac{a_1 b_{12}}{a_1 b_{12} + a_2 b_{22}}.$$

9. (Bayes' Theorem) Generalize Exercise 8. If there are m initial states and n final states, then

$$P(I_j \mid F_k) = \frac{a_j b_{jk}}{\sum_{i=1}^{m} a_i b_{ik}}.$$

4-4 RANDOM VARIABLES

Consider the 36-point sample space representing the results of throwing two dice. With each point of this space there is naturally associated a number giving the total shown on the two dice for each of the possible results. Now, mathematically, associating a number with each point of a space means defining a real-valued function on the space. In probability theory a real-valued function on the sample space is called a *random variable*. Often, as with the example of the total on two dice, random variables represent measurements of interest in the physical problem. Indeed, a typical mathematical model for a probability problem consists of a sample space with probability measure together with appropriate random variables to represent the measurements to be studied.

Let S be a sample space, x a random variable on S, and a a real number. The truth set for the equation

$$x = a$$

is (see Section 1–6)

$$\{p \mid x(p) = a\}.$$

This truth set is an event; that is, it is an element of the domain of the probability measure P. Instead of writing $P(\{p \mid x(p) = a\})$, however, it is customary to write merely

$$P(x = a).$$

That is, notation that seems to refer to "probability of an equation" is shorthand meaning "probability of the truth set for the equation." The same abbreviated notation is applied to inequalities; example:

$$P(x \leq a).$$

For the case of finite sample spaces (which is all we shall discuss here), there is associated with each random variable x a function f_x called the *probability function* for x. Specifically, f_x is a function from the range of x into the unit interval defined by setting

$$f_x(t) = P(x = t) \tag{1}$$

for each t in the range of x.

For example, if z is the random variable measuring the total on two dice, then f_z is as follows:

t	2	3	4	5	6	7	8	9	10	11	12
$f_z(t)$	$\frac{1}{36}$	$\frac{1}{18}$	$\frac{1}{12}$	$\frac{1}{9}$	$\frac{5}{36}$	$\frac{1}{6}$	$\frac{5}{36}$	$\frac{1}{9}$	$\frac{1}{12}$	$\frac{1}{18}$	$\frac{1}{36}$

Clearly,

$$P(3 \leq z \leq 7) = \sum_{t=3}^{7} f_z(t),$$

and in a similar way the probability of any event characterized solely by values of z can be recovered from f_z. However, not every event in the 36-point sample space can be so characterized; so f_z is not a substitute for the probability measure P.

Continuing with the example of the two dice, consider the random variables x and y defined as follows:

$x = $ the number on the first die,
$y = $ the number on the second die.

As the 36-point sample space is usually drawn, x and y actually assume the role of coordinate variables. The probability functions f_x and f_y are as follows:

t	1	2	3	4	5	6
$f_x(t)$	$\frac{1}{6}$	$\frac{1}{6}$	$\frac{1}{6}$	$\frac{1}{6}$	$\frac{1}{6}$	$\frac{1}{6}$
$f_y(t)$	$\frac{1}{6}$	$\frac{1}{6}$	$\frac{1}{6}$	$\frac{1}{6}$	$\frac{1}{6}$	$\frac{1}{6}$

We say that x and y are *identical* random variables because their probability functions are the same. However, in this case we also say that x and y are *independent* random variables because for every a in the range of x and every b in the range of y, $x = a$ and $y = b$ are independent events. The phrase "identical and independent" sounds paradoxical, but this is a case often encountered. It must be borne in mind that the adjective "identical" as applied to a set of random variables applies only to their probability functions; it does not refer to the random variables themselves as functions on the sample space. In the present example, x and y are quite different functions on the sample space, but we call them identical because $f_x = f_y$.

Note, finally, that the variable z, measuring totals, is the sum of x and y. That is, for each point p in the sample space $z(p) = x(p) + y(p)$.

Thus, we say that
$$z = x + y.$$

Other random variables on this space can be obtained by taking other combinations of the coordinates. For example, we might ask for the probability function for $x - y$. This is easily found from Fig. 4–8 and the definition (1) of probability function. The result is

	−5	−4	−3	−2	−1	0	1	2	3	4	5
$f_{x-y}(t)$	$\frac{1}{36}$	$\frac{1}{18}$	$\frac{1}{12}$	$\frac{1}{9}$	$\frac{5}{36}$	$\frac{1}{6}$	$\frac{5}{36}$	$\frac{1}{9}$	$\frac{1}{12}$	$\frac{1}{18}$	$\frac{1}{36}$

Other combinations, such as xy, are also worth investigating.

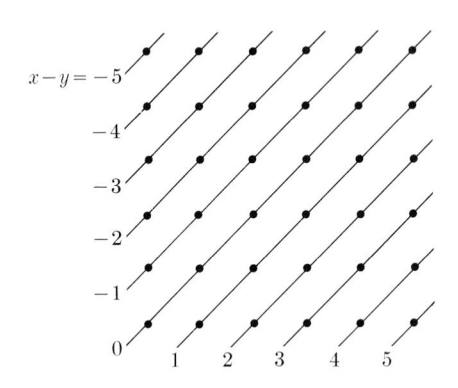

Fig. 4–8

One of the most profitable areas of study in probability theory is involved with sums of random variables (particularly sums of independent random variables). The present discussion is designed merely to indicate what this means. Some few items from the rather extensive theory will appear in subsequent sections.

EXERCISES

1. In the ticket-drawing problem of Exercise 1, Section 4–3, let x be the first number drawn and let y be the second.
    a) Find the probability function for each of the following random variables:
    $$x, \quad y, \quad x + y, \quad x - y + 7, \quad xy.$$
    b) Are x and y identical? Are they independent?
    c) Are $x + y$ and $x - y + 7$ identical? Are they independent?
2. Repeat the questions of Exercise 1 for the ticket-drawing scheme of Exercise 2, Section 4–3.

3. Do the same for Exercise 3, Section 4-3.

4. Referring to Exercise 5, Section 4-1, let $x = 0$ indicate "tails on the first throw," with y and z indicating the other two throws in a similar way. What is the physical significance of the random variable $x + y + z$?

5. There are 25 tickets in an urn, numbered 1-25. Ten times a ticket is drawn and returned. Represent the sum of the numbers drawn as the sum of ten random variables. Find the probability functions for the individual random variables, but do not attempt to find the one for the sum.

6. Repeat Exercise 5 for the case in which the tickets are not replaced in the urn after being drawn.

4-5 EXPECTATION

Let x be a random variable; let R be its range and f_x its probability function. The *expectation* of x, denoted by $\bar{x}$ or $E(x)$, is defined as

$$\bar{x} = E(x) = \sum_{t \in R} t f_x(t). \tag{1}$$

For example, if z is the random variable measuring the total thrown on two dice, then

$$E(z) = 2 \cdot \tfrac{1}{36} + 3 \cdot \tfrac{1}{18} + 4 \cdot \tfrac{1}{12} + 5 \cdot \tfrac{1}{9} + 6 \cdot \tfrac{5}{36} + 7 \cdot \tfrac{1}{6}$$
$$+ 8 \cdot \tfrac{5}{36} + 9 \cdot \tfrac{1}{9} + 10 \cdot \tfrac{1}{12} + 11 \cdot \tfrac{1}{18} + 12 \cdot \tfrac{1}{36} = 7.$$

An alternative definition of $E(x)$ is as follows. Let S be the sample space and P the probability measure; then

$$E(x) = \sum_{p \in S} x(p) P(\{p\}). \tag{2}$$

If in the sum (2), we group together all those terms for which $x(p) = t$, the sum of such terms is

$$\sum_{x(p)=t} x(p) P(\{p\}) = t P(x = t) = t f_x(t).$$

So the sum (1) is merely the sum (2) with terms rearranged and appropriately grouped.

The notation $\bar{x}$ is used to suggest the idea of "average x" and indeed $\bar{x}$ is a weighted average of the values assumed by x. The weight assigned to each value is its probability.

The word "expectation" is intended to be suggestive, and indeed $E(x)$ is often referred to as the "expected value of x." The mathematical meaning of "expect" in this connection will be discussed in subsequent sections, and it is best not to form preconceived ideas. [Note Exercise 1 (d) below.] For the present, let "expectation" be merely a new technical word standing for a quantity that can be computed by either formula (1) or formula (2) above.

In formula (2), the symbol x is merely a symbol for an arbitrary function on S. If the function happens to be denoted by $x + y$, the formula still applies equally well. This observation leads to a very important result:

$$E(x + y) = \sum_{p \in S} (x + y)(p)P(\{p\}) = \sum_{p \in S} [x(p) + y(p)]P(\{p\})$$
$$= \sum_{p \in S} x(p)P(\{p\}) + \sum_{p \in S} y(p)P(\{p\}) = E(x) + E(y).$$

The expectation of the sum of two random variables is the sum of their expectations.

Let us illustrate the use of this result. Suppose there are 100 tickets in an urn, numbered 1–100. Suppose that 20 times a ticket is drawn and replaced; what is the expectation of the sum of the numbers drawn? We introduce random variables $x_1, x_2, \ldots, x_{20}$, where x_i is the number on the ith ticket drawn. To find $E(x_i)$, we recall the formula

$$\sum_{k=1}^{n} k = \frac{n(n+1)}{2}.$$

Using this, we have

$$E(x_i) = \sum_{k=1}^{100} k \cdot \frac{1}{100} = \frac{100(101)}{2} \cdot \frac{1}{100} = 50.5.$$

Now the variable whose expectation we seek is

$$z = \sum_{i=1}^{20} x_i;$$

therefore

$$E(z) = \sum_{i=1}^{20} E(x_i) = 20 \times 50.5 = 1010.$$

With the same setup, suppose the tickets are not replaced. What, then, is the expectation of the total? We introduce variables x_i as before. Again the variables x_i are identical (have identical probability functions). The beginning of an argument to this effect is suggested in Exercise 2(a, b) of Section 4–3; we omit further details. Since the x_i are identical, it is clear from (1) that they all have the same expectation, and again this is 50.5. Now the important thing is that, *just as in the case of independent variables* discussed above, the expectation of the total is 20×50.5.

The addition theorem for expectations holds regardless of how the variables are related. This is a major reason why a common maneuver in probability theory is to set up the problem in such a way that pertinent random variables appear as sums of simpler ones.

EXERCISES

1. The expected total on two dice was found above as a direct application of formula (1).
   a) What is the expectation of the number appearing on a single die?
   b) Use part (a) and the addition theorem to get the expected total on two dice again.
   c) What is the expected total thrown on n dice?
   d) What does the answer to part (a) mean as an "expected value" of a random variable?

2. Run a similar analysis on coin tossing.
   a) On the 8-point sample space of Exercise 4, Section 4–1, define a random variable x that gives the number of heads. Find $E(x)$.
   b) What is the expected number of heads on one toss of a coin?
   c) Use part (b) and the addition theorem to get the result in part (a) again.
   d) What is the expected number of heads on n tosses of a coin?

3. In the example discussed in the text we drew 20 tickets from a lot of 100. Consider the simplified model in which we draw 2 (without replacement) from a supply of 3. Let x and y be, respectively, the first and second numbers drawn.
   a) Set up a sample space in which x and y are the coordinate variables and find the probability measure.
   b) Compute $E(x + y)$ directly from the probability measure by formula (2).
   c) Find $E(x)$ and $E(y)$; add and check against part (b).

4. Let aces count 1, kings, queens and jacks, 10, and other cards according to denomination.
   a) A single card is drawn from a standard deck. Find the expected count by the scale listed above.
   b) Ten cards are drawn simultaneously. What is the expected count?

5. In a popular bridge bidding system, basic point count for honor cards is: aces 4, kings 3, queens 2, jacks 1. Ignoring other bases for point count (long, short suits, etc.), find the expected point count in a 13-card bridge hand.

6. There are n balls, numbered $1-n$, to be placed one each in n pockets, likewise numbered $1-n$.
   a) Let $n = 3$. List the six possible orders in which the balls can be arranged. Assume these represent the way they go into the pockets and that these orderings are equally likely.
   b) From part (a), find the probability that ball 2 goes in pocket 2; that ball 3 goes in pocket 3.
   c) Assuming ball 1 is placed first in a randomly chosen pocket, then ball 2 in a randomly chosen empty pocket, give a conditional probability argument to justify the probability assumptions suggested in part (a).
   d) Generalize to arbitrary n. What is the probability that ball k goes in pocket k?

e) We call it a match if ball and pocket number are the same. Find the expected number of matches.

7. (St. Petersburg problem) Any random variable on a finite sample space obviously has an expectation. On an infinite sample space, this may not be the case. The following is a classical example. To raise money for the czar, the Russian government once proposed to bank a game in which the player tossed a coin until it came up tails. If he tossed n heads before the first tails, he was to be paid 2^n rubles. Find the expected payoff. [*Hint:* There is an infinite set of possible results: T, H T, H H T, H H H T, etc.]

4-6 VARIANCE

Let x be a random variable. The *variance* of x, denoted by var (x), is defined as
$$\text{var}(x) = E[(x - \bar{x})^2].$$

Direct computation from the probability function would involve summing $(t - \bar{x})^2 f_x(t)$ over all t in the range of x. However, we can obtain a simpler computational scheme as follows. Note that if c is a constant, then $E(c) = c$ and $E(cx) = c\bar{x}$. Using these facts and the addition theorem for expectations, we have

$$\begin{aligned}\text{var}(x) = E[(x - \bar{x})^2] &= E(x^2 - 2\bar{x}x + \bar{x}^2) \\ &= E(x^2) - 2\bar{x}E(x) + \bar{x}^2 = E(x^2) - \bar{x}^2.\end{aligned} \quad (1)$$

Variance is the average of the squares of the deviations of x from its expected value. In some of the older literature this average is called the *dispersion* of x. In many ways this is more suggestive, but the word variance seems to be the generally accepted one today.

The variance of a sum does not always turn out to be as simple as the expectation of a sum. However, using the addition theorem for expectations, we have the following.

$$\begin{aligned}\text{var}(x + y) &= E[(x + y - \bar{x} - \bar{y})^2] \\ &= E(x^2 + y^2 + \bar{x}^2 + \bar{y}^2 + 2xy - 2\bar{x}x - 2\bar{y}y - 2\bar{y}x - 2\bar{x}y + 2\bar{x}\bar{y}) \\ &= E(x^2) + E(y^2) + \bar{x}^2 + \bar{y}^2 + 2E(xy) - 2\bar{x}^2 - 2\bar{y}^2 - 4\bar{x}\bar{y} + 2\bar{x}\bar{y} \\ &= E(x^2) - \bar{x}^2 + E(y^2) - \bar{y}^2 + 2E(xy) - 2\bar{x}\bar{y} \\ &= \text{var}(x) + \text{var}(y) + 2[E(xy) - \bar{x}\bar{y}].\end{aligned}$$

So the variance of a sum reduces to the sum of the variances if and only if the expectation of the product is the product of the expectations. Thus we seek a multiplication theorem for expectations. This is not unrestrictedly true as is the addition theorem, but it is true for independent random variables. Recall that if x and y are independent, then

$$P(x = s \text{ and } y = t) = P(x = s)P(y = t) = f_x(s)f_y(t).$$

Hence, letting R be the range of x and R' the range of y, we have, for x and y independent, that

$$E(xy) = \sum_{s \in R} \sum_{t \in R'} stf_x(s)f_y(t) = \sum_{s \in R} \left[sf_x(s) \sum_{t \in R'} tf_y(t) \right]$$

$$= \left[\sum_{s \in R} sf_x(s) \right] \left[\sum_{t \in R'} tf_y(t) \right] = E(x)E(y).$$

Therefore, if x and y are independent, then

$$\text{var } (x + y) = \text{var } (x) + \text{var } (y).$$

Variance may be additive for dependent variables, but it is not unrestrictedly so, as is expectation. We shall be content here with the result just proved: that for independent variables the variance of the sum is the sum of the variances.

To turn to a numerical example, let us find the variance of the number thrown on one die. The expectation is 3.5; so by definition the variance is

$$(1 - 3.5)^2 \cdot \tfrac{1}{6} + (2 - 3.5)^2 \cdot \tfrac{1}{6} + \cdots + (6 - 3.5)^2 \cdot \tfrac{1}{6}.$$

The arithmetic is simpler, however, if we use formula (1):

$$\text{var } (x) = E(x^2) - \bar{x}^2$$
$$= \tfrac{1}{6}(1 + 4 + 9 + 16 + 25 + 36) - (3.5)^2 = \tfrac{91}{6} - \tfrac{49}{4} = \tfrac{35}{12}.$$

EXERCISES

1. What is the variance of the total thrown
   a) on two dice?
   b) on n dice?

2. Consider the problem of two out of three numbered tickets drawn, without replacement, from an urn. Set up the sample space and coordinate variables as suggested in Exercise 3, Section 4–5.
   a) Find directly from the definition var (x), var (y), var $(x + y)$, $E(xy)$.
   b) Show that var $(x + y) \neq$ var $(x) +$ var (y).
   c) Show that $E(xy) \neq E(x)E(y)$.
   d) Show that var $(x + y) =$ var $(x) +$ var $(y) + 2E(xy) - 2\bar{x}\bar{y}$.

3. Let x and y be random variables and let c be a constant. Prove the following formulas.
   a) $E(x + c) = \bar{x} + c$
   b) $E(cx) = c\bar{x}$
   c) var $(x + c) =$ var (x)
   d) var $(cx) = c^2$ var (x)

4. In Exercise 4, Section 4–3, we introduced the idea of total independence as contrasted with independence by pairs. Which of these notions is needed to extend the addition theorem for variance to n random variables? That is,

$$\operatorname{var}\left(\sum_{i=1}^{n} x_i\right) = \sum_{i=1}^{n} \operatorname{var}(x_i),$$

provided the x_i are independent in whch sense? [*Hint:* Study the proof for $n = 2$; $E(xy)$ is involved because variance is the expectation of a quadratic.]

5. Find the expectation and variance of the number of heads
   a) on one toss of a coin;
   b) on n tosses.
6. Generalize Exercise 5. Suppose the coin is biased so that the probability of heads is p, rather than $\frac{1}{2}$.

4–7 BERNOULLIAN TRIALS

The problem of the biased coin (Exercise 6, Section 4–6) is the prototype of what is known as a Bernoullian sequence of trials. Specifically, any sequence of trials with the following properties is called Bernoullian.

1. Each trial has exactly two possible results, referred to as success and failure.
2. The probability of success is the same for all trials; standard notation: $p = $ probability of success, $q = $ probability of failure.
3. The trials are totally independent.

Suppose we have a sequence of n Bernoullian trials. A point in the sample space can be denoted by a sequence of S's and F's:

$$S\ F\ F\ S\ F\ S\ S \ldots F\ S\ F\ (n\ \text{symbols}).$$

It follows from properties 2 and 3 of Bernoullian sequences that each such point has probability

$$p^t q^{n-t},$$

where t is the number of S's in the representation of the point. Now the number of points that represent exactly t successes is given by the number of ways of placing the S's in the n slots. That is (see Section 1–2), it is

$$\binom{n}{t}.$$

Thus the probability of exactly t successes in n Bernoullian trials is

$$\binom{n}{t} p^t q^{n-t}.$$

Another way of saying this is as follows: On the sample space for n Bernoullian trials, let r be a random variable measuring the number of successes; then

$$f_r(t) = \binom{n}{t} p^t q^{n-t}. \tag{1}$$

Describing the problem this way leads to another interesting analysis. On this sample space for n Bernoullian trials, let random variables $x_1, x_2, \ldots, x_n$ be defined in the following way. Let x_k have the value 1 at each point where the kth trial resulted in success, and let $x_k = 0$ wherever the kth trial resulted in failure. The variables x_k are identical, each having the probability function

$$\begin{array}{l} t\colon 0 \quad 1, \\ f_{x_k}(t)\colon q \quad p. \end{array} \tag{2}$$

Furthermore, the x_k are totally independent. Another way of describing the x's is to say that x_k measures the number of successes on the kth trial. When they are described this way it is clear that the variable r measuring the number of successes on n trials is the sum of the x's; that is,

$$r = \sum_{k=1}^{n} x_k. \tag{3}$$

Thus a purely mathematical formulation of the theory of Bernoullian trials is as follows. Let $x_1, x_2, \ldots, x_n$ be totally independent and identical random variables, each having a probability function given by (2), and let r be defined by (3). Then the probability function for r is given by (1).

Any procedure involving independent repetitions of an experiment will lead to a sum of independent and identical random variables. The Bernoullian case is the simplest example of this, and in this simplest case the probability function for the sum is easily found. In more complicated problems this may not be so. However (see Section 4–9), such problems may be studied profitably, provided expectations and variances can be computed. Thus it is important to note that $E(r)$ and var (r) can be found without recourse to formula (1). Indeed, this was assigned as an exercise (6, Section 4–6) before the theory of Bernoullian trials was developed. Specifically, we have for each k,

$$E(x_k) = 0 \cdot q + 1 \cdot p = p;$$
$$\text{var }(x_k) = E(x_k^2) - \bar{x}_k^2 = p - p^2 = p(1-p) = pq.$$

Therefore

$$E(r) = \sum_{k=1}^{n} E(x_k) = np; \quad \text{var }(r) = \sum_{k=1}^{n} \text{var }(x_k) = npq.$$

Though the Bernoullian model is relatively simple, it still fits a number of problems. Some illustrations are given in the exercises that follow.

EXERCISES

1. Find the probability that in 5 throws of a single die there will be exactly two sixes.
2. Find the probability that in 5 throws of a pair of dice there will be exactly two sevens.
3. On a throw of two dice the expected total is 7. What is the probability of getting within 1 of the expected value (that is, 6, 7 or 8)? (a) 9 times out of 10, (b) 8 times out of 10, (c) at least 5 times out of 10.
4. A man claims he can distinguish between two brands of cigarettes by smoking them while he is blindfolded. At least he claims, "I can do it four times out of five."
    a) Suppose he is only guessing; what is the probability that he will make 4 or more correct guesses in 5 trials?
    b) Suppose there really is a probability $\frac{4}{5}$ that he will get the right answer on any one trial. What is the probability that he will get 4 or more right out of 5?
    c) He runs 5 trials a day for 10 days. Again using the assumption in part (b), find the probability that he will get at least 4 out of 5 every day.
    d) Repeat part (c), using the assumption in part (a).
5. Prove each of the following results, using the theories developed in this and the preceding two sections.

    a) $\sum_{k=1}^{n} k \binom{n}{k} p^k (1-p)^{n-k} = np$

    b) $\sum_{k=1}^{n} k^2 \binom{n}{k} p^k (1-p)^{n-k} = np(1 - p + np)$

4-8 POISSON DISTRIBUTIONS

A bacteriologist has a culture containing a large population of bacteria. From this culture (which fills a fairly large vessel) he takes a single drop. He places the drop on a microscope slide and with suitable magnification he is able to count the bacteria in the drop. Let r be the number of bacteria per drop in this experiment. We want to find the probability function for r.

If we interpret certain assumptions rather loosely we can represent this as a Bernoullian problem. If we focus our attention on an individual bacterium in the culture, it seems that the probability of its being in the crucial drop is equal to the volume of the drop divided by the total volume

4-8 POISSON DISTRIBUTIONS

of the culture. We call this volume ratio p, consider each bacterium as a "trial," and define "success" as being in the drop that goes under the microscope. The independence assumption needed to make this strictly Bernoullian is a little strained here, but we ignore this point and say that a reasonable probability function for r is given by

$$f_r(t) = \binom{n}{t} p^t (1-p)^{n-t}, \tag{1}$$

where p is the volume ratio and n is the total number of bacteria in the culture.

Bernoullian theory tells us that, assuming (1), we have

$$E(r) = np.$$

That is, the expected number of bacteria per drop is the total number of bacteria times the ratio of drop volume to total volume. At least, this consequence of assuming (1) to hold seems reasonable.

In practice this expected number per drop is easier to estimate than are n and p; so we set

$$a = np$$

and rewrite (1) as follows.

$$\begin{aligned} f_r(t) &= \binom{n}{t} \left(\frac{a}{n}\right)^t \left(1 - \frac{a}{n}\right)^{n-t} \\ &= \frac{n(n-1)\cdots(n-t+1) a^t [1-(a/n)]^n}{t!} \cdot \frac{1}{n^t [1-(a/n)]^t} \\ &= \frac{1}{[1-(a/n)]^t} \binom{n}{n} \left(1 - \frac{1}{n}\right) \cdots \left(1 - \frac{t-1}{n}\right) \frac{a^t}{t!} \left(1 - \frac{a}{n}\right)^n. \end{aligned} \tag{2}$$

Since n is large (millions) and a and t are medium-sized (in the range 5–50), we approximate this last expression for $f_r(t)$ by its limit as $n \to \infty$. Now

$$\left(1 - \frac{a}{n}\right)^t \to 1,$$

$$\frac{n}{n} = 1,$$

$$\left(1 - \frac{1}{n}\right) \to 1,$$

$$\vdots$$

$$\left(1 - \frac{t-1}{n}\right) \to 1,$$

and it can be shown (proof omitted here) that

$$\left(1 - \frac{a}{n}\right)^n \to e^{-a},$$

where e is a well-known constant given correct to five decimal places by

$$e = 2.71828\ldots$$

Therefore the probability function usually assigned to the random variable r in this problem is

$$f_r(t) = \frac{a^t e^{-a}}{t!}. \tag{3}$$

This is known as the Poisson probability function. Extensive tables of this function are available. The following excerpts from the tables give some idea of how the function behaves.

t	$f_r(t)$		
	$a = 0.1$	$a = 1$	$a = 5$
0	0.905	0.368	0.007
1	0.091	0.368	0.034
2	0.005	0.184	0.086
3	0.000	0.061	0.142
4		0.015	0.179
5		0.003	0.179
6		0.001	0.149
7		0.000	0.106
8			0.058
9			0.033
10			0.017
11			0.007
12			0.003
13			0.001
14			0.000

Recall that a is the expected value of r. The case $a = 5$ gives a typical picture of a Poisson distribution. As seen in the above table, the distribution looks somewhat different when the expected value is 1 or less.

We turn now to another physical example. A radioactive source is emitting alpha particles and a nearby Geiger counter is detecting those particles that come in its direction. The setup is such that the experimenter can actually count the number of particles detected by the counter in, say, a 10-second period. We let r be the number so counted and again we seek $f_r(t)$.

To analyze this problem, we make the following assumptions about very short time intervals:

1. The probability of detecting exactly 1 particle in such a short time interval is proportional to the length of the interval.
2. Probabilities for detection in a short time interval are independent of when the interval started and of what happened in other such time intervals.
3. The probability of detecting more than one particle in a very short time interval is so small that this possibility can be ignored in our calculations.

We now take the stated time interval (10 seconds in the problem outlined above) and divide it into a large number n of equal subintervals. By assumption 1, the probability of detecting one particle in one of these subintervals is a/n, where a is a suitable proportionality constant. By assumption 3, we suppose that in each subinterval there is detected either one particle or none. Thus, by assumption 2, the problem is Bernoullian and the probability of detecting t particles in n subintervals is

$$\binom{n}{t}\left(\frac{a}{n}\right)^t\left(1-\frac{a}{n}\right)^{n-t}.$$

We are now back to formula (2); so just as above we conclude that

$$f_r(t) = \frac{a^t e^{-a}}{t!}.$$

This last problem is an example of a general type that may be described informally as follows. We deal with random occurrences in time, and the variable that measures the number of such occurrences in a stated time has a Poisson distribution.

We used quite different analyses on the bacteria-counting and radioactive-emission problems. It is instructive to summarize these analyses and also to analyze each of these problems in the other way.

Bacteria Counting Problem

Bernoullian trials analysis

  Trial: bacterium
  Success: in drop that goes under the microscope
  Variable with Poisson distribution: number of bacteria in the drop under the microscope

Random occurrences in time analysis
　Time: volume
　Occurrence: presence of a bacterium
　Stated time: drop that goes under microscope
　Variable with Poisson distribution: number of bacteria in the drop under the microscope

Radioactive Emission Problem

Bernoullian trials analysis
　Trial: atom of radioactive material
　Success: emits particle during stated time period and particle hits counter
　Variable with Poisson distribution: number of particles counted during stated time period

Random occurrences in time analysis
　Time: time
　Occurrence: emitted particle hits counter
　Stated time: time of counting
　Variable with Poisson distribution: number of particles counted during stated time period

EXERCISES

1. A business firm has its own telephone switchboard with a large number of office extensions and a certain number of trunk lines to the outside. They figure that an outside call lasts five minutes of a normal business day.
   a) Explain why the number of requests for an outside line in five minutes should have a Poisson distribution. Analyze the problem by both of the methods illustrated in the text.
   b) Assume that the expected number of requests for an outside line in a stated period is 5. Use the table in the text to determine how many lines are needed so that all these requests can be accommodated on different lines with probability ≥ 0.8; with probability ≥ 0.95.
   c) Assume that the expected number of requests in the critical time is only 1. Discuss the question of how many lines are needed.
2. Leading off a busy turnpike is a side road that leads to an island resort. Traffic on the side road averages one car every six minutes. Finally, you get to the island by a ferry that makes a round trip every half hour. What should the capacity of the ferry be so that with probability 0.95 it can carry all the cars that are waiting for it on a given trip?
3. Explain why each of the following should have a Poisson distribution. Analyze each problem in two ways.
   a) The number of grit particles in a drop of used lubricating oil.

b) The number of times per day your phone rings.
c) The number of nuts in a chocolate-almond bar.
d) The number of typographical errors per page in a newspaper.

4. Find some other examples of Poisson distributions.

4-9 LIMIT THEOREMS

Suppose we have a Bernoullian sequence of trials. Let x_i be the random variable that is 1 or 0 according as the ith trial results in success or failure. Then

$$r = \sum_{i=1}^{n} x_i$$

is the random variable measuring the number of successes in n trials. Now for each i,

$$E(x_i) = 1 \cdot p + 0 \cdot q = p \quad \text{and} \quad E(x_i^2) = 1 \cdot p + 0 \cdot q = p.$$

Therefore

$$\text{var}(x_i) = E(x_i^2) - \bar{x}_i^2 = p - p^2 = p(1-p) = pq.$$

Thus $E(r) = np$, and, since the x_i are independent, $\text{var}(r) = npq$.

We want to get some insight into the significance of expectation; so let us look at the random variable

$$r - E(r) = r - np.$$

This variable has variance npq and therefore for large n must assume relatively large values with reasonable probability. That is, we really do not "expect" that the total number of successes will be close to its expected value.

A better variable to study is the average number of successes:

$$\frac{r - np}{n} = \frac{r}{n} - p.$$

Recalling that $\text{var}(cx) = c^2 \text{var}(x)$, we see that $(r/n) - p$ has variance

$$\frac{npq}{n^2} = \frac{pq}{n}.$$

Thus, if n is large, $(r/n) - p$ must assume small values with large probability. A precise statement of this result is given by the *weak law of large numbers:*

For each fixed positive number ϵ,

$$P\left(\left|\frac{r}{n} - p\right| < \epsilon\right) \to 1 \quad \text{as } n \to \infty.$$

The proof of this stems directly from the fact that var $(r/n) \to 0$; the calculations are not very enlightening and are omitted here.

The variance of $r - np$ tends to ∞ while that of $(r/n) - p$ tends to 0. How about stabilizing the variance? Specifically,

$$\frac{r - np}{\sqrt{npq}}$$

has variance 1 for every n. Let us call this variable S_n. The *central limit theorem* states that for each fixed a and b,

$$P(a \leq S_n \leq b) \to \int_a^b \frac{1}{\sqrt{2\pi}} e^{-t^2/2} \, dt \quad \text{as } n \to \infty. \tag{1}$$

We are not prepared to indicate any proof of this theorem.

Actually, the central limit theorem is much more general than we have indicated here. We began with variables x_i relating to success or failure on the various trials of a Bernoullian sequence, set

$$r = \sum_{i=1}^{n} x_i,$$

and went on from there. More generally, if $x_1, x_2, x, \ldots$ is any sequence of identical and independent random variables for which variance is defined, and if we set

$$S_n = \frac{\text{sum of } n \text{ } x\text{'s} - \text{expectation of sum}}{\sqrt{\text{variance of sum}}},$$

then (1) still holds regardless of what the specific variables x_i were. This is a sample of the rather powerful kind of result that can be obtained by the methods of mathematical probability theory.

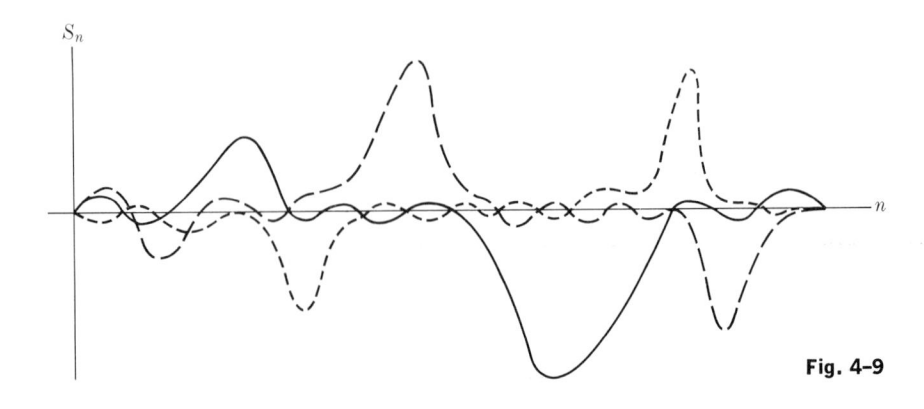

Fig. 4-9

It is important to note that the weak law of large numbers and central limit theorem apply to aggregates of runs of fixed length. That is, we take a *fixed* (though large) n and consider the sample space of all possible runs of length n. The central-limit theorem says that on this sample space $P(a \leq S_n \leq b)$ is given approximately by the integral in (1). By contrast, for a single run of indefinite extent there are other probability-limit theorems that say that with large probability we can expect wide fluctuations in S_n as n changes. Roughly, the situation is like that pictured in Fig. 4–9. Each curve represents a single extended run. At each stage (central-limit theorem), most curves are nicely in bounds, but each curve (theory of single runs) keeps getting out of bounds.

EXERCISES

1. It is claimed that Swami has extrasensory perception. Experiments are run in which Swami's partner takes numbered cards from a shuffled deck and concentrates on the number so that Swami can give the correct number from across the room without seeing it. They hold a seance every day for quite a while, and point out that the results are at variance with what the central-limit theorem would indicate if Swami were only guessing. A cynic points out that they go through a different number of cards each day. The explanation of this is that mental telepathy is hard work and to be fair they have to quit when Swami gets tired. Adopt the point of view of the cynic that "tired" means "ahead" and show that the central-limit theorem is not the proper criterion for evaluating these data.

2. Jones agrees to bet \$1 on tails on each of n tosses of a coin. Jones has a total capital of C dollars, but his opponent does not know this, and they merely keep score with the idea of settling up after the game.

   a) Letting r be the number of heads in n tosses, show that Jones must declare bankruptcy if $r - (n/2) > C/2$.

   b) Show that the inequality in part (a) is equivalent to

   $$S_n > \frac{C}{\sqrt{n}},$$

   and use the central-limit theorem to show that, if Jones agrees to stay for a very large number of tosses, the probability is close to $\frac{1}{2}$ that he will be unable to pay off.

   c) Suppose the coin is slightly biased against Jones (as are all professional gambling games against the customer). That is, suppose the probability of heads is $p > \frac{1}{2}$. Show that now the inequality in part (a) is equivalent to

   $$S_n > \frac{C}{2\sqrt{npq}} - \sqrt{\frac{n}{pq}}(p - \tfrac{1}{2}),$$

and conclude that if the agreed-upon game is sufficiently long there is a probability close to 1 that Jones will be unable to pay his debt.

d) In part (c), let $C = \$100$ and $p = 0.51$. By the integral formula in the central-limit theorem, $P(S_n > 0) = 0.5$, $P(S_n > -1) = 0.841$, and $P(S_n > -2) = 0.977$. Make some numerical estimates of n for these various probabilities of disaster for Jones.

3. Apropos of the discussion in the last paragraph of this section, note the difference between the game of Exercise 2 and a cash game in which Jones must quit whenever his capital is exhausted. Suppose the coin is honest; let Jones have $2 capital, and consider 4 tosses.

a) Show that in the credit game he is broke or in debt after 4 tosses with probability $\frac{5}{16}$.

b) Show that in the cash game he goes broke with probability $\frac{6}{16}$. (The situation is much worse for large n.)

c) Note that part (a) is a Bernoullian problem (which the central-limit theorem approximates for large n), while part (b) is a problem of quite a different type.

LINEAR ALGEBRA 5

5-1 MATRICES

A rectangular array of symbols, such as

$$\begin{bmatrix} a_{11} & a_{12} & a_{13} \\ a_{21} & a_{22} & a_{23} \end{bmatrix}$$

is called a *matrix* (plural, *matrices*). The individual symbols may have first one meaning and then another, although in the present study they will usually be either numbers or variables. The essential requirement is that one be able to add and multiply them in order to define the operations of matrix algebra.

The above matrix has two *rows* and three *columns*, and is called a 2×3 matrix. When double-subscript notation is used for matrix entries, the above pattern is always followed. The first subscript gives the row number and the second gives the column number. Often

$$[a_{ij}]$$

is used to denote the matrix with entry a_{ij} in the ith row and jth column. That is, a symbol for a general matrix entry enclosed in brackets constitutes a symbol for the matrix itself. When such notation is used, the dimensions of the matrix must be clear from the context. Frequently, a single capital letter is also used to denote a matrix; thus one can write

$$A = [a_{ij}]$$

and use these symbols interchangeably.

The following operations with matrices form the basis for their principal applications.

i) *Multiplication.* For reasons that will appear very shortly, multiplication of matrices is defined in the following way. If $[a_{ij}]$ is $m \times n$ and $[b_{ij}]$ is $n \times s$, then the product $[a_{ij}][b_{ij}]$ is the $m \times s$ matrix $[c_{ij}]$, defined by

$$c_{ik} = \sum_{j=1}^{n} a_{ij} b_{jk}.$$

In words, to get the (i, k) entry in the product AB, line up the ith row of A with the kth column of B; multiply corresponding entries and add.

Note that, for multiplication of matrices to be defined, the dimensions must match, as shown in Fig. 5–1.

A more important point to be noted is that, in computing AB, one lines up rows of A with columns of B; this rule is not symmetric. If A and B are both square matrices of the same dimension, then both AB and BA are defined, but in general these are not equal. For example, let

$$A = \begin{bmatrix} 1 & 2 \\ 3 & 4 \end{bmatrix}, \quad B = \begin{bmatrix} 5 & 6 \\ 7 & 8 \end{bmatrix}.$$

Then

$$AB = \begin{bmatrix} 1 \cdot 5 + 2 \cdot 7 & 1 \cdot 6 + 2 \cdot 8 \\ 3 \cdot 5 + 4 \cdot 7 & 3 \cdot 6 + 4 \cdot 8 \end{bmatrix} = \begin{bmatrix} 19 & 22 \\ 43 & 50 \end{bmatrix},$$

$$BA = \begin{bmatrix} 5 \cdot 1 + 6 \cdot 3 & 5 \cdot 2 + 6 \cdot 4 \\ 7 \cdot 1 + 8 \cdot 3 & 7 \cdot 2 + 8 \cdot 4 \end{bmatrix} = \begin{bmatrix} 23 & 34 \\ 31 & 46 \end{bmatrix}.$$

Perhaps this is the student's first encounter with noncommutative multiplication. Such operations are common in modern algebra, and other examples will appear later in this book.

On the other hand, matrix multiplication is associative. That is, if

$$A(BC)$$

is defined, so is

$$(AB)C,$$

and the two are equal. For this reason, it is unambiguous to write ABC.

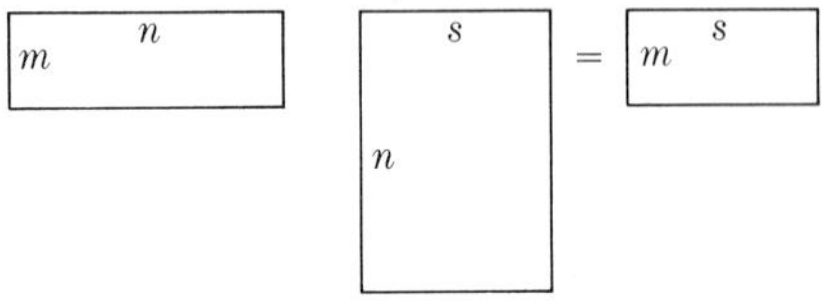

Fig. 5–1

The following considerations introduce the principal application of matrices, indicate why matrix multiplication is defined as it is, and incidentally suggest a simple proof of the associative law.

The pair of linear equations,

$$u = a_{11}x + a_{12}y, \quad v = a_{21}x + a_{22}y, \tag{1}$$

define a mapping T_1 which carries ordered pairs (x, y) into ordered pairs (u, v); that is,

$$(u, v) = T_1(x, y). \tag{2}$$

A mapping of pairs into pairs is usually called a *transformation*, and one defined by a pair of linear equations is called a *linear transformation*. Now suppose that there is another linear transformation T_2 such that

means
$$(z, w) = T_2(u, v) \qquad (3)$$
$$z = b_{11}u + b_{12}v, \qquad w = b_{21}u + b_{22}v. \qquad (4)$$

By the definition of a composite mapping, given (2) and (3),

$$(z, w) = (T_2 \circ T_1)(x, y).$$

To find equations describing $T_2 \circ T_1$, substitute (1) into (4):

$$\begin{aligned} z &= b_{11}(a_{11}x + a_{12}y) + b_{12}(a_{21}x + a_{22}y) \\ &= (b_{11}a_{11} + b_{12}a_{21})x + (b_{11}a_{12} + b_{12}a_{22})y, \\ w &= b_{21}(a_{11}x + a_{12}y) + b_{22}(a_{21}x + a_{22}y) \\ &= (b_{21}a_{11} + b_{22}a_{21})x + (b_{21}a_{12} + b_{22}a_{22})y. \end{aligned} \qquad (5)$$

Now each of these systems of linear equations may be written in matrix form. By the definition of matrix multiplication, (1) is the same as

$$\begin{bmatrix} u \\ v \end{bmatrix} = \begin{bmatrix} a_{11} & a_{12} \\ a_{21} & a_{22} \end{bmatrix} \begin{bmatrix} x \\ y \end{bmatrix}. \qquad (1')$$

Similarly, Eq. (4) may be written

$$\begin{bmatrix} z \\ w \end{bmatrix} = \begin{bmatrix} b_{11} & b_{12} \\ b_{21} & b_{22} \end{bmatrix} \begin{bmatrix} u \\ v \end{bmatrix}. \qquad (4')$$

Converting (5) in a similar way and noting again the definition of matrix multiplication yields

$$\begin{aligned} \begin{bmatrix} z \\ w \end{bmatrix} &= \begin{bmatrix} b_{11}a_{11} + b_{12}a_{21} & b_{11}a_{12} + b_{12}a_{22} \\ b_{12}a_{11} + b_{22}a_{21} & b_{21}a_{12} + b_{22}a_{22} \end{bmatrix} \begin{bmatrix} x \\ y \end{bmatrix} \\ &= \begin{bmatrix} b_{11} & b_{12} \\ b_{21} & b_{22} \end{bmatrix} \begin{bmatrix} a_{11} & a_{12} \\ a_{21} & a_{22} \end{bmatrix} \begin{bmatrix} x \\ y \end{bmatrix}. \end{aligned} \qquad (5')$$

Thus, if ordered pairs are written as 2×1 matrices, a linear transformation is given by multiplication by a square matrix. Furthermore, comparison of (1'), (4'), and (5') shows that composition of linear transformations corresponds to multiplication of the associated matrices.

The associative law for matrix multiplication thus follows from the associativity of the ∘ operator.

ii) *Addition.* Definition:

$$[a_{ij}] + [b_{ij}] = [a_{ij} + b_{ij}].$$

In words, matrices with identical dimensions are added by adding corresponding entries. Key properties (proofs left to the student):

$$A + B = B + A, \qquad A + (B + C) = (A + B) + C,$$
$$A(B + C) = AB + AC, \qquad (A + B)C = AC + BC.$$

iii) *Multiplication by scalars.* Definition:

$$[a_{ij}]c = c[a_{ij}] = [ca_{ij}].$$

In words, to multiply a matrix by a scalar, multiply each entry by the scalar. Key properties:

$$c(AB) = (cA)B = A(Bc), \qquad c(A + B) = cA + cB.$$

iv) *Transposition.* Definition:

$$[a_{ij}]' = [a_{ji}].$$

In words, the transpose of A, denoted by A', is obtained from A by converting rows into columns, and vice versa. In the case of a square matrix, transposition may also be described as reflection through the main diagonal. Note that if A is $m \times n$, then A' is $n \times m$. The student should check the following properties:

$$(A + B)' = A' + B', \qquad (AB)' = B'A'.$$

Note carefully the reversal of order when a product is transposed.

EXERCISES

1. Let

$$A = \begin{bmatrix} 1 & -1 \\ 1 & 0 \end{bmatrix}, \qquad B = \begin{bmatrix} 1 & 2 & 0 \\ 0 & -1 & 2 \end{bmatrix}$$

$$C = \begin{bmatrix} 1 & -1 \\ 0 & 1 \\ 2 & 0 \end{bmatrix}, \qquad D = \begin{bmatrix} 1 & -1 & 0 \\ 0 & 1 & 2 \\ 2 & -1 & 1 \end{bmatrix}$$

a) Which of these products is defined? $AB, BA, AC, CA, AD, DA, BC, CB, BD, DB, CD, DC$.

b) Compute each of the products mentioned in part (a) that is properly defined.
c) Find A', B', C', and D'.
d) Find the transpose of each of the products in part (b), and show that each is the appropriate product of transposes.

2. Write each of the following systems of equations in matrix form.

a) $u = 2x - 3y$
   $v = 4x - y$

b) $u = x + y$
   $v = -2y$

c) $u = 2x - 3y + z$
   $v = x - 2y + 3z$
   $w = 4x - y + 5z$

d) $u = x - y$
   $v = y - z$
   $w = z - x$

3. Let

$$X = \begin{bmatrix} x \\ y \end{bmatrix}, \quad U = \begin{bmatrix} u \\ v \end{bmatrix}, \quad A = \begin{bmatrix} 3 & -2 \\ 4 & 0 \end{bmatrix}.$$

Write the relation $U = AX$ as a system of linear equations.

5-2 MATRIX INVERSION

Consider the matrix $[\delta_{ij}]$, where δ_{ij} is the so-called Kronecker δ, defined by

$$\delta_{ij} = \begin{cases} 1 & \text{for } i = j, \\ 0 & \text{for } i \neq j. \end{cases}$$

Thus $[\delta_{ij}]$ is a square matrix with 1's down the main diagonal and 0's elsewhere. The 2×2 and 3×3 cases are

$$\begin{bmatrix} 1 & 0 \\ 0 & 1 \end{bmatrix}, \quad \begin{bmatrix} 1 & 0 & 0 \\ 0 & 1 & 0 \\ 0 & 0 & 1 \end{bmatrix}.$$

Now it is easily verified that, for any matrix A,

$$A[\delta_{ij}] = A \quad \text{and} \quad [\delta_{ij}]A = A,$$

provided that the dimension of $[\delta_{ij}]$ is properly chosen. For this reason, $[\delta_{ij}]$ is called the *identity matrix*. It is often denoted by I, sometimes with a subscript to indicate dimension, I_n.

The *inverse* of a square matrix A is a matrix denoted by A^{-1}, such that

$$A^{-1}A = AA^{-1} = [\delta_{ij}].$$

Only a square matrix can have an inverse (see Exercise 4 below), but not all square matrices do.

136 LINEAR ALGEBRA

Suppose A^{-1} exists: how does one find it? Consider the case in which A is $n \times n$. Let X and U each be $n \times 1$, and write a system of linear equations as in (1') of Section 5–1:

$$U = AX.$$

If A^{-1} exists, this system is easily solved in matrix form:

$$A^{-1}U = A^{-1}AX = [\delta_{ij}]X = X.$$

Thus finding the inverse of a square matrix is equivalent to solving a system of linear equations.

Let

$$A = \begin{bmatrix} 1 & -1 \\ 2 & 1 \end{bmatrix}.$$

To find A^{-1}, write

$$u = x - y, \qquad v = 2x + y,$$

and solve. Adding the two equations, one gets

$$u + v = 3x;$$

subtracting twice the first equation from the second yields

$$-2u + v = 3y.$$

Thus

$$x = \tfrac{1}{3}u + \tfrac{1}{3}v, \qquad y = -\tfrac{2}{3}u + \tfrac{1}{3}v,$$

and it appears that

$$A^{-1} = \begin{bmatrix} \tfrac{1}{3} & \tfrac{1}{3} \\ -\tfrac{2}{3} & \tfrac{1}{3} \end{bmatrix}.$$

For 2×2 matrices, we can obtain a workable formula for inversion. It is easily checked by routine computation that

$$\begin{bmatrix} a_{11} & a_{12} \\ a_{21} & a_{22} \end{bmatrix} \begin{bmatrix} a_{22} & -a_{12} \\ -a_{21} & a_{11} \end{bmatrix} = \begin{bmatrix} a_{11}a_{22} - a_{12}a_{21} & 0 \\ 0 & a_{11}a_{22} - a_{12}a_{21} \end{bmatrix}$$

$$= (a_{11}a_{22} - a_{12}a_{21}) \begin{bmatrix} 1 & 0 \\ 0 & 1 \end{bmatrix}.$$

Therefore

$$\begin{bmatrix} a_{11} & a_{12} \\ a_{21} & a_{22} \end{bmatrix}^{-1} = \frac{\begin{bmatrix} a_{22} & -a_{12} \\ -a_{21} & a_{11} \end{bmatrix}}{a_{11}a_{22} - a_{12}a_{21}}. \tag{1}$$

The number $a_{11}a_{22} - a_{12}a_{21}$ in the denominator is the determinant of the original matrix. It is the product of the main diagonal entries minus that of the secondary diagonal entries (suggestive picture in Fig. 5-2). Formula (1) can be summarized in words as follows: To invert a 2×2 matrix, interchange the main diagonal entries, change the signs of the secondary diagonal entries, and divide by the determinant.

The theory of determinants leads to generalizations of formula (1) to higher dimensions, but these are not at all simple, even in the 3×3 case. We shall not pursue the subject any further. Matrix inversion is important in many applications, but today it is usually done on computers. Interestingly enough, the efficient method on a computer is not to generalize formula (1), but to employ a systematic form of the addition-subtraction process we used in our initial example above.

Note, finally, that

$$(B^{-1}A^{-1})(AB) = B^{-1}(A^{-1}A)B$$
$$= B^{-1}[\delta_{ij}]B = B^{-1}B = [\delta_{ij}];$$

so that

$$(AB)^{-1} = B^{-1}A^{-1}.$$

We see that inversion reverses the order of factors, just as transposition does.

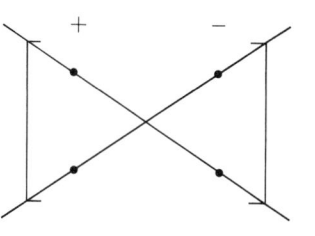

Fig. 5-2

EXERCISES

1. Let
$$A = \begin{bmatrix} 1 & 3 \\ -4 & 2 \end{bmatrix}, \quad B = \begin{bmatrix} -4 & 3 \\ -1 & 2 \end{bmatrix};$$
find A^{-1}, B^{-1}, AB, $(AB)^{-1}$, BA, $(BA)^{-1}$, A^{-1}, B^{-1}, $B^{-1}A^{-1}$.

2. Write the system of equations
$$x - 3y = 1, \quad 2x + y = -2$$
in matrix form.
   a) Give the solution (for x and y) in matrix form.
   b) Use formula (1) to solve these equations (for x and y simultaneously).

3. Use addition and subtraction of equations to find the inverse of the matrix D of Exercise 1, Section 5-1. Check that $DD^{-1} = D^{-1}D = [\delta_{ij}]$.

4. Suppose that
$$BA = [\delta_{ij}] \quad \text{and} \quad AC = [\delta_{ij}].$$
   a) Apply the associative law to the product BAC to show that $B = C$.
   b) Show from part (a) that only square matrices have inverses.
   c) Show from part (a) that if A^{-1} exists it is unique.

Fig. 5-3   **Fig. 5-4**

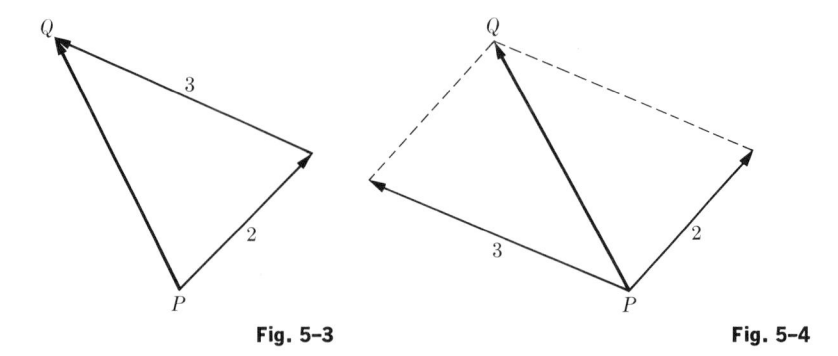

5-3 VECTOR SPACES

Consider the following simple problem. Suppose that a boat leaves a pier on a large lake, sails 2 miles NE, then turns and sails 3 miles WNW. What is its final position relative to the pier? Quite obviously, Fig. 5-3 gives a graphical solution to the problem. The final position relative to the pier is given by the arrow from P to Q.

Consider another problem. There are two horizontal forces operating on an object. There is a 2-pound push NE and a 3-pound push WNW. What is the total horizontal force on the object? An elementary principle of physics is that there is a "parallelogram law" for the composition of forces, which yields—as a solution to this problem—that the total horizontal force is represented by the arrow from P to Q in Fig. 5-4.

Loosely speaking, things representable by arrows in this way are called *vectors*, and these two simple examples illustrate the fact that displacements are vectors and so are forces. There are three points worthy of note.

1. We are talking here about directed magnitudes. An arrow describes a direction in an obvious way, and its length indicates a magnitude.
2. We have introduced a scheme for adding directed magnitudes. Figures 5-3 and 5-4 describe in slightly different ways the same notion of the sum of two directed magnitudes.
3. The trouble with representing directed magnitudes by arrows is that you have to draw the arrow somewhere, and the position of the arrow is not significant. The WNW arrow is in different positions in Figs. 5-3 and 5-4; yet the two figures describe exactly the same idea.

Of these three observations, the second is the really important one. Directed magnitudes are not vectors unless you agree to add them. Actually we must also agree to multiply them by real numbers. That is, for forces, for example, we must define "twice a given force" (obvious definition), "−1.5 times a given force" (1.5 times the magnitude and going in the opposite direction), etc. To the mathematician, vectors are things that can be added to each other and multiplied by real numbers. Directed magnitudes are examples of vectors, but as we shall see there are many other examples.

A *vector space* is a set V whose elements are called *vectors* such that addition of vectors and multiplication of vectors by real numbers are defined so as to satisfy the following rules. (In the statement of these rules, each boldface letter **u**, **v**, ... represents an arbitrary vector in V, and each lightface letter a, b, ... represents an arbitrary real number.)

1. $\mathbf{u} + \mathbf{v} \in V$ and $a\mathbf{u} \in V$. V is *closed* under addition and multiplication by real numbers.
2. $\mathbf{u} + \mathbf{v} = \mathbf{v} + \mathbf{u}$. Vector addition is *commutative*.
3. $(\mathbf{u} + \mathbf{v}) + \mathbf{w} = \mathbf{u} + (\mathbf{v} + \mathbf{w})$. Vector addition is *associative*.
4. There is one vector **0** such that $\mathbf{u} + \mathbf{0} = \mathbf{u}$ for every $\mathbf{u} \in V$.
5. $a(b\mathbf{u}) = (ab)\mathbf{u}$. Multiplication by real numbers is *associative*.
6. $a(\mathbf{u} + \mathbf{v}) = a\mathbf{u} + a\mathbf{v}$ and $(a + b)\mathbf{u} = a\mathbf{u} + b\mathbf{u}$. Multiplication by real numbers is *distributive* over addition of both vectors and real numbers.
7. $1\mathbf{u} = \mathbf{u}$.

These are the basic postulates for a vector space. Some additional working rules of vector algebra are indicated in Exercise 6 below. In many vector spaces (particularly the spaces of directed magnitudes used in elementary physics) it is profitable to define other algebraic operations, notably some that look like multiplication of vectors by vectors. Our discussion here will be limited to ideas that are based on the fundamental vector-space operations: addition of vectors and multiplication of vectors by real numbers. Often in vector analysis these real-number multipliers are called *scalars*.

To illustrate many ideas in this chapter, we shall turn to the *space of plane vectors*. This is the space of directed magnitudes in the plane, with addition defined by a parallelogram rule (as in Fig. 5–4) or equivalently by placing arrows head-to-toe (as in Fig. 5–3). Multiplication by scalars is defined by saying that the magnitude of $a\mathbf{u}$ is the absolute value of a times the magnitude of **u**, and the direction of $a\mathbf{u}$ is that of **u** if $a > 0$ and opposite to that of **u** if $a < 0$.

With these same definitions of addition and multiplication by scalars, the set of all directed magnitudes in 3-space forms an interesting and useful vector space.

There are also interesting and useful nongeometric examples. In Section 1–4 we defined the sum of two functions by saying that

$$(f + g)(a) = f(a) + g(a), \tag{1}$$

and we defined a number times a function by

$$(cf)(a) = cf(a). \tag{2}$$

As noted in Section 1–4, it does not matter what the common domain of these functions is; in both (1) and (2) the right-hand side makes sense if the functions have ranges consisting of real numbers. Thus, if A is any set whatsoever, (1) and (2) define addition and multiplication by scalars in such a way that the set of all functions from A into the real-number system becomes an example of a vector space.

If A is a large set, this function space may be a very elaborate example of a vector space. For example, if A is the real-number system, the number of real-valued functions on A reaches what might be called the "third order of infinity." It could be that A is this function space, in which case the space of functions on A is even bigger, and so on, *ad infinitum*. The idea of a space of functions introduces an unlimited number of examples of vector spaces.

In connection with the idea of function space, it is profitable to consider not only different examples of domains but also different limited classes of functions on a fixed domain. For example, on the real-number system, the set of all polynomial functions,

$$\sum_{k=0}^{n} a_k I^k, \quad n = 0, 1, 2, \ldots$$

is an excellent example of a vector space. The only question about a specialized class of functions is whether or not the closure postulate (No. 1) is satisfied. In this case it obviously is; the sum of two polynomials is a polynomial, and so is a constant times a polynomial.

We shall call this space of polynomials P, and pursuing further the idea of considering restricted sets of functions, we shall denote by P_n the space of all polynomials of degree n or less. In subsequent sections of this chapter we shall often use P_2 as an illustrative example. This means the set of all functions of the form

$$aI^2 + bI + cI^0,$$

where any (or all) of the coefficients a, b, c may be zero. P_2 is the space of quadratic functions, including the degenerate ones (linear and constant).

5-4 BASES 141

EXERCISES

1. A function f is bounded on a set A if there is a number M such that $|f(a)| \leq M$ for every $a \in A$. Show that if A is any set, the set of all bounded functions on A forms a vector space.

2. Addition of matrices and multiplication of matrices by numbers is defined in Section 5–1. Show that with these definitions each of the following sets forms a vector space, and that these three spaces are essentially the same: (a) the set of all 6×1 matrices, (b) the set of all 1×6 matrices, (c) the set of all 3×2 matrices.

3. Show that one of the following sets forms a vector space and the other does not: (a) the set of all 1×3 matrices with middle entry 1, (b) the set of all 1×3 matrices with middle entry 0.

4. Is the set of nondegenerate quadratics $(aI^2 + bI + cI^0$, with $a \neq 0)$ a vector space?

5. Show that the set of all polynomials f such that $f(1) = 0$ forms a vector space. How about the set of polynomials g such that $g(0) = 1$?

6. Prove each of the following from the vector-space postulates.
   a) $0\mathbf{u} = \mathbf{0}$. [*Hint:* $\mathbf{u} = (1 + 0)\mathbf{u} = \mathbf{u} + 0\mathbf{u}$.]
   b) $\mathbf{u} + (-1)\mathbf{u} = \mathbf{0}$. [Thus it is natural to define $-\mathbf{u}$ to mean $(-1)\mathbf{u}$.]
   c) $a\mathbf{0} = \mathbf{0}$. [*Hint:* Use part (b) to show that $a\mathbf{0} = a\mathbf{u} - a\mathbf{u}$.]
   d) If $a\mathbf{u} = \mathbf{0}$, then either $a = 0$ or $\mathbf{u} = \mathbf{0}$. [*Hint:* If $a \neq 0$, divide by a.]
   e) If $\mathbf{u} \neq \mathbf{0}$ and $a\mathbf{u} = b\mathbf{u}$, then $a = b$.
   f) If $a \neq 0$ and $a\mathbf{u} = a\mathbf{v}$, then $\mathbf{u} = \mathbf{v}$.
   g) The following statements are equivalent. (i) $a\mathbf{u} + b\mathbf{v} = \mathbf{0}$ implies $a = b = 0$. (ii) There is no c such that $\mathbf{u} = c\mathbf{v}$. [*Hint:* Use contrapositives; not (i) implies not (ii) and not (ii) implies not (i).]

5-4 BASES

Figure 5–5 shows two plane vectors **i** and **j**, each with magnitude 1, **i** being horizontal and **j** vertical. It also shows two other plane vectors **u** and **v** and indicates geometrically that

$$\mathbf{u} = 3\mathbf{i} + 3\mathbf{j}, \quad \mathbf{v} = -\mathbf{i} + 4\mathbf{j}. \quad (1)$$

The pair of vectors (**i**, **j**) is called a *basis* for the space of plane vectors and the coefficients appearing in (1) are called *components* of the vectors **u** and **v**. Specifically, we say that

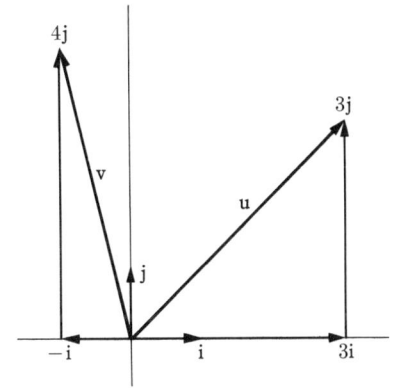

Fig. 5–5

with respect to the basis (**i**, **j**), **u** has components (3, 3) and **v** has components (−1, 4).

Though the two situations differ in detail, there is an obvious analogy between introducing a basis into the space of plane vectors and introducing a coordinate system on the plane as a point set. In this analogy, components of a vector correspond to coordinates of a point. Let us carry the analogy still further. To describe the foundations of analytic geometry, we introduced (Section 1–6) coordinate variables—mappings which carried points of the plane into their respective coordinates. So here we introduce *component variables*. Let x_1 and x_2 be the component variables for the basis (**i**, **j**). (We use x_1 and x_2 rather than x and y, because we have another use in mind for the symbol y in this discussion.) By this we mean that if
$$\mathbf{w} = a\mathbf{i} + b\mathbf{j},$$
then
$$x_1(\mathbf{w}) = a, \qquad x_2(\mathbf{w}) = b.$$

That is, each vector has a unique expansion in terms of **i** and **j**, and x_1 is the mapping that carries each vector into the coefficient of **i** in its expansion; x_2 carries the vector into its **j**-coefficient. To put it succinctly, for each vector **w**,

$$\mathbf{w} = x_1(\mathbf{w})\mathbf{i} + x_2(\mathbf{w})\mathbf{j}.$$

To discuss the two component variables simultaneously, we introduce a matrix
$$X = \begin{bmatrix} x_1 \\ x_2 \end{bmatrix}.$$

Then we write $X(\mathbf{w})$ to mean
$$\begin{bmatrix} x_1(w) \\ x_2(w) \end{bmatrix}.$$

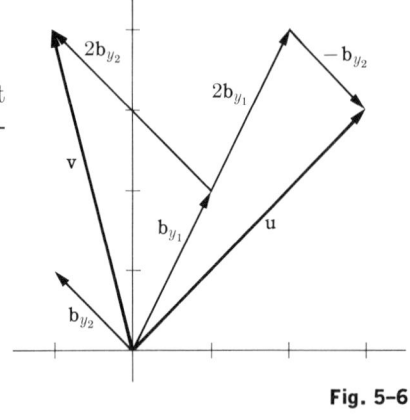

Fig. 5–6

That is, X is a mapping that carries each vector into a 2×1 matrix of numbers, the numbers being the components of the vector with respect to **i** and **j**. In particular, for the vectors **u** and **v** shown in Fig. 5–5,

$$X(\mathbf{u}) = \begin{bmatrix} 3 \\ 3 \end{bmatrix}, \qquad X(\mathbf{v}) = \begin{bmatrix} -1 \\ 4 \end{bmatrix}. \tag{2}$$

Turning now to Fig. 5–6, we see the same vectors **u** and **v** that appeared in Fig. 5–5. This time they are shown as linear combinations,

not of **i** and **j**, but of two other vectors, $\mathbf{b}_{y_1}$ and $\mathbf{b}_{y_2}$. It appears from Fig. 5-6 that
$$\mathbf{u} = 2\mathbf{b}_{y_1} - \mathbf{b}_{y_2}, \quad \mathbf{v} = \mathbf{b}_{y_1} + 2\mathbf{b}_{y_2}.$$
Thus if
$$Y = \begin{bmatrix} y_1 \\ y_2 \end{bmatrix}$$
is the matrix of component variables for the basis $(\mathbf{b}_{y_1}, \mathbf{b}_{y_2})$, then
$$Y(\mathbf{u}) = \begin{bmatrix} 2 \\ -1 \end{bmatrix}, \quad Y(\mathbf{v}) = \begin{bmatrix} 1 \\ 2 \end{bmatrix}. \tag{3}$$

It should be stressed that the vectors **u** and **v** in (2) are exactly the same as the **u** and **v** in (3). As seen in (2), the matrix X associates each of these vectors with a pair of numbers. In (3), the matrix Y associates each of these vectors with a different number pair. Introduction of a basis in the space of plane vectors leads to the association of each vector with a pair of numbers. However, there is no intrinsic number-pair representation for a vector; this depends on the basis chosen.

In studying these ideas we shall use the following notation. A basis and a component-variable matrix form a "package," and we shall identify them by repetition of a letter. Thus
$$Y = \begin{bmatrix} y_1 \\ y_2 \end{bmatrix} \quad \text{and} \quad \mathbf{b}_{y_1}, \mathbf{b}_{y_2}$$
go together. If we had another basis in the same problem, we might call the pertinent items
$$Z = \begin{bmatrix} z_1 \\ z_2 \end{bmatrix} \quad \text{and} \quad \mathbf{b}_{z_1}, \mathbf{b}_{z_2}.$$

We recognize that $(\mathbf{i}, \mathbf{j})$ is a "special" basis, and reserve X as the symbol for its component-variable matrix. To be consistent we should write $\mathbf{b}_{x_1}$ and $\mathbf{b}_{x_2}$ instead of **i** and **j**, but the latter are commonly used in physics and vector analysis generally, and we shall continue to use them here.

We have written component variables in 2×1 matrices because when we write them this way we can use matrix multiplication to study the effect of changing from one basis to another. For example, if Y is the component-variable matrix for the basis $(\mathbf{b}_{y_1}, \mathbf{b}_{y_2})$ shown in Fig. 5-6, and if X has its agreed-upon meaning, then there is a 2×2 matrix A of numbers such that for every vector **w**,
$$Y(\mathbf{w}) = AX(\mathbf{w}). \tag{4}$$

144 LINEAR ALGEBRA 5–4

If we think of $(\mathbf{i}, \mathbf{j})$ as the "old" basis and change to the "new" basis $(\mathbf{b}_{y_1}, \mathbf{b}_{y_2})$, then (4) gives the new components of a vector $\mathbf{w}$ in terms of its old components. How can we find the matrix A in (4)? In Fig. 5–6 it appears that

$$\mathbf{b}_{y_1} = \mathbf{i} + 2\mathbf{j}, \qquad \mathbf{b}_{y_2} = -\mathbf{i} + \mathbf{j}.$$

Another way of saying this is

$$X(\mathbf{b}_{y_1}) = \begin{bmatrix} 1 \\ 2 \end{bmatrix}, \qquad X(\mathbf{b}_{y_2}) = \begin{bmatrix} -1 \\ 1 \end{bmatrix}. \tag{5}$$

Now clearly,

$$\mathbf{b}_{y_1} = \mathbf{b}_{y_1} + 0\mathbf{b}_{y_2}, \qquad \mathbf{b}_{y_2} = 0\mathbf{b}_{y_1} + \mathbf{b}_{y_2},$$

which is to say that

$$Y(\mathbf{b}_{y_1}) = \begin{bmatrix} 1 \\ 0 \end{bmatrix}, \qquad Y(\mathbf{b}_{y_2}) = \begin{bmatrix} 0 \\ 1 \end{bmatrix}. \tag{6}$$

If we substitute $\mathbf{w} = \mathbf{b}_{y_1}$ in (4) and use (5) and (6), we have

$$\begin{bmatrix} 1 \\ 0 \end{bmatrix} = A \begin{bmatrix} 1 \\ 2 \end{bmatrix}. \tag{7}$$

There is a useful trick that we can employ at this point. It is readily verified from the rules of matrix multiplication that for any 2×2 matrix B,

$$B \begin{bmatrix} 1 \\ 0 \end{bmatrix}$$

is just the first column of B. This does not apply directly to (7), but it does if we multiply both sides of (7) by A^{-1}:

$$A^{-1} \begin{bmatrix} 1 \\ 0 \end{bmatrix} = \begin{bmatrix} 1 \\ 2 \end{bmatrix}.$$

This tells us the first column of A^{-1}. Similarly, if we substitute $\mathbf{w} = \mathbf{b}_{y_2}$ in (4) and multiply by A^{-1}, we have

$$A^{-1} \begin{bmatrix} 0 \\ 1 \end{bmatrix} = \begin{bmatrix} -1 \\ 1 \end{bmatrix},$$

and this gives us the second column of A^{-1}. Therefore

$$A^{-1} = \begin{bmatrix} 1 & -1 \\ 2 & 1 \end{bmatrix},$$

and by the rule of Section 5–2 for inverting 2×2 matrices, we have

$$A = \begin{bmatrix} \frac{1}{3} & \frac{1}{3} \\ -\frac{2}{3} & \frac{1}{3} \end{bmatrix}.$$

With this matrix for A, formula (4) should now apply to the vector **u** of Figs. 5–5 and 5–6. That is, we want to check that

$$Y(\mathbf{u}) = AX(\mathbf{u}).$$

Noting (2) and (3), we see that this means that

$$\begin{bmatrix} 2 \\ -1 \end{bmatrix} = \begin{bmatrix} \frac{1}{3} & \frac{1}{3} \\ -\frac{2}{3} & \frac{1}{3} \end{bmatrix} \begin{bmatrix} 3 \\ 3 \end{bmatrix};$$

this does indeed check. We leave it to the reader to check that formula (4) also transforms the components of **v** correctly.

Note that in this example

$$\mathbf{i} = \tfrac{1}{3}\mathbf{b}_{y_1} - \tfrac{2}{3}\mathbf{b}_{y_2}, \qquad \mathbf{j} = \tfrac{1}{3}\mathbf{b}_{y_1} + \tfrac{1}{3}\mathbf{b}_{y_2}$$

(check this geometrically), and if the information on change of basis had been given in this form the techniques used above would have found A directly rather than A^{-1}.

In general, a set $\mathbf{b}_1, \mathbf{b}_2, \ldots, \mathbf{b}_n$ of elements of a vector space V is called a *basis* for V if every $\mathbf{w} \in V$ has a unique expansion

$$\mathbf{w} = \sum_{i=1}^{n} a_i \mathbf{b}_i.$$

Not every vector space has a basis consisting of a finite set of elements. For example, the space P of all polynomials has none. However, it can be shown that if V has a basis consisting of n vectors, then every basis for V has exactly n vectors in it. In this case, V is said to be *n-dimensional*. Though we have mentioned some infinite-dimensional spaces (such as P), our discussion will in general be concerned only with finite-dimensional vector spaces.

In any finite-dimensional vector space, a change of basis can be described by a matrix equation

$$Y(\mathbf{w}) = AX(\mathbf{w}),$$

where X and Y are $n \times 1$ and A is $n \times n$. In the 2-dimensional example discussed above, we used a trick to find the matrix A, and this works equally well in the general case. That is, if B is $n \times n$ and C is $n \times 1$, with 1 in the kth row and all other entries 0, then BC is the kth column

146 LINEAR ALGEBRA 5-4

of B. Dimension becomes an issue only if (as may well happen) the problem calls for inversion of a matrix.

We conclude with a nongeometric example. Consider the space P_2 of quadratic polynomials. The three polynomials

$$I^2, \quad I, \quad I^0$$

form a basis. Let X be the component-variable matrix for this basis; that is,

$$X(aI^2 + bI + cI^0) = \begin{bmatrix} a \\ b \\ c \end{bmatrix}.$$

As a new basis let us take

$$(I + I^0)^2, \quad I + I^0, \quad (I + I^0)^0.$$

In terms of elementary algebra, this says "convert all quadratic polynomials in x to polynomials in $x + 1$." Now

$$(I + I^0)^2 = I^2 + 2I + I^0,$$
$$I + I^0 = I + I^0,$$
$$(I + I^0)^0 = I^0,$$

which is to say

$$X[(I+I^0)^2] = \begin{bmatrix} 1 \\ 2 \\ 1 \end{bmatrix}, \quad X(I+I^0) = \begin{bmatrix} 0 \\ 1 \\ 1 \end{bmatrix}, \quad X[(I+I^0)^0] = \begin{bmatrix} 0 \\ 0 \\ 1 \end{bmatrix}.$$

Thus, if Y is the component variable matrix for the new basis and

$$Y(\mathbf{w}) = AX(\mathbf{w}),$$

substituting $\mathbf{w} = (I + I^0)^2$ yields

$$\begin{bmatrix} 1 \\ 0 \\ 0 \end{bmatrix} = A \begin{bmatrix} 1 \\ 2 \\ 1 \end{bmatrix} \quad \text{or} \quad A^{-1} \begin{bmatrix} 1 \\ 0 \\ 0 \end{bmatrix} = \begin{bmatrix} 1 \\ 2 \\ 1 \end{bmatrix},$$

and we have the first column of A^{-1}. Continuing in this way, we get

$$A^{-1} = \begin{bmatrix} 1 & 0 & 0 \\ 2 & 1 & 0 \\ 1 & 1 & 1 \end{bmatrix}.$$

5-4

We are not concerned with techniques for inverting 3×3 matrices, but the reader can check (by showing $AA^{-1} = [\delta_{ij}]$) that, in this case,

$$A = \begin{bmatrix} 1 & 0 & 0 \\ -2 & 1 & 0 \\ 1 & 1 & 1 \end{bmatrix}$$

Let us apply this to a specific vector (polynomial). In terms of matrices,

$$\begin{bmatrix} 1 & 0 & 0 \\ -2 & 1 & 0 \\ 1 & -1 & 1 \end{bmatrix} \begin{bmatrix} 3 \\ 4 \\ 5 \end{bmatrix} = \begin{bmatrix} 3 \\ -2 \\ 4 \end{bmatrix};$$

in terms of polynomials, this says that

$$3x^2 + 4x + 5 = 3(x+1)^2 - 2(x+1) + 4.$$

EXERCISES

1. For each of the following descriptions of a change of basis in the space of plane vectors, find the matrix A such that $Y(\mathbf{w}) = AX(\mathbf{w})$ for every plane vector $\mathbf{w}$.
   a) $\mathbf{b}_{y_1} = 3\mathbf{i} - 2\mathbf{j}$, $\mathbf{b}_{y_2} = -2\mathbf{i} + \mathbf{j}$ b) $\mathbf{b}_{y_1} = \mathbf{i} - 2\mathbf{j}$, $\mathbf{b}_{y_2} = 2\mathbf{i} - 3\mathbf{j}$
   c) $\mathbf{i} = \mathbf{b}_{y_1} + \mathbf{b}_{y_2}$, $\mathbf{j} = \mathbf{b}_{y_1} - 2\mathbf{b}_{y_2}$ d) $\mathbf{i} = \mathbf{b}_{y_1} - \mathbf{b}_{y_2}$, $\mathbf{j} = \mathbf{b}_{y_1} + 2\mathbf{b}_{y_2}$

2. For each of the changes of basis listed in Exercise 1, find each of the following equations algebraically and check it geometrically.
   a) An equation giving $3\mathbf{i} + 2\mathbf{j}$ in terms of $\mathbf{b}_{y_1}$ and $\mathbf{b}_{y_2}$.
   b) An equation giving $4\mathbf{b}_{y_1} - 3\mathbf{b}_{y_2}$ in terms of $\mathbf{i}$ and $\mathbf{j}$.

3. Given that, for every plane vector $\mathbf{w}$,

$$Y(\mathbf{w}) = \begin{bmatrix} 2 & 3 \\ 1 & 2 \end{bmatrix} X(\mathbf{w}).$$

   a) Find $\mathbf{b}_{y_1}$ and $\mathbf{b}_{y_2}$ in terms of $\mathbf{i}$ and $\mathbf{j}$.
   b) Find $\mathbf{i}$ and $\mathbf{j}$ in terms of $\mathbf{b}_{y_1}$ and $\mathbf{b}_{y_2}$.

4. The set of 2×1 matrices forms a vector space, but the numbers appearing in an element of the space must not be confused with components.
   a) Show that with $\begin{bmatrix} 1 \\ 0 \end{bmatrix}$ and $\begin{bmatrix} 0 \\ 1 \end{bmatrix}$ taken as a basis, the numbers in a matrix are its components.
   b) Find the components of $\begin{bmatrix} 2 \\ 3 \end{bmatrix}$ with respect to $\begin{bmatrix} -1 \\ 2 \end{bmatrix}$ and $\begin{bmatrix} 2 \\ 1 \end{bmatrix}$ as a basis.

5. In the space P_2 of quadratic polynomials, let X be the component-variable matrix for the basis (I^2, I, I^0). Let Y be the matrix for another basis

(f_1, f_2, f_3). Specific changes of basis are described below, and each can be described by a matrix equation

$$Y(g) = AX(g),$$

valid for every quadratic function g. In each case, find either A or A^{-1} and indicate which matrix you have found.

a) $f_1 = I^2 + I, f_2 = I + I^0, f_3 = I - I^0$
b) $I^2 = f_1 + f_2 + f_3, I = f_1 - f_2 + f_3, I^0 = f_1 + f_2 - f_3$

6. A set $v_1, v_2, \ldots, v_n$ of vectors is called *linearly independent* if

$$\sum_{i=1}^{n} a_i v_i = 0$$

implies that $a_i = 0$ ($i = 1, 2, \ldots, n$). Show that a set of n vectors is linearly independent if and only if no one of them is a linear combination of the other $n - 1$ vectors. [*Note:* For $n = 2$ this is Exercise 6(g), Section 5–3.]

7. Let $v_1, v_2, \ldots, v_n$ be a set of vectors in a vector space V such that for every $u \in V$ there is an expansion

$$u = \sum_{i=1}^{n} a_i v_i.$$

For $v_1, v_2, \ldots, v_n$ to be a basis for V, the coefficients a_i must be uniquely determined by u. Show that this is the case if and only if the v_i form a linearly independent set. [*Hint:* To prove "if," suppose that u has two expansions and subtract them; to prove "only if," use Exercise 6.]

5–5 LINEAR TRANSFORMATIONS; PLANE VECTORS

Let (i, j) and X be as in Section 5–4, and consider the equation

$$X(v) = BX(w), \qquad (1)$$

where B is a 2×2 matrix of numbers. Equation (1) describes a vector-to-vector mapping

$$w \to v.$$

Such a mapping is called a *transformation*. Let us denote the mapping itself by T. It is customary to write the result of applying a transformation T to a vector w by Tw rather than $T(w)$. Thus (1) may be rewritten

$$X(Tw) = BX(w). \qquad (2)$$

Equation (2) is a matrix description of T in terms of the (i, j) basis, and

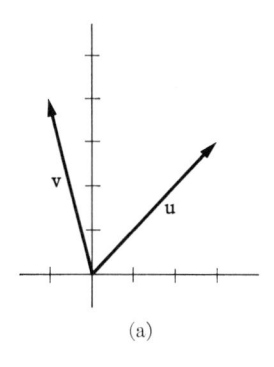

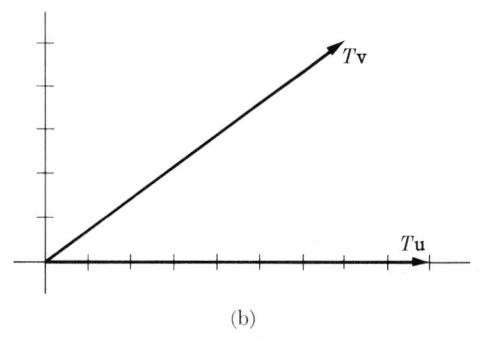

Fig. 5-7

we say that B is the matrix of the transformation T with respect to the basis $(\mathbf{i}, \mathbf{j})$.

It is easily verified that if T is described by a matrix equation of the form (2), then
$$T(a\mathbf{u} + b\mathbf{v}) = aT\mathbf{u} + bT\mathbf{v}. \tag{3}$$

A transformation T satisfying (3) is called a *linear transformation*. It can be shown that any linear transformation on a finite-dimensional vector space can be described by a matrix equation similar to (2). Indeed, matrices first appeared in the study of linear transformations.

By way of example, let the matrix B in (2) be
$$\begin{bmatrix} 1 & 2 \\ -1 & 1 \end{bmatrix}.$$

Figure 5-7(a) shows the two vectors $\mathbf{u}$ and $\mathbf{v}$ introduced for illustrative purposes in Fig. 5-5 (Section 5-4). Since
$$X(\mathbf{u}) = \begin{bmatrix} 3 \\ 3 \end{bmatrix},$$
we have
$$X(T\mathbf{u}) = \begin{bmatrix} 1 & 2 \\ -1 & 1 \end{bmatrix} \begin{bmatrix} 3 \\ 3 \end{bmatrix} = \begin{bmatrix} 9 \\ 0 \end{bmatrix}.$$
Similarly,
$$X(T\mathbf{v}) = \begin{bmatrix} 1 & 2 \\ -1 & 1 \end{bmatrix} \begin{bmatrix} -1 \\ 4 \end{bmatrix} = \begin{bmatrix} 7 \\ 5 \end{bmatrix}.$$

Figure 5-7(b) shows the vectors $T\mathbf{u}$ and $T\mathbf{v}$. The only reasonable way to draw a picture of a linear transformation of the space of plane vectors

150 LINEAR ALGEBRA

into itself is to draw two planes and show certain vectors on one and their transforms on the other.

Still referring to this same transformation T, we see that

$$X(T\mathbf{i}) = \begin{bmatrix} 1 & 2 \\ -1 & 1 \end{bmatrix}\begin{bmatrix} 1 \\ 0 \end{bmatrix} = \begin{bmatrix} 1 \\ -1 \end{bmatrix}, \quad X(T\mathbf{j}) = \begin{bmatrix} 1 & 2 \\ -1 & 1 \end{bmatrix}\begin{bmatrix} 0 \\ 1 \end{bmatrix} = \begin{bmatrix} 2 \\ 1 \end{bmatrix}.$$

Figure 5-8 shows $T\mathbf{i}$ and $T\mathbf{j}$ and also the expansion of $T\mathbf{u}$ and $T\mathbf{v}$ in terms of $T\mathbf{i}$ and $T\mathbf{j}$. Note the following relations:

$$\mathbf{u} = 3\mathbf{i} + 3\mathbf{j}, \quad \mathbf{v} = -\mathbf{i} + 4\mathbf{j}; \tag{4}$$

$$T\mathbf{u} = 3T\mathbf{i} + 3T\mathbf{j}, \quad T\mathbf{v} = -T\mathbf{i} + 4T\mathbf{j}; \tag{5}$$

$$T\mathbf{u} = 9\mathbf{i} + 0\mathbf{j}, \quad T\mathbf{v} = 7\mathbf{i} + 5\mathbf{j}. \tag{6}$$

Note carefully the distinction between (5) and (6). The coefficients in (6) are what the matrix equation (2) is designed to give us. The coefficients in (5) must be the same as those in (4) if the linearity condition (3) is to be satisfied. That is, Fig. 5-8 is illustrating that the transformation T is linear.

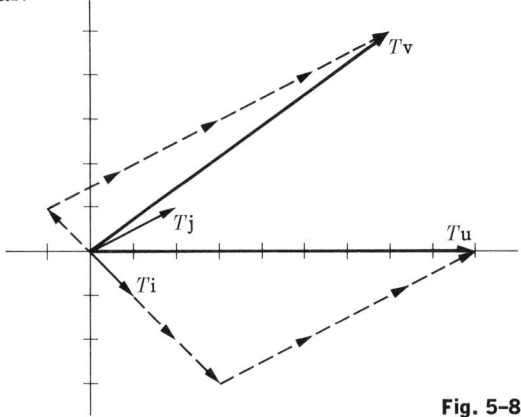

Fig. 5-8

To put it another way, Fig. 5-8 illustrates that if we know $T\mathbf{i}$ and $T\mathbf{j}$, we can find $T\mathbf{u}$, $T\mathbf{v}$ and, indeed, the transform of any vector whose $(\mathbf{i}, \mathbf{j})$ components are given. That is, $T\mathbf{i}$ and $T\mathbf{j}$ determine T completely. So suppose we are told that T is a linear transformation such that

$$T\mathbf{i} = \mathbf{i} - \mathbf{j}, \quad T\mathbf{j} = 2\mathbf{i} + \mathbf{j}. \tag{7}$$

This is enough to determine T uniquely; so it should determine the matrix B such that

$$X(T\mathbf{w}) = BX(\mathbf{w}) \tag{8}$$

for every vector **w**. To find B from the information in (7), we use the same technique that we used in Section 5-4 to find the matrix for a change of basis. By definition,

$$X(\mathbf{i}) = \begin{bmatrix} 1 \\ 0 \end{bmatrix},$$

and by the first equation in (7),

$$X(T\mathbf{i}) = \begin{bmatrix} 1 \\ -1 \end{bmatrix}.$$

Thus substituting $\mathbf{w} = \mathbf{i}$ in (8) yields

$$\begin{bmatrix} 1 \\ -1 \end{bmatrix} = B \begin{bmatrix} 1 \\ 0 \end{bmatrix},$$

and it follows (see Section 5-4) that the first column of B is

$$\begin{bmatrix} 1 \\ -1 \end{bmatrix}.$$

We find the second column by setting $\mathbf{w} = \mathbf{j}$ in (8), and

$$B = \begin{bmatrix} 1 & 2 \\ -1 & 1 \end{bmatrix}.$$

So far we have used only the $(\mathbf{i}, \mathbf{j})$ basis in discussing linear transformations. Now a linear transformation is merely a mapping that satisfies (3), and this has nothing to do with bases. Bringing in a basis yields a matrix formula—such as (8)—for the transformation. However, the matrix formula depends on the basis chosen as well as on the transformation being described. To illustrate this, let T be the same linear transformation we have been discussing throughout this section and let $(\mathbf{b}_{y_1}, \mathbf{b}_{y_2})$ be the basis used as an illustration in Section 5-4. What is the matrix of T with respect to this new basis? The easiest way to answer this specific question is to derive a general formula. We suppose that (8) describes T with respect to the X-basis and that the change of basis is given by

$$Y(\mathbf{w}) = AX(\mathbf{w}). \tag{9}$$

From (9), we have

$$X(\mathbf{w}) = A^{-1}Y(\mathbf{w}) \quad \text{and also} \quad X(T\mathbf{w}) = A^{-1}Y(T\mathbf{w}),$$

because (9) holds for $T\mathbf{w}$ as well as $\mathbf{w}$; it holds for all vectors. Substituting these results in (8), we have

$$A^{-1}Y(T\mathbf{w}) = BA^{-1}Y(\mathbf{w}) \quad \text{or} \quad Y(T\mathbf{w}) = ABA^{-1}Y(\mathbf{w}).$$

Thus ABA^{-1} is the matrix for T with respect to the Y-basis.

To return to our specific example, the matrix B in (8) is

$$\begin{bmatrix} 1 & 2 \\ -1 & 1 \end{bmatrix}.$$

For the change of basis

$$\mathbf{b}_{y_1} = \mathbf{i} + 2\mathbf{j}, \qquad \mathbf{b}_{y_2} = -\mathbf{i} + \mathbf{j},$$

we have (see Section 5-4)

$$A^{-1} = \begin{bmatrix} 1 & -1 \\ 2 & 1 \end{bmatrix}, \qquad A = \begin{bmatrix} \frac{1}{3} & \frac{1}{3} \\ -\frac{2}{3} & \frac{1}{3} \end{bmatrix}.$$

Therefore

$$BA^{-1} = \begin{bmatrix} 1 & 2 \\ -1 & 1 \end{bmatrix} \begin{bmatrix} 1 & -1 \\ 2 & 1 \end{bmatrix} = \begin{bmatrix} 5 & 1 \\ 1 & 2 \end{bmatrix}$$

and

$$ABA^{-1} = \begin{bmatrix} \frac{1}{3} & \frac{1}{3} \\ -\frac{2}{3} & \frac{1}{3} \end{bmatrix} \begin{bmatrix} 5 & 1 \\ 1 & 2 \end{bmatrix} = \begin{bmatrix} 2 & 1 \\ -3 & 0 \end{bmatrix}.$$

Therefore the matrix equations

$$X(T\mathbf{w}) = \begin{bmatrix} 1 & 2 \\ -1 & 1 \end{bmatrix} X(\mathbf{w}), \qquad Y(T\mathbf{w}) = \begin{bmatrix} 2 & 1 \\ -3 & 0 \end{bmatrix} Y(\mathbf{w}) \tag{10}$$

describe the same transformation T.

We now again use the specific vectors $\mathbf{u}$ and $\mathbf{v}$ that we have employed throughout the last two sections for illustrative purposes. We recall from Section 5-4 (note Fig. 5-6) that

$$Y(\mathbf{u}) = \begin{bmatrix} 2 \\ -1 \end{bmatrix}, \qquad Y(\mathbf{v}) = \begin{bmatrix} 1 \\ 2 \end{bmatrix};$$

therefore, by the second equation in (10),

$$Y(T\mathbf{u}) = \begin{bmatrix} 2 & 1 \\ -3 & 0 \end{bmatrix} \begin{bmatrix} 2 \\ -1 \end{bmatrix} = \begin{bmatrix} 3 \\ -6 \end{bmatrix}, \qquad Y(T\mathbf{v}) = \begin{bmatrix} 2 & 1 \\ -3 & 0 \end{bmatrix} \begin{bmatrix} 1 \\ 2 \end{bmatrix} = \begin{bmatrix} 4 \\ -3 \end{bmatrix}.$$

Figure 5-9 shows the transformation T again, with vectors given in the Y-basis. Note that $\mathbf{u}$, $\mathbf{v}$, $T\mathbf{u}$, $T\mathbf{v}$ are exactly the same in Figs. 5-7 and 5-9. Only the bases are different.

5-5   LINEAR TRANSFORMATIONS; PLANE VECTORS

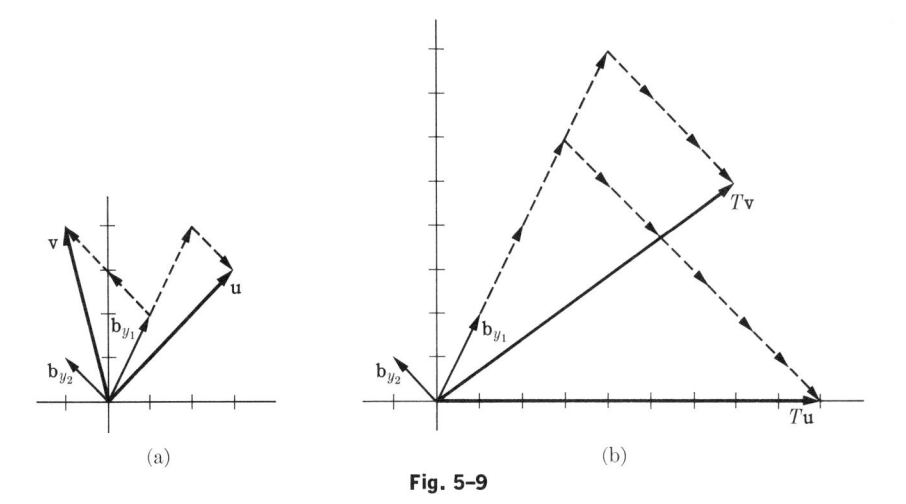

Fig. 5-9

EXERCISES

1. Let T be the linear transformation such that
$$Ti = i - 3j, \qquad Tj = 2i + j.$$

a) Find the matrix B such that, for all vectors $\mathbf{w}$,
$$X(T\mathbf{w}) = BX(\mathbf{w}).$$

b) Let $\mathbf{u} = \mathbf{i} + \mathbf{j}$. Sketch (on different planes) $\mathbf{u}$ and $T\mathbf{u}$.

c) Introduce a new basis by
$$\mathbf{b}_{y1} = 2\mathbf{i} - \mathbf{j}, \qquad \mathbf{b}_{y2} = -3\mathbf{i} + 2\mathbf{j}.$$

Find the matrix C such that, for every vector $\mathbf{w}$,
$$Y(T\mathbf{w}) = CY(\mathbf{w}).$$

d) Show Y-components of $\mathbf{u}$ and $T\mathbf{u}$ on the sketches of part (b).

2. Consider two bases related as follows:
$$\mathbf{b}_{y1} = 3\mathbf{i} - 2\mathbf{j}, \qquad \mathbf{b}_{y2} = 2\mathbf{i} - \mathbf{j}.$$

Let T be the linear transformation such that
$$T\mathbf{b}_{y1} = \mathbf{b}_{y1} - 3\mathbf{b}_{y2}, \qquad T\mathbf{b}_{y2} = 4\mathbf{b}_{y1} - \mathbf{b}_{y2}.$$

a) Find the matrix C such that, for every vector $\mathbf{w}$,
$$Y(T\mathbf{w}) = CY(\mathbf{w}).$$

b) Find the matrix B such that, for every vector **w**,

$$X(T\mathbf{w}) = BX(\mathbf{w}).$$

3. Each of the following equations describes a linear transformation T. In each case give a geometric description of the effect of T on a vector, and find the matrix for T with respect to the (**i**, **j**) basis.
   a) $T(a\mathbf{i} + b\mathbf{j}) = (a + b)\mathbf{i} + b\mathbf{j}$
   b) $T(a\mathbf{i} + b\mathbf{j}) = a\mathbf{i}$
   c) $T(a\mathbf{i} + b\mathbf{j}) = a\mathbf{i} - b\mathbf{j}$

5–6 LINEAR TRANSFORMATIONS; OTHER SPACES

In Section 5–5 we looked at matrix representation of linear transformations of the space of plane vectors into itself. The format for this representation was

$$X(T\mathbf{w}) = BX(\mathbf{w}). \qquad (1)$$

If V is any n-dimensional vector space and X is an $n \times 1$ component-variable matrix for V and B is $n \times n$, then (1) gives a matrix representation of a linear transformation T of V into itself. The geometric pictures of Section 5–5 may be missing, but the algebraic theory is exactly like that of Section 5–5.

We get a useful generalization by permitting the domain and range spaces of T to be different, even to differ in dimension. Consider the following situation:

V_1 is a vector space of dimension k.
X is a $(k \times 1)$ component variable matrix for V_1.
V_2 is a vector space of dimension n (n may be either larger or smaller than k).
Y is a $(n \times 1)$ component-variable matrix for V_2.
T is a mapping from V_1 into V_2 such that

$$T(a\mathbf{u} + b\mathbf{v}) = aT\mathbf{u} + bT\mathbf{v}.$$

Given this situation, the matrix representation for T assumes the form

$$Y(T\mathbf{w}) = BX(\mathbf{w}), \qquad (2)$$

where B is $n \times k$.

Let us look at an example. Suppose V_1 is the space P_2 of quadratic polynomials with basis (I^2, I, I^0). Let V_2 be the space P_1 of linear polynomials with basis (I, I^0). Let T be the derivative operator; that is, for any quadratic function f, let Tf be the linear function f'. This is a linear transformation from V_1 to V_2 because

$$T(af + bg) = (af + bg)' = af' + bg' = aTf + bTg.$$

Turning now to the bases, we have

$$TI^2 = 2I, \quad TI = I^0, \quad TI^0 = 0.$$

As in Section 5–5, transforms of the basis elements determine the columns of the matrix; so the matrix for T here is

$$\begin{bmatrix} 2 & 0 & 0 \\ 0 & 1 & 0 \end{bmatrix}.$$

For example,

$$\begin{bmatrix} 2 & 0 & 0 \\ 0 & 1 & 0 \end{bmatrix} \begin{bmatrix} 5 \\ -3 \\ 2 \end{bmatrix} = \begin{bmatrix} 10 \\ -3 \end{bmatrix}$$

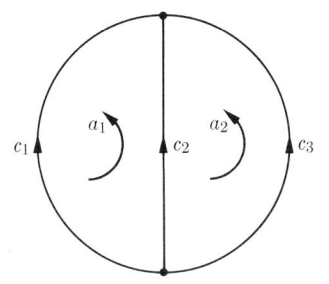

which is to say the derivative of $5I^2 - 3I + 2I^0$ is $10I - 3I^0$.

Fig. 5–10

Another interesting example comes from algebraic topology. Figure 5–10 shows three oriented curves c_1, c_2, c_3, and two oriented areas a_1 and a_2. The topologist considers what he calls chains. A 1-dimensional chain (abbreviated 1-chain) for Fig. 5–10 is a linear combination of the oriented curves c_1, c_2, and c_3. Formally,

$$\alpha_1 c_1 + \alpha_2 c_2 + \alpha_3 c_3, \tag{3}$$

where the α's are numbers, is a 1-chain. Strictly speaking, chains are just algebraic formalisms, but we might think of (3) as a plan for carrying weights along the curves. We carry a weight α_1 along c_1, α_2 along c_2, etc. A negative weight means that we move in the direction opposite to the arrow. Algebraically, the 1-chains for Fig. 5–10 form a 3-dimensional vector space with c_1, c_2, and c_3 as basis vectors. Similarly, 2-chains are linear combinations of the a's, and for Fig. 5–10 these form a 2-dimensional vector space with a_1, a_2 as basis.

An important notion in algebraic topology is that of boundary. In Fig. 5–10, it is reasonable to say that the boundary of a_1 is $c_2 - c_1$. That is, to go around the edge of a_1 you traverse c_2 in the direction of its arrow and c_1 in the direction opposite to its arrow. Similarly, the boundary of a_2 is $c_3 - c_2$. For any 2-chain $\beta_1 a_1 + \beta_2 a_2$, we define the boundary as β_1 times the boundary of a_1 plus β_2 times that of a_2. With this definition the boundary operator becomes a linear transformation from the space of 2-chains into the space of 1-chains. Let T be this boundary transformation. From Fig. 5–10, we have

$$Ta_1 = -c_1 + c_2, \qquad Ta_2 = -c_2 + c_3;$$

so these coefficients form the columns of the matrix for T, and this matrix is

$$\begin{bmatrix} -1 & 0 \\ 1 & -1 \\ 0 & 1 \end{bmatrix}.$$

Now look at some sample computations.

$$\begin{bmatrix} -1 & 0 \\ 1 & -1 \\ 0 & 1 \end{bmatrix} \begin{bmatrix} 1 \\ 1 \end{bmatrix} = \begin{bmatrix} -1 \\ 0 \\ 1 \end{bmatrix}$$

This says that the boundary of $a_1 + a_2$ is $-c_1 + c_3$. Geometrically, if we go around a_1 and then a_2, we traverse c_3 positively, c_1 negatively, and c_2 once each way. Another computation,

$$\begin{bmatrix} -1 & 0 \\ 1 & -1 \\ 0 & 1 \end{bmatrix} \begin{bmatrix} 1 \\ -1 \end{bmatrix} = \begin{bmatrix} -1 \\ 2 \\ -1 \end{bmatrix},$$

tells us that the boundary of $a_1 - a_2$ is $-c_1 + c_2 - c_3$. Again look at the picture. If we go around a_1 in the direction of the arrow and around a_2 in the opposite direction, we traverse c_2 twice in the direction of the arrow and c_1 and c_3 once each against the arrows.

Change of basis in connection with transformations of the type we are discussing here is accomplished very much as in Section 5–5. The difference is that since the transformations here go from one space to another, there are two changes of basis to consider in one problem: one in the domain space and one in the range space. Suppose T goes from V_1 with component matrix X to V_2 with component matrix Y, and has matrix B with respect to these bases; that is,

$$Y(T\mathbf{w}) = BX(\mathbf{w}). \tag{4}$$

Let

$$Z(\mathbf{w}) = AX(\mathbf{w}) \tag{5}$$

describe a basis change in V_1 and let

$$W(\mathbf{w}) = CY(\mathbf{w}) \tag{6}$$

describe one in V_2. From (5) we have $X(\mathbf{w}) = A^{-1}Z(\mathbf{w})$, and from (6) with $\mathbf{w}$ replaced by $T\mathbf{w}$ we have $Y(T\mathbf{w}) = C^{-1}W(T\mathbf{w})$. Substitution in (4) yields $C^{-1}W(T\mathbf{w}) = BA^{-1}Z(\mathbf{w})$ or

$$W(T\mathbf{w}) = CBA^{-1}Z(\mathbf{w}) \tag{7}$$

as the matrix equation for T with respect to the two new bases.

Suppose we change bases for the derivative transformation from P_2 into P_1 by taking

$$(I + I^0)^2, \qquad I + I^0, \qquad (I + I^0)^0$$

as the basis in P_2 and

$$I + I^0, \qquad I - I^0$$

as the basis in P_1. This change of basis for P_2 was discussed in Section 5–4 and the inverse of the change-of-basis matrix [which is what we want in (7)] was found to be

$$A^{-1} = \begin{bmatrix} 1 & 0 & 0 \\ 2 & 1 & 0 \\ 1 & 1 & 1 \end{bmatrix}.$$

If C is the change-of-basis matrix in P_1, we have, by the usual procedure,

$$C^{-1} = \begin{bmatrix} 1 & 1 \\ 1 & -1 \end{bmatrix};$$

so

$$C = \begin{bmatrix} \tfrac{1}{2} & \tfrac{1}{2} \\ \tfrac{1}{2} & -\tfrac{1}{2} \end{bmatrix}.$$

Thus the matrix of constants in (7) is

$$\begin{bmatrix} \tfrac{1}{2} & \tfrac{1}{2} \\ \tfrac{1}{2} & -\tfrac{1}{2} \end{bmatrix} \begin{bmatrix} 2 & 0 & 0 \\ 0 & 1 & 0 \end{bmatrix} \begin{bmatrix} 1 & 0 & 0 \\ 2 & 1 & 0 \\ 1 & 1 & 1 \end{bmatrix}$$

$$= \begin{bmatrix} \tfrac{1}{2} & \tfrac{1}{2} \\ \tfrac{1}{2} & -\tfrac{1}{2} \end{bmatrix} \begin{bmatrix} 2 & 0 & 0 \\ 2 & 1 & 0 \end{bmatrix} = \begin{bmatrix} 2 & \tfrac{1}{2} & 0 \\ 0 & -\tfrac{1}{2} & 0 \end{bmatrix}.$$

A sample computation with this new matrix is

$$\begin{bmatrix} 2 & \tfrac{1}{2} & 0 \\ 0 & -\tfrac{1}{2} & 0 \end{bmatrix} \begin{bmatrix} 3 \\ 4 \\ 5 \end{bmatrix} = \begin{bmatrix} 8 \\ -2 \end{bmatrix},$$

158 LINEAR ALGEBRA 5-6

which says that the derivative of

$$3(I + I^0)^2 + 4(I + I^0) + 5(I + I^0)^0$$

is $8(I + I^0) - 2(I - I^0)$.

We return now to Fig. 5–10 and the boundary transformation from the space of 2-chains to the space of 1-chains. For a new basis in the 2-chain space, we use

$$a_1 + a_2, \quad a_1 - a_2.$$

The matrix A^{-1} in (7) is then

$$A^{-1} = \begin{bmatrix} 1 & 1 \\ 1 & -1 \end{bmatrix}.$$

In the 1-chain space, we introduce the new basis

$$-c_1 + c_3, \quad -c_1 + 2c_2 - c_3, \quad 2c_1 - c_3.$$

For the matrix C of (7), we have

$$C^{-1} = \begin{bmatrix} -1 & -1 & 2 \\ 0 & 2 & 0 \\ 1 & -1 & -1 \end{bmatrix}.$$

The inverse turns out to be

$$C = \begin{bmatrix} 1 & \frac{3}{2} & 2 \\ 0 & \frac{1}{2} & 0 \\ 1 & 1 & 1 \end{bmatrix}.$$

(The reader should check that $C^{-1}C = [\delta_{ij}]$.) So, with respect to these new bases, the boundary transformation for Fig. 5–10 is given by the matrix

$$\begin{bmatrix} 1 & \frac{3}{2} & 2 \\ 0 & \frac{1}{2} & 0 \\ 1 & 1 & 1 \end{bmatrix} \begin{bmatrix} -1 & 0 \\ 1 & -1 \\ 0 & 1 \end{bmatrix} \begin{bmatrix} 1 & 1 \\ 1 & -1 \end{bmatrix}$$

$$= \begin{bmatrix} 1 & \frac{3}{2} & 2 \\ 0 & \frac{1}{2} & 0 \\ 1 & 1 & 1 \end{bmatrix} \begin{bmatrix} -1 & -1 \\ 0 & 2 \\ 1 & -1 \end{bmatrix} = \begin{bmatrix} 1 & 0 \\ 0 & 1 \\ 0 & 0 \end{bmatrix}.$$

The final result here tells us that

$-c_1 + c_3$ is the boundary of $a_1 + a_2$;
$-c_1 + 2c_2 - c_3$ is the boundary of $a_1 - a_2$;
$2c_1 - c_3$ is not a boundary.

This kind of basis change is very useful in algebraic topology. An important idea there is to count the linearly independent boundary chains, and this is most easily done if each basis 2-chain has a single basis 1-chain for a boundary.

EXERCISES

1. Each of the following equations gives the inverse of a 3 × 3 matrix. Check each of these by multiplication. This exercise contains all 3 × 3 matrix inversions that are needed below (and some that are not needed). It may be used as a reference in solving the problems that follow.

a) $\begin{bmatrix} 1 & 0 & 0 \\ 2 & 1 & 0 \\ 1 & 1 & 1 \end{bmatrix}^{-1} = \begin{bmatrix} 1 & 0 & 0 \\ -2 & 1 & 0 \\ 1 & -1 & 1 \end{bmatrix}$

b) $\begin{bmatrix} 1 & 0 & 0 \\ 1 & 1 & 1 \\ 0 & 1 & -1 \end{bmatrix}^{-1} = \begin{bmatrix} 1 & 0 & 0 \\ -\frac{1}{2} & \frac{1}{2} & \frac{1}{2} \\ -\frac{1}{2} & \frac{1}{2} & -\frac{1}{2} \end{bmatrix}$

c) $\begin{bmatrix} 1 & \frac{4}{5} & \frac{3}{5} \\ 0 & 1 & 2 \\ 0 & 0 & 1 \end{bmatrix}^{-1} = \begin{bmatrix} 1 & -\frac{4}{5} & 1 \\ 0 & 1 & -2 \\ 0 & 0 & 1 \end{bmatrix}$

d) $\begin{bmatrix} 1 & 1 & 1 \\ 0 & 1 & 0 \\ 0 & 0 & 1 \end{bmatrix}^{-1} = \begin{bmatrix} 1 & -1 & -1 \\ 0 & 1 & 0 \\ 0 & 0 & 1 \end{bmatrix}$

2. Let T be the derivative transformation from P_2 to P_1.
   a) Take $(I^2 + I)$, $(I + I^0)$, $(I - I^0)$ as a basis in P_2 and $(I + 2I^0)$, $(2I - I^0)$ as a basis in P_1. Find the matrix for T.
   b) Find the derivative with respect to x of $2(x^2 + x) - 4(x + 1) + 3(x - 1)$ in terms of $(x + 2)$ and $(2x - 1)$.

3. Let T be the antiderivative transformation from P_1 into P_2. That is, let

$$TI = \tfrac{1}{2}I^2, \qquad TI^0 = I.$$

a) Find the matrix for T with respect to the natural bases in these spaces.
b) Take $(I + 2I^0)$, $(2I - I^0)$ as a basis in P_1 and $(I + I^0)^2$, $(I + I^0)$, $(I + I^0)^0$ as a basis in P_2. Find the matrix for T.
c) Evaluate the integral

$$\int_{-1}^{0} [3(x+2) - 5(2x-1)]\, dx.$$

4. Let T be the antiderivative transformation from P_2 into P_3 defined by

$$TI^2 = \tfrac{1}{3}I^3, \qquad TI = \tfrac{1}{2}I^2, \qquad TI^0 = I.$$

a) Find the matrix for T with respect to the natural bases in these spaces.
b) Change the basis in P_2 to $(I + I^0)^2$, $(I + I^0)$, $(I + I^0)^0$ and leave I^3, I^2, I, I^0 as the basis in P_3. Find the matrix for T.
c) Evaluate the integral

$$\int_{0}^{1} [3(x+1)^2 - 5(x+1)]\, dx.$$

5. Figure 5–11 shows the three curves of Fig. 5–10 not serving as boundaries of areas but having boundaries made up of points p_1 and p_2. The boundary of a curve is the point to which it goes minus that from which it came. Thus, in Fig. 5–11, each of the three curves has the 0-chain $p_2 - p_1$ for a boundary.

a) Let T be the boundary transformation from the space of 1-chains to the space of 0-chains. Use c_1, c_2, c_3 as the basis in the 1-chain space and p_1, p_2 as the basis in the 0-chain space. Find the matrix for T.
b) Change the 1-chain basis to c_1, $c_2 - c_1$, $c_3 - c_1$ and the 0-chain basis to $p_2 - p_1$, $p_1 + p_2$. Find the new matrix for T.
c) Interpret the result of part (b) geometrically.

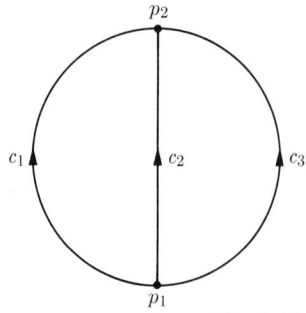

Fig. 5–11

6. One summer lobsters were in very short supply and the seafood wholesale houses were forcing "tie-in" sales on the fish markets. Wholesalers I, II, and III had different policies with regard to a 10-pound order:

   I: 5 pounds lobster, 5 pounds halibut
  II: 4 pounds lobster, 6 pounds halibut
 III: 3 pounds lobster, 7 pounds halibut

For a retail market, introduce procurement vectors

$$\begin{bmatrix} p_1 \\ p_2 \\ p_3 \end{bmatrix},$$

where p_1 is the total number of pounds of lobster and halibut bought from wholesaler I, etc. Also introduce stock vectors

$$\begin{bmatrix} s_1 \\ s_2 \end{bmatrix},$$

where s_1 is the number of pounds of lobster stocked and s_2 the number of pounds of halibut.

a) Find the matrix of the linear transformation T that maps procurement vectors into stock vectors.
b) Use the result of part (a) to find how much of each kind of seafood is stocked if 50 pounds are bought from I, 30 from II, and 25 from III.
c) Compute the matrix product

$$\begin{bmatrix} \frac{1}{5} & 0 \\ -\frac{1}{2} & \frac{1}{2} \end{bmatrix} \begin{bmatrix} 5 & 4 & 3 \\ 5 & 6 & 7 \end{bmatrix} \begin{bmatrix} 1 & -\frac{4}{5} & 1 \\ 0 & 1 & -2 \\ 0 & 0 & 1 \end{bmatrix}.$$

d) Interpret part (c) as a change of bases in the spaces of procurement and stock vectors. Interpret the physical significance (or lack thereof) of the new basis vectors. [*Note:* This is a typical pattern for the use of vectors in economics. Two comments are in order. (i) Often only a portion of the vector space is economically significant. (ii) Sometimes a simplifying change of basis is useful even though the new basis vectors are not in the significant part of the space. This occurs in the simplex method for linear programming (Section 6–5), where the results of the simplification are useful and the meaningless new basis vectors never really appear.]

5–7 DUALITY

Let M_2 be the vector space of all 2×1 matrices of numbers, and let

$$\begin{bmatrix} u_1 \\ u_2 \end{bmatrix}$$

be an arbitrary element of M_2. Let us take a specific 1×2 matrix, say [2 3], and multiply:

$$[2 \quad 3] \begin{bmatrix} u_1 \\ u_2 \end{bmatrix} = 2u_1 + 3u_2. \qquad (1)$$

The result is just a number. Another way of looking at this is to say that [2 3] is the matrix of a linear transformation from M_2 into a 1-dimensional vector space (the real-number system). Linear transformations with 1-dimensional ranges are called *linear functionals*. The set of all linear functionals on M_2 is called the *dual* space to M_2 and is denoted by M_2^*. Clearly M_2^* is represented by the set of all 1×2 matrices of numbers.

Now let M_3 be the vector space of all 3×1 matrices of numbers, and let

$$\begin{bmatrix} v_1 \\ v_2 \\ v_3 \end{bmatrix} \in M_3.$$

A 2×3 matrix such as

$$\begin{bmatrix} 2 & -1 & 3 \\ 1 & 2 & -2 \end{bmatrix}$$

describes a linear transformation T from M_3 to M_2 by the matrix equation

$$\begin{bmatrix} u_1 \\ u_2 \end{bmatrix} = \begin{bmatrix} 2 & -1 & 3 \\ 1 & 2 & -2 \end{bmatrix} \begin{bmatrix} v_1 \\ v_2 \\ v_3 \end{bmatrix}.$$

Substituting this into (1), we have

$$\begin{bmatrix} 2 & 3 \end{bmatrix} \begin{bmatrix} u_1 \\ u_2 \end{bmatrix} = \begin{bmatrix} 2 & 3 \end{bmatrix} \left(\begin{bmatrix} 2 & -1 & 3 \\ 1 & 2 & -2 \end{bmatrix} \begin{bmatrix} v_1 \\ v_2 \\ v_3 \end{bmatrix} \right)$$

$$= \left(\begin{bmatrix} 2 & 3 \end{bmatrix} \begin{bmatrix} 2 & -1 & 3 \\ 1 & 2 & -2 \end{bmatrix} \right) \begin{bmatrix} v_1 \\ v_2 \\ v_3 \end{bmatrix}$$

$$= \begin{bmatrix} 7 & 4 & 0 \end{bmatrix} \begin{bmatrix} v_1 \\ v_2 \\ v_3 \end{bmatrix}.$$

The first entry here is a description of a linear functional on M_2, while the last describes a linear functional on M_3. In this way a linear transformation T from M_3 to M_2 maps linear functionals on M_2 into linear functionals on M_3. That is to say, T from M_3 to M_2 determines a transformation denoted by T^* from M_2^* to M_3^*. The transformation T^* is called the *dual transformation* to T.

In terms of matrices, the relation between T and T^* is very simple. They have the same matrix; T is effected by multiplying a column matrix from the left; T^* is effected by multiplying a row matrix from the right.

EXERCISES

1. In the example discussed in the text, denote the linear functional on M_2 by f. Then the matrix multiplication

$$[2 \ \ 3] \begin{bmatrix} u_1 \\ u_2 \end{bmatrix}$$

is a computation of $f(\mathbf{u})$. The matrix equation

$$\begin{bmatrix} u_1 \\ u_2 \end{bmatrix} = \begin{bmatrix} 2 & -1 & 3 \\ 1 & 2 & -2 \end{bmatrix} \begin{bmatrix} v_1 \\ v_2 \\ v_3 \end{bmatrix}$$

may be rendered in non-matrix form as $\mathbf{u} = T\mathbf{v}$. Show that in this non-matrix notation the definition of T^* may be written

$$f(T\mathbf{v}) = (T^*f)(\mathbf{v}),$$

which is to say

$$T^*f = f \circ T.$$

2. Use the basis I^2, I, I^0 in the space P_2 of quadratic polynomials and the basis I, I^0 in the space P_1 of linear polynomials. The *natural representative* of $aI^2 + bI + cI^0$ in the space P_2^* is the linear functional with matrix $[a \ \ b \ \ c]$, and the natural representative of $aI + bI^0$ in P_1^* is the functional with matrix $[a \ \ b]$. Let T_1 be the derivative transformation from P_2 into P_1 and let T_2 be the antiderivative transformation from P_1 into P_2.
   a) Show that $T_1 \circ T_2$ is the identity map on P_1.
   b) Compare the action of T_1 on quadratic polynomials with that of T_2^* on their natural representatives.
   c) Compare T_1^* and T_2 in a similar way.
   d) Discuss the relation (or lack thereof) between inverses and duals.

3. Let T be the transformation of the space of plane vectors into itself such that

$$T\mathbf{i} = 2\mathbf{i} + 3\mathbf{j}, \qquad T\mathbf{j} = \mathbf{i} - 4\mathbf{j}.$$

Let f be the functional such that

$$f(a\mathbf{i} + b\mathbf{j}) = 5a - 2b.$$

Find T^*f; that is, give its value on an arbitrary vector $a\mathbf{i} + b\mathbf{j}$.

4. Let V_1 be the space of 3×1 matrices and let V_2 be the space of 2×1 matrices. Let T be the transformation from V_1 to V_2 having the matrix

$$\begin{bmatrix} 1 & -2 & 0 \\ 2 & 1 & -3 \end{bmatrix};$$

let
$$\mathbf{u} = \begin{bmatrix} 2 \\ -1 \\ 3 \end{bmatrix} \in V_1;$$

let
$$f = [4 \quad 1] \in V_2^*$$

Find each of the following in matrix form.

a) $T\mathbf{u}$, b) $f(T\mathbf{u})$, c) T^*f, d) $(T^*f)(\mathbf{u})$.

5. Repeat the plan of Exercise 4, with T having the matrix

$$\begin{bmatrix} 2 & 4 \\ -1 & 0 \\ 0 & -2 \\ 3 & 1 \end{bmatrix}$$

and with

$$\mathbf{u} = \begin{bmatrix} -4 \\ 3 \end{bmatrix} \quad \text{and} \quad f = [1 \quad 2 \quad -1 \quad 3].$$

What are V_1 and V_2 in this case? Answer questions (a)–(d) of Exercise 4.

6. This is a continuation of Exercise 6, Section 5–6. The wholesalers do not quote separate prices for lobster and halibut; each quotes an overall price per pound for his package deal. The retailer assigns what are called accounting prices or "shadow" prices to lobster and halibut separately, so as to reflect wholesale costs. Because of the lobster shortage, the Better Business Bureau is keeping a careful watch on retail prices. It will recognize accounting prices as a factor in determining fair retail prices, provided all the accounting prices attributed to a given wholesaler do not exceed the price charged by that wholesaler. Show that, mathematically, this means the following. Let a_1 be the accounting price of lobster and a_2 that of halibut. Introduce an accounting price functional f with matrix $[a_1 \quad a_2]$ on the space of stock vectors. Compute T^*f, where T is the transformation of Exercise 6(a), Section 5–6, and compare this with the wholesaler's package prices.

7. Continuing the lobster-halibut problem, suppose the wholesalers charge, respectively, 75, 60, and 55 cents a pound. Which of the following sets of accounting prices are allowable?

a) Lobster $0.80, halibut $0.40
b) Lobster $1.00, halibut $0.30
c) Lobster $0.70, halibut $0.50
d) Lobster $1.50, halibut zero

LINEAR PROGRAMMING 6

6-1 CONVEX SETS

In Section 3-13, we saw how derivatives can be used to find maximum and minimum values of certain functions. The general pattern there was that the quantity to be maximized or minimized was first given in terms of two coordinate variables. One coordinate variable was then eliminated by substitution from an equation that described a side condition on the problem. After that, calculus methods were used to locate maxima and minima.

The side condition in a max-min problem is called a *constraint*, and problems such as those in Section 3-13 are called *constrained-max-min* problems. With the limited amount of calculus studied in Chapter 3, we were able to solve a number of constrained max-min problems, but they all had the feature that the constraints reduced them to one-dimensional problems. That is, when the time came to take derivatives, we had a function of a single argument. There are calculus methods for higher-dimensional max-min problems, but they will not be discussed in this book.

Linear programming is also concerned with constrained max-min problems, but of a very special kind. The key to identifying these is the word *linear*. Recall that a linear function in n arguments is a function f of the form

$$f(x_1, x_2, \ldots, x_n) = \sum_{i=1}^{n} a_i x_i.$$

A linear-programming problem is a constrained max-min problem in which the function to be maximized or minimized is linear, and in which the constraints consist of linear inequalities. In these strictly linear problems, calculus methods are of little or no use, and purely algebraic methods have been devised to handle them.

In this section we shall look at the geometric interpretation of linear constraints. In Section 6-2 we shall note the extremely simple general principle for solving linear programming problems. This general principle applies to linear max-min problems of all dimensions, but for dimensions higher than two it is often cumbersome to apply directly. The remainder

166   LINEAR PROGRAMMING

of the chapter is devoted to additional theory leading to a workable method for a linear programming problem of any dimension.

A *convex set* (in Euclidean space of any dimension) is a set A such that if $p \in A$ and $q \in A$, then the line segment from p to q is contained in A. In Fig. 6-1, the set A is convex, while B is not. Informally, a convex set is sometimes described as one without "dimples."

The first observation to be made about convex sets is that if A and B are both convex, then $A \cap B$ is convex. Suppose that

$$p \in A \cap B \quad \text{and} \quad q \in A \cap B;$$

then p and q are both in A, and hence the line segment from p to q is in A. Similarly, this line segment is also in B, and so in $A \cap B$. Thus $A \cap B$ is convex.

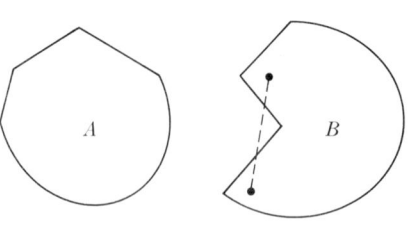

Fig. 6-1

In the plane, a linear inequality $ax + by \leq c$ has for a locus a *half-plane* (Fig. 6-2). More generally, in n-space a linear inequality

$$\sum_{i=1}^{n} a_i x_i \leq c \tag{1}$$

has for a locus a *half-space*.

It is geometrically evident that a half-space is convex. An analytic proof is obtained by noting that the line segment from p to q consists of those points r such that for some number t between 0 and 1,

$$x_i(r) = t x_i(p) + (1 - t) x_i(q)$$

for each coordinate variable x_i. Suppose, now, that the inequality (1) holds at p and q; then

$$\sum_{i=1}^{n} a_i x_i(r) = \sum_{i=1}^{n} a_i [t x_i(p) + (1 - t) x_i(q)]$$

$$= t \sum_{i=1}^{n} a_i x_i(p) + (1 - t) \sum_{i=1}^{n} a_i x_i(q) \leq tc + (1 - t)c = c.$$

So r is also in the half-space.

The constraint in a linear-programming problem consists of a set of simultaneous linear inequalities. Each of these determines a half-space and the locus of the set of inequalities is thus a convex set—the intersection of these half-spaces. An intersection of half-spaces is called a *convex polyhedral set*.

6-1
CONVEX SETS

We turn now to an example. An automobile manufacturer produces a standard model and a deluxe model. These are assembled at different plants. The standard-model plant has a maximum capacity of 6000 cars a month, while the deluxe-model plant can produce at most 2000 cars a month. It costs $2000 to produce a standard car and $3000 to produce a deluxe one. There is a budget of $12 million for next month's production costs. Let us picture geometrically the constraints on the manufacturer's production program.

Let x be the number of standard cars (in thousands) to be produced, and let y be the number of deluxe ones (also in thousands). Obviously,

$$x \geq 0, \quad y \geq 0,$$

and the plant capacities require that

$$x \leq 6, \quad y \leq 2.$$

Finally, the budget requires that

$$2x + 3y \leq 12.$$

An effective way to sketch the locus of a linear inequality is to sketch the locus of the corresponding equation (this will be a straight line) and then indicate by an arrow on which side of the line the locus of the inequality lies. To graph an equation like $2x + 3y = 12$, recall that two points determine a line, and the easiest two points to find quickly are those where the line crosses the axis. For this particular line:

$$x = 0, \quad y = 4; \quad y = 0, \quad x = 6.$$

Using these devices, we have the sketch in Fig. 6–3.

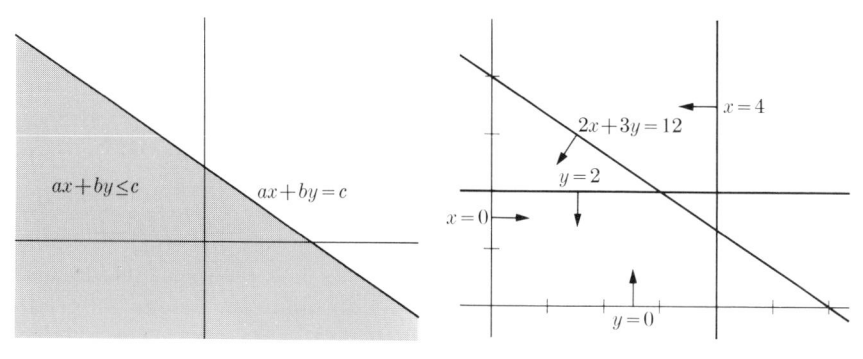

Fig. 6–2

Fig. 6–3

168   LINEAR PROGRAMMING   6-1

Each point p in the plane is a "production plan"—produce $x(p)$ thousand standard models and $y(p)$ thousand deluxe ones. The feasible production plans, given the constraints listed above, are those represented by points in the shaded area of Fig. 6-4.

Let us consider another example. An oil refinery has contracted to supply the government with at least 3 million gallons of aviation fuel and 2 million gallons of diesel fuel. It has two sources of crude oil. A certain amount (which we shall call a unit) of oil from Source I will produce 3 gallons of aviation and 1 gallon of diesel fuel. A unit of oil from Source II will produce 1 gallon of aviation and 2 of diesel fuel. We want to plot the feasible plans for purchasing crude oil.

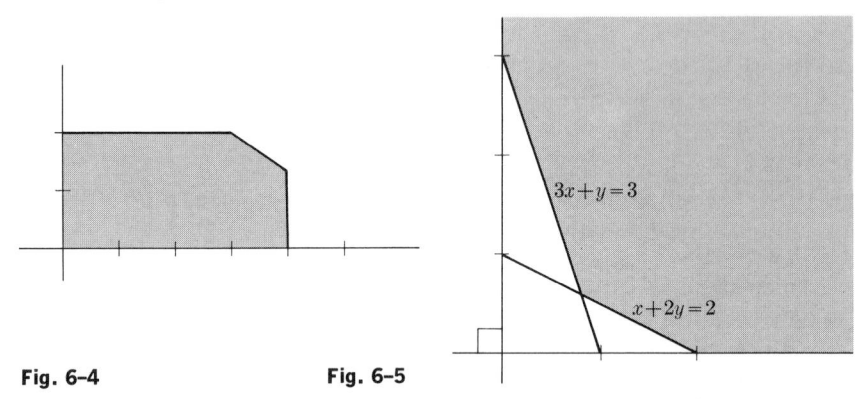

Fig. 6-4   **Fig. 6-5**

Let x be the number (in millions) of units of oil bought from Source I and let y similarly give the amount bought from Source II. As in the previous example, we have

$$x \geq 0, \quad y \geq 0.$$

We get $3x$ million gallons of aviation fuel from the Source I oil and y million gallons from the Source II oil. So to fulfill the contract, we must have

$$3x + y \geq 3.$$

In terms of diesel fuel yield, the contract also requires that

$$x + 2y \geq 2.$$

Figure 6-5 shows the feasible purchase plans. It shows an unbounded convex region, indicating that we can buy an unlimited amount of crude oil from either source. This is not realistic, but as we shall see in Section 6-2, the suggested additional constraints are not vital to the problem. By contrast, the constraints $x \geq 0$, $y \geq 0$ are vital, though at first glance

6-1 CONVEX SETS

it might seem that they are just there to make things "realistic." An informal general rule on this is as follows. In meeting minimal requirements, practical maximum constraints are usually not pertinent, but nonnegativity constraints are usually an essential part of a linear-programming problem. We shall comment on this point again in Section 6-2.

EXERCISES

1. Sketch the locus of each of the following sets of simultaneous linear inequalities.
   a) $x \geq 0, y \geq 0, 3x + 2y \leq 6$
   b) $x \geq 0, y \geq 0, 2x + 5y \geq 10$
   c) $x \geq 0, y \geq 0, 2x + y \geq 5, x + 3y \geq 10$
   d) $x \geq 0, y \geq 0, x + 2y \leq 2, 3x + y \leq 3$
   e) $x \geq 0, y \geq 0, x + 2y \leq 2, 3x + y \leq 3, 5x + 5y \leq 6$
   f) $x \geq 0, y \geq 0, 2x + y \geq 5, x + 3y \geq 10, 2x + 2y \geq 9$

2. In the example of the refinery discussed in the text, suppose that crude oil from Source I costs 50¢ a unit and that crude oil from Source II costs 25¢ a unit. When the refinery is negotiating the contract prices of the finished products, it submits what are called "accounting prices" or "shadow prices" attributable to crude-oil costs. That is, it wants to put z_1 cents per gallon into the price of aviation fuel and z_2 cents per gallon into the price of diesel fuel on the basis of crude-oil costs. The government accountants will allow this, provided the total shadow price charged against oil from a given source does not exceed the actual cost of oil obtained from that source. In a z_1z_2-plane, sketch the shadow prices due to crude oil costs that the government will allow.

3. Mr. Smith and Mr. Jones have been bragging around the Drones' Club that by performing in shifts they can keep one of the twosome standing on his head almost indefinitely. The club needs a new rug and TV set for the private lounge room. A group of club members has agreed to contribute toward the rug $1 for every minute Smith is upside down and $2 for every minute Jones is. Another group will contribute toward the TV set $3 for every minute Smith performs and $1 for every minute Jones does. The club manager has made a side bet with Smith and Jones that they cannot keep the act going as long as three hours. Draw a sketch showing the possible total time on his head for each of the men if they are to raise at least $200 for the rug and $240 for the TV set and also win their side bet.

4. Following the head-standing marathon, the club social committee serves martinis. For this function the manager has put out 100 ounces of vermouth and 400 ounces of gin. The bartender uses 1 ounce of vermouth and 2 ounces of gin in a regular martini and he uses 0.5 ounces of vermouth and 2.5 ounces of gin in an extra-dry martini. Draw a sketch showing how many of each kind of martini the club can serve.

5. The club manager wants to have transferred from the social-committee budget to the bar budget 50¢ for each extra-dry martini and 45¢ for each regular one. The club treasurer, however, wants to record the transaction as so much vermouth at z_1 cents an ounce and so much gin at z_2 cents an ounce. Sketch possible values of z_1 and z_2 so that the price assigned to each drink is at least what the manager is asking.

6-2 LINEAR MAX-MIN PROBLEMS

In Section 6–1 we looked at some typical sets of constraints for linear-programming problems. They are representable geometrically as convex polyhedral sets. Think of a 3-dimensional polyhedral set for a moment. It has faces (portions of bounding planes), edges (intersections of pairs of faces), and corners (intersections of triples of bounding planes). In general, a *corner point* of an n-dimensional polyhedral set is the intersection of exactly n bounding hyperplanes.

Now the basic principle of linear programming is very simply described. The maximum and minimum values of a linear function on a convex polyhedral set are assumed at corner points. We shall not give a complete proof of this, but we shall consider informally the case of a bounded, convex polygon in the plane. Suppose (Fig. 6–6) that p is in the interior. We draw a line through p, which (because the figure is bounded and convex) intersects the boundary in two points q and r. It is easily verified directly that any linear function on the plane must have a value at either q or r at least as great as it has at p. Suppose this is at q; by a similar argument it has a value at least this great at either s or t. Thus, given any point p, there is a corner point at which the linear function has a value greater than or equal to that at p. So the maximum value is assumed at a corner point.

In theory, then, linear programming is extremely simple. To maximize or minimize a linear function over a convex polyhedral set, find the corner points, evaluate the function at these corner points, and pick out the largest and smallest of these corner-point values.

In this section we apply the direct approach to some two-dimensional problems. In higher dimensions, finding all the corner points involves a lot of arithmetic, and there are simpler calculating procedures that depend on more sophisticated theory. We shall consider these in the remaining sections of the chapter.

In Section 6–1 we considered two examples of constraint sets: the automobile manufacturer and the oil refinery. Let us return to these now and make a complete linear-programming problem out of each of them.

The automobile manufacturer was constrained by plant capacity and budget to those production plans represented by points in the bounded polygonal set in Fig. 6–7. Recall that x is (in thousands) the number of standard models and y the number of deluxe models (also in thousands).

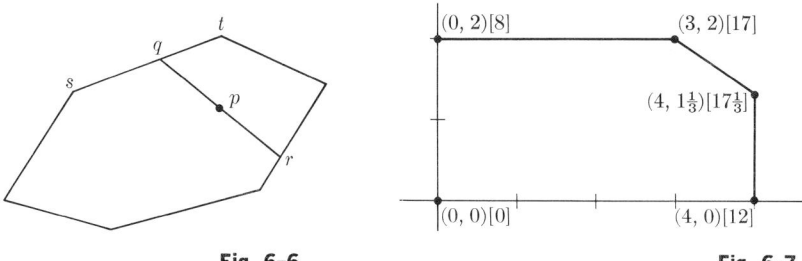

Fig. 6-6

Fig. 6-7

Suppose the profit is $300 on a standard model and $400 on a deluxe model. Assuming that he can sell all he produces, what production plan yields maximum profit? Figure 6–7 shows the coordinates of the corner points, and in brackets the value of

$$3x + 4y$$

at each corner point. This latter is the profit in ten-thousands; so the best plan is to produce 4000 standard models and 1333 deluxe ones, for a profit of $1,733,300.

As for the oil refinery problem, suppose (as in Exercise 2, Section 6–1) that crude oil from Source I costs 50¢ a unit and that crude oil from Source II costs 25¢ a unit. What purchase plan gives the minimum crude-oil cost? In Fig. 6–8 we reproduce Fig. 6–5, adding the coordinates of the corner points, and in brackets the values at the corner points of

$$0.5x + 0.25y.$$

For minimum cost the refinery should buy 800,000 units of oil from Source I and 600,000 from Source II, at a total cost of $550,000.

Suppose the price of oil from Source I goes up to 80¢ and that from Source II stays at 25¢. We then have the revised figures shown in Fig. 6–9, and it pays to get all the oil from Source II for $750,000.

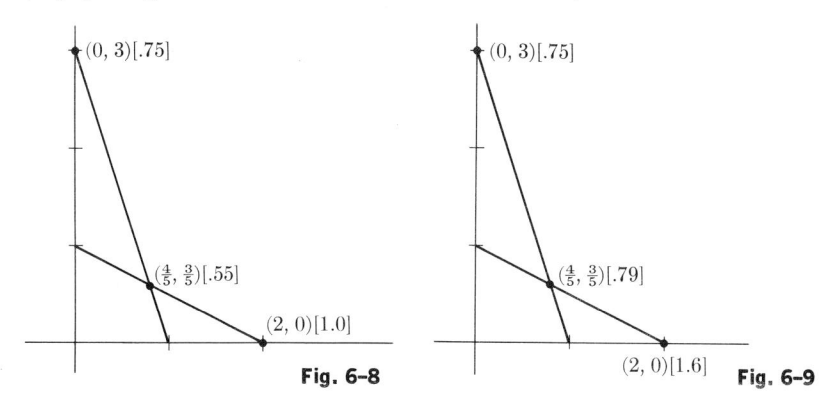

Fig. 6-8

Fig. 6-9

172 LINEAR PROGRAMMING

We are concerned with maximizing and minimizing

$$ax + by,$$

where in all cases of practical importance

$$a \geq 0 \quad \text{and} \quad b \geq 0. \quad (1)$$

It facilitates the theoretical discussion considerably to assume that (1) always holds; therefore we shall limit our discussion to those cases.

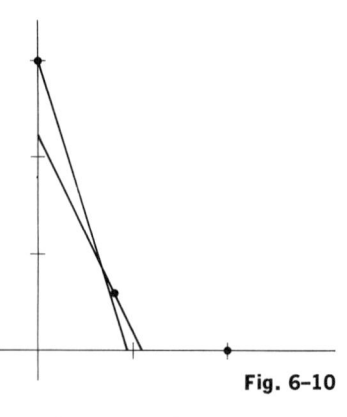

Fig. 6-10

A convenient way to picture a linear function over the plane is to draw a few of its level lines; that is, draw lines

$$ax + by = c$$

for several values of c. For given a and b, these are parallel, and by (1), they have negative slope for all cases in which we are interested. Maxima and minima are easy to see from level lines because, given (1), if we have two level lines for $ax + by$ going through the first quadrant, we get smaller values on the level line closer to the origin.

To return to the oil-refinery problem, the constraints give a convex region with three corner points. If the crude oil prices are 0.50 and 0.25, the level lines for the linear function have slope -2; if the prices are 0.80 and 0.25, the level lines have slope -3.2. Figure 6-10 gives another picture of the minimum problems. The line through $(\frac{4}{5}, \frac{3}{5})$ with slope -2 leaves the other two corner points on the opposite side from the origin, as does the line through $(0, 3)$ with slope -3.2.

This geometric approach to the minimum problem shows why additional maximal constraints are irrelevant. Suppose that, in the oil-refinery problem, we add the constraints

$$x \leq 10, \quad y \leq 15,$$

because that is all the oil that the two sources can come up with. This would "box in" the figure and add three more corner points (Fig. 6–11). Now no line with negative slope can pass through one of these new corner points and leave all other corner points on the opposite side from the origin; so no matter what is to be minimized [provided it satisfies (1)], the maximal constraints are irrelevant. By contrast, note that if we forgot the constraints

$$x \geq 0, \quad y \geq 0,$$

we would lose two very significant corner points.

Fig. 6-11   **Fig. 6-12**

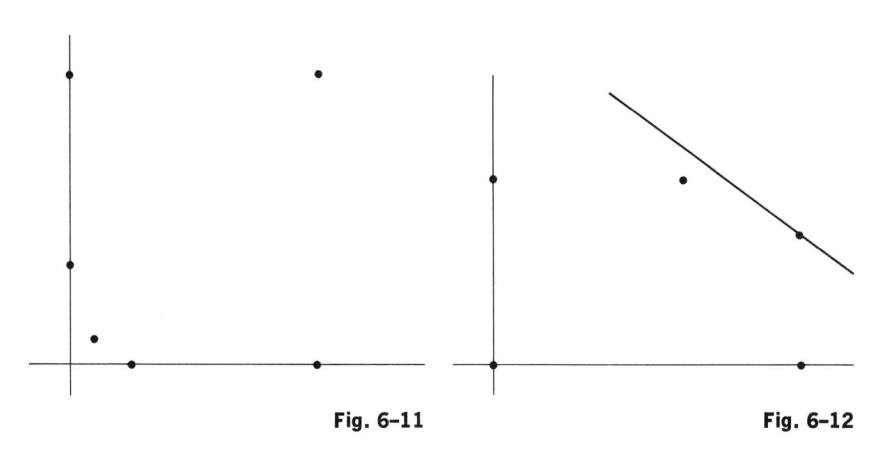

Finally, to solve a maximum problem by drawing level lines, the idea is to draw a level line through a corner point so that all other corner points are on the same side as the origin. Figure 6-12 shows in these terms the solution already obtained for the problem of the automobile manufacturer. If the profits are $300 and $400, we are interested in level lines of slope $-\frac{3}{4}$.

EXERCISES

1. Return to Exercise 2, Section 6-1, and note that if the contract is for 3 million gallons of aviation fuel and 2 million gallons of diesel fuel, then

$$3z_1 + 2z_2$$

gives (in units of $10,000) the total shadow cost for the operation due to crude-oil prices.
   a) Using exactly the data given in Exercise 2, Section 6-1, maximize the total shadow cost due to crude-oil prices.
   b) Compare the answer to part (a) with the minimum actual cost of crude oil at 50¢ and 25¢ (found in the text).
   c) Following the discussion in the text, change the prices of crude oil to 80¢ and 25¢ and rework Exercise 2, Section 6-1. [*Note:* One constraint is superfluous in this case.]
   d) Using the constraints in part (c), maximize the total shadow cost due to crude-oil prices.
   e) With the 80-25 crude-oil prices, how much diesel fuel is actually produced and what is its shadow price? [*Note:* This is typical; a product that is overproduced is called a by-product, and by-products have zero shadow prices.]

2. In connection with the head-standing stunt of Exercise 3, Section 6-1, Mrs. Smith and Mrs. Jones contend that the whole thing is ridiculous, and they try to stop it by threatening to go shopping.

a) Mrs. Smith says she will spend $1 for every minute that Smith is clocked on his head and Mrs. Jones says she will spend $1.50 for every minute Jones is upside down. Find the Smith-Jones strategy that will win their bet from the manager, raise $200 for the rug and $240 for the TV set, and minimize the total shopping bill.

b) Find the optimal strategy if Mrs. Smith threatens to spend $1.50 per Smith minute in the performance and Mrs. Jones threatens to spend $1 per Jones minute.

c) If the dollars-per-minute threats are $1 from Mrs. Smith and $2.50 from Mrs. Jones, what happens to poor Smith?

3. In this exercise use all the data given in Exercises 4 and 5, Section 6–1.

a) Find the number of regular and extra-dry martinis to maximize the total revenue for the bar.

b) Find the prices to be assigned to gin and vermouth to minimize the total bill to the social committee.

4. In each part of Exercise 1, Section 6–1, a convex region is described by a set of inequalities. In each case complete the description of a linear-programming problem by specifying a linear function to be maximized or minimized. For each bounded region make it a maximum problem and for each unbounded one make it a minimum problem.

a) Complete each problem in several ways. Using the principle of slopes of level lines, choose a linear function to make the answer come out at each corner point of the figure.

b) For each figure characterize precisely those linear functions that will maximize or minimize at a given corner point.

c) What happens when level lines for a function have the same slope as a side of the convex figure?

6–3 MATRIX REPRESENTATION

So far in this chapter we have been doing two-dimensional linear programming geometrically. In general, it pays to describe linear programming problems in matrix form, and in this section we shall look at a few details connected with this procedure.

First let us return to the minimum problem used as an illustrative example in Sections 6–1 and 6–2. This is the oil-refinery problem stated in a nutshell as follows. It is required to produce 3 million gallons of aviation fuel and 2 million gallons of diesel fuel, using crude oil from Source I at 50¢ a unit that gives 3 gallons of aviation and 1 gallon of diesel fuel per unit, and crude oil from Source II at 25¢ a unit that gives 1 gallon of aviation and 2 gallons of diesel fuel per unit. The problem is to minimize the cost of crude oil.

6-3
MATRIX REPRESENTATION 175

Letting x_1 be the amount of crude oil from Source I and x_2 be the amount from Source II, we can state the problem as follows:

$$x_1 \geq 0, \quad x_2 \geq 0, \quad 3x_1 + x_2 \geq 3, \quad x_1 + 2x_2 \geq 2;$$
$$\text{minimize } 0.5x_1 + 0.25x_2.$$

We can say this with matrices as follows:

$$\begin{bmatrix} x_1 \\ x_2 \end{bmatrix} \geq \begin{bmatrix} 0 \\ 0 \end{bmatrix}, \quad \begin{bmatrix} 3 & 1 \\ 1 & 2 \end{bmatrix} \begin{bmatrix} x_1 \\ x_2 \end{bmatrix} \geq \begin{bmatrix} 3 \\ 2 \end{bmatrix};$$
$$\text{minimize } [0.5 \quad 0.25] \begin{bmatrix} x_1 \\ x_2 \end{bmatrix}.$$

Note that we write an inequality between two matrices of like dimension and interpret it to mean that the indicated inequality holds between each pair of corresponding elements.

Introducing single letters for matrices, we have the condensed version of the problem. Let

$$X = \begin{bmatrix} x_1 \\ x_2 \end{bmatrix}, \quad A = \begin{bmatrix} 3 & 1 \\ 1 & 2 \end{bmatrix}, \quad B = \begin{bmatrix} 3 \\ 2 \end{bmatrix}, \quad C = [0.5 \quad 0.25].$$

The problem then reads

$$\left.\begin{array}{r} X \geq 0, \\ AX \geq B; \\ \text{minimize } CX. \end{array}\right\} \qquad (1)$$

This is the general form for a minimum problem.

The maximum problem worked out in Sections 6–1 and 6–2 is that of the automobile manufacturer. Briefly, it is this. He is limited by plant capacity to 4000 standard cars and 2000 deluxe ones and by budget to $12 million in production costs. A standard car costs $2000 to produce and makes a profit of $300; a deluxe one costs $3000 with a profit of $400. The problem is to maximize profit.

Letting z_1 be the number of standard cars and z_2 the number of deluxe ones, and choosing appropriate units, we can state the problem this way:

$$z_1 \geq 0, \quad z_2 \geq 0, \quad 2z_1 + 3z_2 \leq 12, \quad z_1 \leq 4, \quad z_2 \leq 2;$$
$$\text{maximize } 3z_1 + 4z_2.$$

In rendering this into matrix form, we choose a different format from that used above to describe the minimum problem.

$$[z_1 \; z_2] \geq [0 \; 0], \quad [z_1 \; z_2]\begin{bmatrix} 2 & 1 & 0 \\ 3 & 0 & 1 \end{bmatrix} \leq [12 \; 4 \; 2];$$

$$\text{maximize } [z_1 \; z_2]\begin{bmatrix} 3 \\ 4 \end{bmatrix}.$$

Again we introduce single letters for matrices to get a picture of the general form of the problem. Let

$$Z = [z_1 \; z_2], \quad A = \begin{bmatrix} 2 & 1 & 0 \\ 3 & 0 & 1 \end{bmatrix}, \quad B = \begin{bmatrix} 3 \\ 4 \end{bmatrix}, \quad C = [12 \; 4 \; 2];$$

then the problem can be written

$$\left.\begin{array}{r} Z \geq 0, \\ ZA \leq C; \\ \text{maximize } ZB. \end{array}\right\} \tag{2}$$

This is the general form for a maximum problem.

With regard to the change in format from minimum problem to maximum problem, reference to Section 5–7 would indicate that we seem to be posing the minimum problem in the base space and the maximum problem in the dual space. It will appear in Section 6–4 that this is precisely what we are doing, and for good reason.

The notation in the general forms (1) and (2) is so designed that in either case we need three matrices of constants with dimensions matching as follows.

$$A: m \times n, \quad B: m \times 1, \quad C: 1 \times n.$$

In matrix form, then a linear-programming problem is described by giving A, B, and C meeting these specifications and telling which kind of problem (max or min) it is.

EXERCISES

1. In Exercises 1(a), 1(d), 2(a), 2(b), 2(c), 3(a), and 3(b) of Section 6–2 there appear seven different linear-programming problems. Give the matrix form for the statement of each of these. Use the notation of (1) and (2) above and give each answer in the form

    $A =$
    $B =$
    $C =$

    followed by a notation "max" or "min."

6-4 DUALITY

From Section 6–3, we repeat here for reference the general forms for linear-programming problems:

$$\left.\begin{array}{r}X \geq 0, \\ AX \geq B; \\ \min CX.\end{array}\right\} \quad (1)$$

$$\left.\begin{array}{r}Z \geq 0, \\ ZA \leq C; \\ \max ZB.\end{array}\right\} \quad (2)$$

Suppose we pose two problems, one in the form (1) and the other in the form (2), and use the same A, B, and C in each problem. The two problems so posed are called *dual* problems.

For a specific example, let us return to the problem of the automobile manufacturer. The maximum problem was given in matrix form in Section 6–3. The dual minimum problem is

$$\begin{bmatrix}x_1\\x_2\\x_3\end{bmatrix} \geq \begin{bmatrix}0\\0\\0\end{bmatrix};$$

$$\begin{bmatrix}2 & 1 & 0\\3 & 0 & 1\end{bmatrix}\begin{bmatrix}x_1\\x_2\\x_3\end{bmatrix} \geq \begin{bmatrix}3\\4\end{bmatrix};$$

$$\min \begin{bmatrix}12 & 4 & 2\end{bmatrix}\begin{bmatrix}x_1\\x_2\\x_3\end{bmatrix}.$$

The original problem in this case was the maximum problem:

$$[z_1 \ z_2] \geq [0 \ 0];$$

$$[z_1 \ z_2]\begin{bmatrix}2 & 1 & 0\\3 & 0 & 1\end{bmatrix} \leq [12 \ 4 \ 2];$$

$$\max [z_1 \ z_2]\begin{bmatrix}3\\4\end{bmatrix}.$$

As we shall point out in Exercise 5 below, these are called dual problems because they involve an interlocking system of vectors and functionals. Without any recourse to the general notion of duality in linear spaces, we shall prove here the theorem that serves as the basis for the simplex method in linear programming. Though our present discussion will involve only manipulation with matrices, this theorem is really a rather potent example of what duality in linear algebra can accomplish.

First we recall that a "nonnegative matrix" means one with all entries nonnegative. It is clear from the definition of matrix multiplication that the product of two nonnegative matrices is nonnegative. It therefore follows that a matrix inequality is preserved on multiplying through by a nonnegative matrix. We use this fact several times in the following discussion.

Theorem. Given the constraints

$$X \geq 0, \tag{3}$$
$$AX \geq B, \tag{4}$$
$$Z \geq 0, \tag{5}$$
$$ZA \leq C, \tag{6}$$

if these are satisfied for $X = X_1$ and $Z = Z_1$ and if also $CX_1 = Z_1 B$, then $X = X_1$ solves the minimum problem (1) and $Z = Z_1$ solves the maximum problem (2).

Proof. Take any X satisfying (3); then

$$\begin{aligned} CX &\geq Z_1 AX &&\text{by (6) and (3)} \\ &\geq Z_1 B &&\text{by (4) and (5)} \\ &= CX_1 &&\text{by hypothesis.} \end{aligned}$$

Therefore $X = X_1$ does give the minimum value for CX. A similar manipulation shows that $Z = Z_1$ solves the maximum problem.

This leads to a completely different method in linear programming from that discussed in Section 6–2. We consider not one problem but two dual ones: get $CX = ZB$ and satisfy all the constraints and both problems are solved.

The *duality theorem for linear programming* involves this theorem and its converse. We have shown that if the constraints are satisfied and $CX = ZB$, then the problems are solved. The other part of the duality theorem states that if the dual problems are solved, then $CX = ZB$.

EXERCISES

1. Exercise 1, Section 6–3, refers to seven linear-programming problems that have appeared in this chapter. There are some duals among these, but there are others for which the duals do not appear. Expand the list to get a complete set of dual problems.

2. Discuss the interpretation of each new problem added to the list in Exercise 1. [*Note:* Sometimes the interpretation of the dual follows a standard pattern. For example, minimum cost and maximum shadow-price problems come in pairs. In other cases the interpretation of the dual may not be particularly illuminating.]
3. The martini problems of Exercise 3, Section 6–2, are duals: Solve them and show that $CX = ZB$.
4. Write out the other half of the proof of the theorem given in this section.
5. Let M_k be the vector space of $k \times 1$ matrices. For the dual problems of the automobile manufacturer, given in matrix form in this section, identify appropriate matrices with vectors, functionals, and transformations to show that the problems may be stated as follows:

$$\mathbf{u} \geq 0, \quad T\mathbf{u} \geq \mathbf{v}_0, \quad \min g_0(\mathbf{u}),$$
$$f \geq 0, \quad T^*f \leq g_0, \quad \max f(\mathbf{v}_0).$$

[*Hint:* $\mathbf{u} \in M_3$; T is from M_3 into M_2; $\mathbf{v}_0 \in M_2$; $g_0 \in M_3^*$; $f \in M_2^*$.]

6. Let a, b, and c be numbers with $a > 0$, $b \geq 0$, $c \geq 0$. Consider the one-dimensional linear-programming problem.

$$x \geq 0, \quad ax \geq b; \quad \min cx.$$

a) Solve this minimum problem.
b) State and solve the dual problem.
c) Prove both parts of the duality theorem for this simplified case.

6–5 THE SIMPLEX METHOD

We conclude our discussion of linear programming with a description of a computational procedure for solving problems of any dimension. The basic idea is that we solve not one problem, but a dual pair of problems simultaneously. Even if we are not interested in the dual problem, it helps to put it in the hopper.

Let us pose the problems in matrix form. Suppose we want to solve one of the problems

$$X \geq 0, \quad AX \geq B; \quad \min CX.$$
$$Z \geq 0, \quad ZA \leq C; \quad \max ZB.$$

We formulate the other whether we want its solution or not and consider the two problems together. The key to the method is the duality theorem. We do not look directly for maxima and minima at all. We merely look for X and Z satisfying all four inequalities above, and also satisfying the equation

$$CX = ZB.$$

180 LINEAR PROGRAMMING   6-5

The duality theorem tells us that once we have found these the problems are solved.

We replace the condition $AX \geq B$ by

$$AX - Y = B, \qquad Y \geq 0,$$

and replace $ZA \leq C$ by

$$ZA + W = C, \qquad W \geq 0.$$

The problem then is this. We want to find X, Y, Z, W such that

$$X \geq 0, \qquad Y \geq 0, \qquad (1)$$

$$Z \geq 0, \qquad W \geq 0, \qquad (2)$$

$$AX - Y = B, \qquad (3)$$

$$ZA + W = C, \qquad (4)$$

$$CX = ZB. \qquad (5)$$

The plan of attack is as follows. We start with

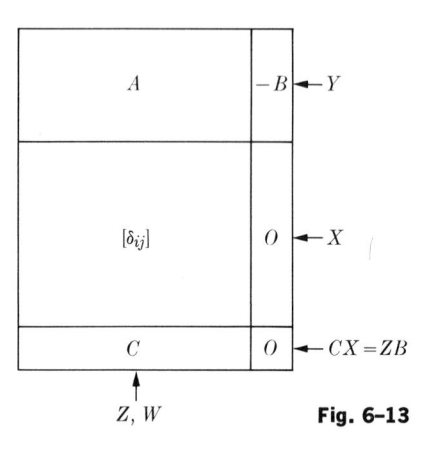

$$X = 0, \qquad Y = -B,$$

$$Z = 0, \qquad W = C.$$

Fig. 6-13

This satisfies (2), (3), (4), and (5), but not (1). The simplex algorithm computes new values of X, Y, Z, W in such a way that the relations (2), (3), (4), and (5) are always preserved. Therefore, as soon as it produces nonnegative X and Y, the problem is solved.

The algorithm is somewhat complicated. We introduce it through a specific example. Consider the problem of the automobile manufacturer. In Section 6-3 we saw that the matrix formulation for this involves

$$A = \begin{bmatrix} 2 & 1 & 0 \\ 3 & 0 & 1 \end{bmatrix}, \qquad B = \begin{bmatrix} 3 \\ 4 \end{bmatrix}, \qquad C = [12 \ 4 \ 2].$$

We now build up a rectangular array of numbers. In the top left corner we put the matrix A. Right below A we put an identity matrix $[\delta_{ij}]$. Below that we put C. Then we add another column on the right. Opposite A we put Y ($= -B$ to start with); opposite $[\delta_{ij}]$ we put X (initially 0). Finally, the lower right entry is the common value of CX and ZB (0 to start with). Schematically it looks like Fig. 6-13 to begin with. In this figure we have put inside the boxes the initial entries and indicated by arrows and outside labels the significance of these entries.

For the automobile problem, the initial array is

$$\begin{array}{ccc|c} 2 & 1 & 0 & -3 \\ 3 & 0 & 1 & -4 \\ \hline 1 & 0 & 0 & 0 \\ 0 & 1 & 0 & 0 \\ 0 & 0 & 1 & 0 \\ \hline 12 & 4 & 2 & 0 \end{array}$$

The object is to get rid of the negative entries in X and Y. We can start with any one of them, but the program usually gets there faster if you always go after the most negative one; so we work on the -4. This is in the second row; so we list the second row, below it the bottom row, and below that the quotients (bottom-row entry divided by second-row entry) for every positive second-row entry.

$$\begin{array}{cccc} 3 & 0 & 1 & -4 \\ 12 & 4 & 2 & 0 \\ 4 & & 2 & \end{array}$$

The smallest of these quotients is in column 3; so that will be our operating column. First we divide column 3 by its row-2 entry (1 in this case, so no visible effect). Now we add multiples of column 3 to the other columns, so as to produce zeros across row 2. For this specific array,

$$\text{column 1} \rightarrow \text{column 1} - 3 \times \text{column 3},$$
$$\text{column 2 unchanged},$$
$$\text{column 4} \rightarrow \text{column 4} + 4 \times \text{column 3}.$$

The result is the following array.

$$\begin{array}{ccc|c} 2 & 1 & 0 & -3 \\ 0 & 0 & 1 & 0 \\ \hline 1 & 0 & 0 & 0 \\ 0 & 1 & 0 & 0 \\ -3 & 0 & 1 & 4 \\ \hline 6 & 4 & 2 & 8 \end{array}$$

It is now time to talk about the interpretation of the last row. The initial last row meant
$$Z = [0 \ \ 0], \qquad W = [12 \ \ 4 \ \ 2].$$

182 LINEAR PROGRAMMING

Now we have produced zeros in the second row of the top block. According to the rules, this means that we have a new second component of Z, and it is the new last-row entry in the operating (third) column. So the new last row is interpreted to mean

$$Z = [0 \quad 2], \qquad W = [6 \quad 4 \quad 0].$$

Reading the last column, we see that

$$Y = \begin{bmatrix} -3 \\ 0 \end{bmatrix}, \qquad X = \begin{bmatrix} 0 \\ 0 \\ 4 \end{bmatrix}.$$

Clearly (2) is still satisfied (picking the column with the smallest quotient entry does this for us). Let us check (3), (4), and (5).

$$AX - Y = \begin{bmatrix} 2 & 1 & 0 \\ 3 & 0 & 1 \end{bmatrix} \begin{bmatrix} 0 \\ 0 \\ 4 \end{bmatrix} - \begin{bmatrix} -3 \\ 0 \end{bmatrix} = \begin{bmatrix} 0 \\ 4 \end{bmatrix} - \begin{bmatrix} -3 \\ 0 \end{bmatrix} = \begin{bmatrix} 3 \\ 4 \end{bmatrix} = B,$$

$$ZA + W = [0 \quad 2] \begin{bmatrix} 2 & 1 & 0 \\ 3 & 0 & 1 \end{bmatrix} + [6 \quad 4 \quad 0]$$

$$= [6 \quad 0 \quad 2] + [6 \quad 4 \quad 0] = [12 \quad 4 \quad 2] = C,$$

$$CX = [12 \quad 4 \quad 2] \begin{bmatrix} 0 \\ 0 \\ 4 \end{bmatrix} = 8 = [0 \quad 2] \begin{bmatrix} 3 \\ 4 \end{bmatrix} = ZB.$$

So we are ready to do it again. Take the first row, last row, and quotients:

$$\begin{array}{cccc} 2 & 1 & 0 & -3 \\ 6 & 4 & 2 & 8 \\ 3 & 4 & & \end{array}$$

This time, then, the operating column is column 1. Remember, we divide it by 2 and then use it to produce zeros across row 1. The result is

$$\begin{array}{ccc|c} 1 & 0 & 0 & 0 \\ 0 & 0 & 1 & 0 \\ \hline \frac{1}{2} & -\frac{1}{2} & 0 & \frac{3}{2} \\ 0 & 1 & 0 & 0 \\ -\frac{3}{2} & -\frac{3}{2} & 1 & -\frac{1}{2} \\ \hline 3 & 1 & 2 & 17 \end{array}$$

6-5 THE SIMPLEX METHOD

We worked on row 1 in the top block; so we have a new first component for Z in the operating column (column 1) of the last row. Thus, after a second round of computations, we have

$$Z = [3 \quad 2], \qquad W = [0 \quad 1 \quad 0],$$

$$Y = \begin{bmatrix} 0 \\ 0 \end{bmatrix}, \qquad X = \begin{bmatrix} \frac{3}{2} \\ 0 \\ -\frac{1}{2} \end{bmatrix}.$$

At this stage in the last round we stopped to check (2)–(5). Obviously, this is not a part of the algorithm. We do not intend to prove that the algorithm preserves these relations; so we suggest a check that it does for the specific examples considered. It is also worth noting that verification of these relations at each stage is an excellent way to catch arithmetic mistakes. We leave it to the reader to check them this time.

Proceeding to the next round, we turn our attention to row 5.

$$\begin{array}{cccc} -\frac{3}{2} & \frac{3}{2} & 1 & -\frac{1}{2} \\ 3 & 1 & 2 & 17 \\ & \frac{2}{3} & 2 & \end{array}$$

The quotients indicate that we operate with column 2. We multiply column 2 by $\frac{2}{3}$ and then use it to get zeros in row 5. The result:

$$\begin{array}{cccc|c} 1 & 0 & 0 & 0 \\ 0 & 0 & 1 & 0 \\ \hline 0 & -\frac{1}{3} & \frac{1}{3} & \frac{4}{3} \\ 1 & \frac{2}{3} & -\frac{2}{3} & \frac{1}{3} \\ 0 & 1 & 0 & 0 \\ \hline 4 & \frac{2}{3} & \frac{4}{3} & 17\frac{1}{3} \end{array}$$

Since we worked on row 3 of the second block, we have a new third component of W in the operating (second) column. So we read this last array to mean

$$Z = [4 \quad \tfrac{4}{3}], \qquad W = [0 \quad 0 \quad \tfrac{2}{3}]$$

$$Y = \begin{bmatrix} 0 \\ 0 \end{bmatrix}, \qquad X = \begin{bmatrix} \frac{4}{3} \\ \frac{1}{3} \\ 0 \end{bmatrix}.$$

There are no negative components left in either X or Y; so the problem is solved.

In summary, now the simplex algorithm is this. Pick a row (call it row k) that has a negative entry in the last column. Divide each positive entry in row k into the corresponding entry in the last row. The column with the minimum quotient is the operating column. Divide the operating column by its row-k entry, then use addition and subtraction of columns to produce all zeros in row k except for the 1 in the operating column. This completes the computation. To read the results, read Y and X from the last column. Read Z and W from the last row by the following rule. Initially, the last row is W and $Z = 0$. Each round of the algorithm changes the label on the last-row entry in the operating column. If row k is the kth row in the space originally occupied by A (the top block), the entry being relabeled becomes the kth component of Z. If row k is the jth row in the space originally occupied by $[\delta_{ij}]$ (the second block), the entry being relabeled becomes the jth component of W. Any component of Z or W not listed in the last row by this rule will be 0.

In the second step of the above example we introduced a negative component in X. This illustrates that the simplex method must not merely rub out all negative last-column entries that are there at the start. It must also take care of any that it puts in along the way. This suggests the possibility that it may never achieve an all-nonnegative last column. This is possible, and there are theorems characterizing the problems for which the simplex method is guaranteed to work. However, the simplex method is admirably suited to a digital computer; so a practical approach is to put the problem on the computer anyway and have the computer stop if a solution has not appeared after, say, 100 passes. There is further discussion of this in Exercise 12, Section 8–5.

EXERCISES

1. Verify that relations (2) through (5) hold at the end of each step in the example worked out above.
2. Exercise 1, Section 6–4, calls for the compilation of a list of linear-programming problems, paired off by the duality relation. Solve each of these pairs by the simplex method.
3. Apply the simplex method to the general one-dimensional linear-programming problem (Exercise 6, Section 6–4) and analyze the steps involved.

ABSTRACT ALGEBRAIC SYSTEMS   7

7-1 SYMMETRIES

Figure 7-1 indicates that a 90° counterclockwise rotation of a square about its center maps the square onto itself. Figure 7-2 indicates that a reflection of the square through the vertical axis through the center also maps the square onto itself.

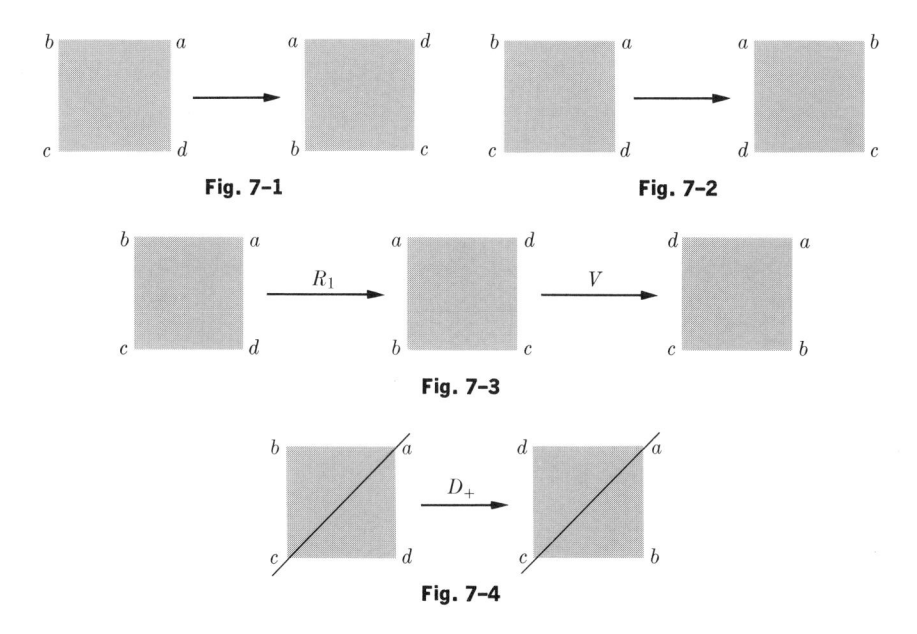

Fig. 7-1

Fig. 7-2

Fig. 7-3

Fig. 7-4

These are examples of symmetries of the square. In general, the symmetries of a geometric figure are the rigid transformations that carry the figure onto itself.

Let the transformation in Fig. 7-1 be denoted by R_1 and that in Fig. 7-2 by V. The composite transformation $V \circ R_1$ (rotate, then reflect) is pictured in Fig. 7-3. Let D_+ be the symmetry consisting of reflection through the diagonal with positive slope. This is shown in Fig. 7-4. Comparison of Figs. 7-3 and 7-4 shows that

$$V \circ R_1 = D_+.$$

185

186 ABSTRACT ALGEBRAIC SYSTEMS

Altogether there are eight symmetries of the square, as follows:

I the identity transformation
R_1 counterclockwise rotation through 90°
R_2 counterclockwise rotation through 180°
R_3 counterclockwise rotation through 270°
H reflection through the horizontal axis
V reflection through the vertical axis
D_+ reflection through the positive-slope diagonal
D_- reflection through the negative-slope diagonal

The composite of any two of these is another one from the list of eight. Indeed, the complete table of composites is shown below. The interpretation of the table is that if we perform the transformation listed at the top and then the one listed at the side, the result is the one shown in the table. Note that, because of the way composites are written, this means that

$$\text{Tabular entry} = \text{side entry} \circ \text{top entry}.$$

	I	R_1	R_2	R_3	H	V	D_+	D_-
I	I	R_1	R_2	R_3	H	V	D_+	D_-
R_1	R_1	R_2	R_3	I	D_+	D_-	V	H
R_2	R_2	R_3	I	R_1	V	H	D_-	D_+
R_3	R_3	I	R_1	R_2	D_-	D_+	H	V
H	H	D_-	V	D_+	I	R_2	R_3	R_1
V	V	D_+	H	D_-	R_2	I	R_1	R_3
D_+	D_+	H	D_-	V	R_1	R_3	I	R_2
D_-	D_-	V	D_+	H	R_3	R_1	R_2	I

In some cases the order of compounding the transformations is significant; in other cases it is not. For example,

$$R_1 \circ R_2 = R_2 \circ R_1 = R_3,$$

but

$$H \circ R_1 = D_- \quad \text{while} \quad R_1 \circ H = D_+.$$

A binary operation is called *commutative* if the order of operands can always be reversed. Since there are cases here in which order cannot be reversed, we say that the composition of symmetries of the square is noncommutative.

Composition of transformations is always *associative*. That is, if T_1, T_2, and T_3 are three transformations of a set onto itself, then

$$T_1 \circ (T_2 \circ T_3) = (T_1 \circ T_2) \circ T_3$$

because each of these triple composites carries an arbitrary element p of

7-1 SYMMETRIES 187

the domain into
$$T_1\{T_2[T_3(p)]\}.$$

Since a symmetry is a one-to-one transformation, it has an *inverse*. This is the transformation that goes the other way. For example, the obvious inverse of R_1 is a clockwise rotation through 90°. This latter is not listed as a symmetry of the square, but clearly it is equivalent to R_3, the 270° rotation. Note that
$$R_1 \circ R_3 = R_3 \circ R_1 = I.$$

Indeed, if T_1 and T_2 are one-to-one transformations of a set onto itself, then the condition
$$T_1 \circ T_2 = T_2 \circ T_1 = I$$

may be taken as a definition of T_1 and T_2 being inverse transformations.

EXERCISES

1. Figure 7–5 shows an equilateral triangle, with the three altitudes labeled 1, 2, and 3. The symmetries of the equilateral triangle are:

   I identity
   R_1 counterclockwise rotation through 120°
   R_2 counterclockwise rotation through 240°
   A_1 reflection through altitude 1
   A_2 reflection through altitude 2
   A_3 reflection through altitude 3

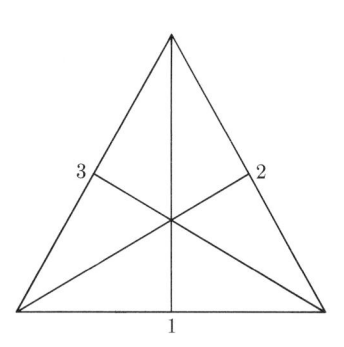

   Fig. 7–5

   a) Construct the table of composites for these symmetries.
   b) Is composition commutative here?
   c) Find the inverse of each of these symmetries.

2. Study the symmetries of an isosceles triangle that is not equilateral.
   a) List and label all the symmetries.
   b) Construct the table of composites.
   c) Determine whether or not composition is commutative.
   d) Find the inverse of each symmetry.

3. Follow the plan of Exercise 2 for a rectangle that is not a square.

4. In each of the following there is listed a subset of one of the sets of symmetries studied. In each case show that all composites of members of the subset lie in the subset; construct the table of composites; check it for commutativity; find inverses.

   a) I, R_1, R_2, R_3 for the square. b) I, R_1, R_2 for the equilateral triangle.
   c) I, R_2, H, V for the square. d) I, R_2, D_+, D_- for the square.

7-2 GROUPS

A common practice in modern mathematics is to study not a single specific mathematical structure but a structure type. That is, we single out certain features that a number of different structures have in common and use these features to define a structure type. Then the abstract study of a structure type yields ideas that are applicable to each specific example of that type.

The symmetries of a geometric figure and composition of these symmetries constitute a mathematical structure of a type referred to as a group. As we shall see, there are many other examples of groups, but the properties of the symmetry groups pointed out in Section 7–1 are those that are used to define the general concept.

A group consists of a set of objects and a binary operation for combining them. In the symmetry groups the objects are the rigid transformations of the geometric figure, and the combining operation is composition. Now, in format, the composition tables studied in Section 7–1 look very much like multiplication tables, and it is customary in the discussion of abstract groups to refer to the group operation as multiplication. We shall do that here and write the "product" of two group elements a and b in the usual format of elementary algebra:

$$ab.$$

Specifically, then, a *group* is a set G and a binary operation known generically as multiplication, for which the following postulates are satisfied.

1. *Closure.* If $a \in G$ and $b \in G$, then $ab \in G$ and $ba \in G$.
2. *Associativity.* For every a, b, c in G,

$$(ab)c = a(bc).$$

3. *Identity.* There is a unique element e of G such that for every $a \in G$,

$$ea = ae = a.$$

4. *Inverses.* For every $a \in G$ there is a unique element $a^{-1} \in G$ such that

$$aa^{-1} = a^{-1}a = e.$$

Nothing has been said here about commutativity. In general, group multiplication is not required to be commutative. It was noted in Section 7–1 that several of the symmetry groups are noncommutative. The commutative cases merit special attention, however, and an *abelian group* is defined as a group which satisfies the additional postulate.

5. *Commutativity.* For every a and b in G,

$$ab = ba.$$

If the set G is finite, the group is called a finite group, and the number of elements in G is called the *order* of the group. The symmetry groups of Section 7–1 are all finite. For example, the group of the square is of order 8 and that of the equilateral triangle is of order 6. Examples of infinite groups are the set of all nonzero real numbers with the operation of ordinary multiplication and the set of all real numbers with the operation of addition.

Another interesting group is the *symmetric group on n objects*, usually denoted by S_n. Let us consider specifically S_3. We take three objects and denote them for convenience by the numerals 1, 2, 3. A *permutation* of this set is a one-to-one function from the set onto itself. There are six such functions:

I		P_{132}		P_{213}	
1	1	1	1	1	2
2	2	2	3	2	1
3	3	3	2	3	3

P_{231}		P_{312}		P_{321}	
1	2	1	3	1	3
2	3	2	1	2	2
3	1	3	2	3	1

To compute the composite of two of these functions, it helps to rearrange the second so that its domain corresponds to the range of the first. For example, we find $P_{132} \circ P_{321}$ as follows:

P_{321}		P_{132}	
1	3	3	2
2	2	2	3
3	1	1	1

1	2
2	3
3	1

Thus

$$P_{132} \circ P_{321} = P_{231}.$$

The symmetric group on 3 objects is this set of six permutation functions with the operation of composition. The complete group "multiplication" table for S_3 follows. As with the table for symmetries of the square, the interpretation is

$$\text{tabular entry} = \text{side entry} \circ \text{top entry},$$

which means perform the permutation at the top then the one at the side.

	I	P_{132}	P_{213}	P_{231}	P_{312}	P_{321}
I	I	P_{132}	P_{213}	P_{231}	P_{312}	P_{321}
P_{132}	P_{132}	I	P_{312}	P_{321}	P_{213}	P_{231}
P_{213}	P_{213}	P_{231}	I	P_{132}	P_{321}	P_{312}
P_{231}	P_{231}	P_{213}	P_{321}	P_{312}	I	P_{132}
P_{312}	P_{312}	P_{321}	P_{132}	I	P_{231}	P_{213}
P_{321}	P_{321}	P_{312}	P_{231}	P_{213}	P_{132}	I

Given a set of objects and an alleged matrix of "products" like the above, we can very simply check, from the table, that all the group postulates except associativity are satisfied.

Closure: The table can be filled in with elements of the given set.

Identity: The first row and first column are merely copies of the top and side entries, respectively. Since the identity is unique, no other row or column duplicates these.

Inverses: The identity element appears exactly once in each row and exactly once in each column. The pattern of identity entries is symmetric about the upper-left to lower-right diagonal.

The postulates require directly that any group multiplication table have these features. There is an easily proved theorem that yields another distinctive feature to group multiplication tables.

Theorem (Cancellation law). If a, b, and c are members of a group and either $ac = bc$ or $ca = cb$, then $a = b$.

Proof. Suppose that $ac = bc$; then

$$(ac)c^{-1} = (bc)c^{-1}.$$

Thus, by the associativity postulate,

$$a(cc^{-1}) = b(cc^{-1}),$$

and by the postulate on inverses, $cc^{-1} = e$; so by the identity postulate

$$a = ae = be = b.$$

The other case is proved in a similar manner.

It follows from this theorem that each group element appears only once in each row and each column of a multiplication table. Clearly, then, each element appears exactly once in each row and in each column.

Note, finally, that a finite abelian group is characterized by the fact that its entire multiplication table is symmetric about the upper-left to lower-right diagonal.

EXERCISES

1. In each of the following there is listed an infinite set and an operation. Show that each of these systems is a group. In each case determine whether or not the group is abelian. For each group name the identity element and indicate for an arbitrary element what its inverse is.
   a) All integers, addition.
   b) All positive rational numbers, multiplication.
   c) All nonzero rational numbers, multiplication.
   d) All 2×2 matrices with nonzero determinants, matrix multiplication.
   e) All functions f such that $f(x) = ax + b$ with $a \neq 0$, composition.

2. Show that each set of symmetries studied in Section 7–1 forms a group with composition as the operation. Determine which of these are abelian. For each group list the identity element and make a list showing the inverse of each element.

3. Neither of the following systems forms a group. Explain why in each case. (a) All integers, subtraction. (b) Positive real numbers, division.

4. What is the order of the symmetric group S_n?

5. Find the one abstract group of order 2. [*Hint:* There must be an identity element e; call the other element a. The first row and first column of the multiplication table must look like this:

	e	a
e	e	a
a	a	

Use the remarks following the cancellation-law theorem to determine what the fourth entry in the table must be.]

6. Follow the pattern of Exercise 5 to show that there is exactly one abstract group of order 3, and find its multiplication table.

7. Consider the transformations I, f_1, f_2, f_3, each carrying an angle into an angle and defined as follows:

$$I(\alpha) = \alpha, \quad f_1(\alpha) = -\alpha, \quad f_2(\alpha) = 180° - \alpha, \quad f_3(\alpha) = 180° + \alpha.$$

   a) Show that these transformations with the operation of composition form a group.
   b) Show that if α and β are any two angles mapped one onto the other by

a member of this group, then

$$|\sin \alpha| = |\sin \beta|.$$

This is described technically by saying that $|\sin \alpha|$ is *invariant* under this group of transformations.

c) Find some other invariants under this group.

8. Let I be the identity function on the real-number system. Show that the set of functions

$$I,\ I^0 - I,\ I^0/I,\ I^0/(I^0 - I),\ I/(I - I^0),\ (I - I^0)/I$$

with the operation of composition forms a group.

9. Show that the set of all functions $T \circ \sin^2$, where T belongs to the group of Exercise 8, is the set $\sin^2, \cos^2, \csc^2, \sec^2, -\tan^2, -\cot^2$. Show that each of these trigonometric functions generates the same set under the group of Exercise 8.

10. Consider the transformations on a conditional statement that transform it into its inverse, converse, and contrapositive. Specifically, let I, f_1, f_2, f_3 be as follows:

$$I(p \to q) = p \to q, \qquad f_2(p \to q) = q \to p,$$
$$f_1(p \to q) = {\sim}p \to {\sim}q, \qquad f_3(p \to q) = {\sim}q \to {\sim}p.$$

Show that I, f_1, f_2, f_3 with the operation of composition form a group.

7-3 ISOMORPHISMS

Examples discussed so far show that the elements of a group may be many different things. Now the essential thing about a (finite) group is the structure of its multiplication table rather than the nature of its elements. That is, if two groups have the same multiplication structure, then so far as group theory is concerned they are effectively the same group, even if the elements are quite different things.

For example, look at the additive group of integers modulo 4. By this we mean the set of integers

$$0,\ 1,\ 2,\ 3$$

with the operation consisting of adding in the usual sense, then dividing by 4 and taking the remainder. This remainder is the "product." It is easily checked that the table is as follows:

	0	1	2	3
0	0	1	2	3
1	1	2	3	0
2	2	3	0	1
3	3	0	1	2

7-3 ISOMORPHISMS

Now, look at the group of rotations of the square. The table of composites is

	I	R_1	R_2	R_3
I	I	R_1	R_2	R_3
R_1	R_1	R_2	R_3	I
R_2	R_2	R_3	I	R_1
R_3	R_3	I	R_1	R_2

It is easily seen that these two tables are basically the same. The only difference is that in one case we think of the elements as numbers and in the other as transformations of the square.

Now look at the mapping f defined by the following table.

f	
0	I
1	R_1
2	R_2
3	R_3

Here f is a one-to-one function from $(0, 1, 2, 3)$ onto (I, R_1, R_2, R_3) which carries one of the above multiplication tables *in toto* into the other. This is the mechanism used to define precisely the notion that two groups (finite or infinite) are "basically the same."

Precisely, suppose that G and G' are groups and suppose that there is a one-to-one function f from G onto G' such that for every a and b in G, $f(ab) = f(a)f(b)$; then G and G' are said to be *isomorphic* (Greek: *isos*, same, plus *morphos*, form) and the mapping f is called an *isomorphism*.

Consider, now, the following abstract groups of order 4:

Group I

	e	a	b	c
e	e	a	b	c
a	a	b	c	e
b	b	c	e	a
c	c	e	a	b

Group II

	e	a	b	c
e	e	a	b	c
a	a	c	e	b
b	b	e	c	a
c	c	b	a	e

Group III

	e	a	b	c
e	e	a	b	c
a	a	e	c	b
b	b	c	a	e
c	c	b	e	a

Each of the following describes a one-to-one mapping of $(e, a, b, c,)$ onto itself.

f	
e	e
a	a
b	c
c	b

g	
e	e
a	c
b	a
c	b

The mapping f is an isomorphism of Group I onto Group II, and g is an isomorphism of Group I onto Group III. To check these statements in detail would require going through every product in the table. Note the following sample.

$$\text{In group I} \qquad \text{In group III}$$
$$ab = c \qquad g(a)g(b) = ca = b = g(c)$$

There is another group of order 4:

Group IV

	e	a	b	c
e	e	a	b	c
a	a	e	c	b
b	b	c	e	a
c	c	b	a	e

This is not isomorphic to the other three because $x^2 = e$ for every x in Group IV and there are squares other than e in the other groups.

Note that, in Group I,

$$a = a, \qquad a^2 = b, \qquad a^3 = ab = c, \qquad a^4 = ac = e.$$

Thus every element of the group is a power of a. There is no element of Group IV whose powers make up the whole group because, since $x^2 = e$ for each x, x^n is either e or x. However, if we take two elements, we can generate the entire group with powers and products:

$$a = a, \qquad a^2 = e, \qquad b = b, \qquad ab = c.$$

We describe these situations technically by saying that in Group I the single element a is a *generator* and that in Group IV the pair (a, b) forms a *set of generators*.

A group with a single generator is called a *cyclic* group. The non-cyclic group of order 4 that we have labeled Group IV above is commonly known as Klein's 4-group.

If two finite groups are isomorphic, the way to set up the isomorphism specifically is to pair off the generators and corresponding combinations thereof.

EXERCISES

1. Show that up to isomorphism there are only two groups of order 4, the cyclic group and the Klein 4-group. [*Hint:* Look for possible multiplication tables. There are only four legal ways to arrange the e's; once these are arranged, the cancellation law determines the rest of the table.]

7-3 ISOMORPHISMS

2. We have previously mentioned five groups of order 4 (listed below). By Exercise 1, each of these must be isomorphic to one of two groups. In each case determine the type and set up the isomorphism with the basic group of that type.
   a) The group of rotations of the square.
   b) The group of symmetries of the rectangle.
   c) The group of transformations on a conditional statement (Exercise 10, Section 7–2).
   d) The additive group of integers modulo 4.
   e) The group of transformations on an angle α that leaves $|\sin \alpha|$ invariant (Exercise 7, Section 7–2).

3. Show that (P_{132}, P_{213}) forms a set of generators for the symmetric group S_3.

4. Informally, Exercise 3 says that all permutations of three objects can be obtained by successively permuting the first two and/or the second two. Use this idea to find a set of three generators for S_4. Finally, describe a set of $n - 1$ generators for S_n.

5. Find a set of generators for the group of functions in Exercise 8, Section 7–2. Show that this group is isomorphic to S_3.

6. The Klein 4-group has the property that $x^2 = e$ for every x. Show that there is no group of order 5 with this property. [*Hint:* The multiplication table would have to have this skeleton:

	e	a	b	c	d
e	e	a	b	c	d
a	a	e			
b	b		e		
c	c			e	
d	d				e

There are two ways to fill in the product ab, and each of these leads to the result that $(aa)b \neq a(ab)$ or to a violation of the cancellation law.]

7. Show that the group of all real numbers with the operation of addition is isomorphic to the set of all positive real numbers with the operation of multiplication. [*Hint:* Let $f(x) = \log x$.]

8. Show that every cyclic group is abelian. [*Hint:* $a^m a^n = a^n a^m$ because of associativity.]

9. Using Exercise 8, show that any two cyclic groups of order n are isomorphic.

10. For an abstract group the operation is usually called multiplication, but composition of transformations is actually the general prototype. This is shown as follows. Let G be a group and for each $a \in G$ let T_a be the mapping of G onto itself defined by
$$T_a(x) = ax.$$
Let G' be the group of all such mappings T_a with the operation of composition. Show that $f(a) = T_a$ defines an isomorphism f from G onto G'.

196   ABSTRACT ALGEBRAIC SYSTEMS

11. Exhibit specifically the set of mappings that constitutes the group of transformations isomorphic to each of the following.
    a) The cyclic group of order 4.
    b) The Klein 4-group.
    c) The multiplicative group of positive real numbers.
    d) The additive group of all real numbers.

7-4 SUBGROUPS

Consider the subset (I, P_{312}, P_{231}) of S_3. A table of products for these three elements is as follows:

	I	P_{312}	P_{231}
I	I	P_{312}	P_{231}
P_{312}	P_{312}	P_{231}	I
P_{231}	P_{231}	I	P_{312}

This set of three permutations itself forms a group! Not every subset of S_3 forms a group. For example, (I, P_{132}, P_{213}) obviously does not satisfy the closure postulate because it contains a set of generators for all of S_3. Clearly, also, if a subset is to form a group it must contain the identity element.

If G is a group and H is a subset of G that also forms a group, then H is called a *subgroup* of G.

If H is a subgroup of G and $a \in G$, we denote by aH the set of all products ah where $h \in H$. If $a \in H$, then $aH = H$ because H is a group. The interesting case is that in which a does not belong to H. Then aH is called the *left coset* of H generated by a. Similarly, Ha is the set of all products ha for $h \in H$ and is the *right coset* of H generated by a. In an abelian group, of course, left and right cosets are always identical and are merely called cosets.

Now suppose b and c are both in aH; that is,

$$b = ah_1 \quad \text{and} \quad c = ah_2,$$

where h_1 and h_2 are in H. Then

$$a = bh_1^{-1}; \quad \text{so} \quad c = bh_1^{-1}h_2.$$

Since H is a group, $h_1^{-1}h_2 \in H$ and we have $c \in bH$. It follows that $aH = bH$, which is to say that a coset may be generated by any one of its elements. Thus two different cosets cannot have an element in common because that common element would be a generator and it cannot generate both cosets.

Let us look at subgroups of S_3 and their cosets. We shall list these in tables that follow the pattern of multiplication tables. For left cosets we list the subgroup at the top and generators at the side; then with products in their usual places we get cosets as rows in the table. For right cosets we list the subgroup down the side and generators at the top, and cosets appear as columns in the table. First consider the subgroup of order 3 noted above.

Left coset

	I	P_{312}	P_{231}
P_{132}	P_{132}	P_{213}	P_{321}

Right coset

		P_{132}
I	P_{132}
P_{312}	P_{321}
P_{231}	P_{213}

These are the same. They come out in different orders, it is true, but cosets are only sets; order is not important.

There are other subgroups of S_3. Take, for example, (I, P_{132}). Since $P_{132}^2 = I$, this is clearly a subgroup. Its cosets are as follows.

Left cosets

	I	P_{132}
P_{213}	P_{213}	P_{231}
P_{312}	P_{312}	P_{321}

Right cosets

		P_{213}	P_{231}
I	P_{213}	P_{231}
P_{132}	P_{312}	P_{321}

Here the right and left cosets are different.

So in the nonabelian group S_3, we find one subgroup with equal right and left cosets and one for which they are unequal. A subgroup H of a group G is called a *normal subgroup* if

$$aH = Ha$$

for all $a \in G$. Among the subgroups of S_3 noted above, the one of order 3 is normal and the one of order 2 is not. In an abelian group, of course, all subgroups are normal.

If A and B are two cosets of a subgroup H, the product AB is defined as the set of all products ab, where $a \in A$ and $b \in B$. Let us look at this for the left cosets of (I, P_{132}):

	P_{213}	P_{231}
P_{312}	P_{132}	I
P_{321}	P_{231}	P_{213}

198 ABSTRACT ALGEBRAIC SYSTEMS

Here the product is a set of four elements. It is not a coset; in fact it is not much of anything.

For the cosets of a normal subgroup, however, the situation is quite different. Let H be the normal subgroup (I, P_{312}, P_{231}) and let A be its coset $(P_{132}, P_{321}, P_{213})$. Clearly,

$$H^2 = H$$

because H is a group; also

$$HA = AH = A$$

because A is both a right and left coset and a coset is generated by each of its elements. For this case, however, look at A^2:

	P_{132}	P_{321}	P_{213}
P_{132}	I	P_{231}	P_{312}
P_{321}	P_{312}	I	P_{231}
P_{213}	P_{231}	P_{312}	I

All we get for products are the elements of H. So

$$A^2 = H.$$

Therefore, for A and H, we have the multiplication table

	H	A
H	H	A
A	A	H

These form a group! This is typical. The general theorem is as follows. (Proof omitted.)

> **Theorem.** The set consisting of a normal subgroup and its cosets forms a group with the subgroup as identity element.

If G is a group and H is a normal subgroup of G, the group of cosets of H is denoted by G/H and is called a *quotient group*.

By way of emphasizing that the elements of a quotient group are cosets, let us rewrite the multiplication table for the quotient group of S_3 without the abbreviations H and A used above. The quotient group

$$S_3/(I, P_{312}, P_{231})$$

has two elements:

$$(I, P_{312}, P_{231}) \quad \text{and} \quad (P_{132}, P_{321}, P_{213}).$$

The multiplication table is

	(I, P_{312}, P_{231})	$(P_{132}, P_{321}, P_{213})$
(I, P_{312}, P_{231})	(I, P_{312}, P_{231})	$(P_{132}, P_{321}, P_{213})$
$(P_{132}, P_{321}, P_{213})$	$(P_{132}, P_{321}, P_{213})$	(I, P_{312}, P_{231})

There is one other important fact about subgroups (normal or not) of finite groups. It follows at once from the cancellation law that each coset has the same number of elements as the subgroup. Since different cosets have no elements in common, it then follows that the order of the original group is the order of the subgroup times the number of cosets (including the subgroup as one of the cosets). This leads to the following classical theorem:

Theorem (Lagrange). If G is a finite group and H is a subgroup of G, then the order of H is a divisor of the order of G.

EXERCISES

1. Two subgroups of S_3 were mentioned above. There are three more. Find them and list their cosets.

2. For the group of symmetries of the square, there are eight subgroups, four of them normal. Find all the subgroups; test for normality; for each normal subgroup find the multiplication table for the quotient group.

3. The cyclic group of order 4 has one subgroup of order 2 and the Klein 4-group has three. Without computing them, explain why all four of these subgroups are normal and why all four quotient groups are isomorphic.

4. Let p be a prime number (no divisors except p and 1) and let G be a group of order p.
    a) Show by Lagrange's Theorem that G has no subgroups except G itself and the trivial group consisting of e alone.
    b) Let $a \in G$ and let n be the smallest positive integer such that $a^n = e$. Show that $n = p$.
    c) Show that G is cyclic.

5. Show that there is no nonabelian group of order less than 6. [*Hint:* See Exercise 4 above, Exercises 5 and 6, Section 7-2, and Exercise 1, Section 7-3.]

6. Let G be the group of integers with the operation of addition and let H be the subgroup of all even integers. Describe the quotient group G/H.

7. Let G be the group of all real numbers with the operation of addition; let a be a real number and let H be the subgroup of all integer multiples of a. Describe G/H.

8. Let $a = 12$ in Exercise 7 and discuss the way in which the idea of a clock is based on the quotient group G/H.

7-5 HOMOMORPHISMS

In Section 7–4 we discussed the quotient group

$$S_3/(I, P_{312}, P_{231}).$$

Consider now the mapping of S_3 onto this quotient group that carries each element of S_3 into the coset to which it belongs. Specifically, this mapping may be displayed as follows:

$$\begin{array}{l} I \\ P_{312} \\ P_{231} \end{array} \longrightarrow (I, P_{312}, P_{231})$$

$$\begin{array}{l} P_{132} \\ P_{321} \\ P_{213} \end{array} \longrightarrow (P_{132}, P_{321}, P_{213})$$

Let us call this mapping f; it is easily checked that for every a and b in S_3,

$$f(ab) = f(a)f(b).$$

For example,
$$P_{321}P_{213} = P_{231}$$
and
$$(P_{132}, P_{321}, P_{213})(P_{132}, P_{321}, P_{213}) = (I, P_{312}, P_{231}).$$

Indeed, it follows at once, from the way multiplication of cosets is defined, that if G is any group, H a normal subgroup of G, and f the mapping of G onto G/H that carries each element of G into the coset to which it belongs, then

$$f(ab) = f(a)f(b). \tag{1}$$

A mapping f of one group onto another satisfying (1) is called a *homomorphism*. If a homomorphism is one-to-one it is an isomorphism (see Section 7–3), but in general homomorphisms are not one-to-one.

We have noted that the so-called "natural map" (each element corresponds to its coset) of a group G onto a quotient group G/H is a homomorphism. However, the connection goes the other way too. If f is a homomorphism of G onto G', then G' is isomorphic to a quotient group of G. Specifically, let e' be the identity in G' and let H be the set of elements of G such that $h \in H$ if and only if

$$f(h) = e'.$$

Then H is called the *kernel* of f and it is easily proved (summary in Exercise 1 below) that H is a normal subgroup of G and that G' is isomorphic to G/H.

A vector space with the vector addition operation is an abelian group and a linear transformation on a vector space is a homomorphism on this group. Recall (Section 5–5) that if T is linear, then

$$T(\mathbf{u} + \mathbf{v}) = T\mathbf{u} + T\mathbf{v}$$

and this is just (1) with addition replacing multiplication. In the additive group of a vector space, the interesting subgroups are those that are also closed under multiplication by scalars. These are called *subspaces*.

For example, let T be defined on the space of plane vectors by

$$T(a\mathbf{i} + b\mathbf{j}) = a\mathbf{i}.$$

Geometrically, this is just vertical projection onto the horizontal axis. The kernel is the vertical axis; that is $T(\mathbf{u}) = \mathbf{0}$ if and only if $\mathbf{u} = b\mathbf{j}$. Cosets of this kernel are vertical lines, and the quotient space is this space of lines. Now T maps the plane onto the horizontal axis; so the theory we have summarized here says that the horizontal axis is isomorphic to the space whose elements are vertical lines. This should be quite evident in this specific example.

EXERCISES

1. Let G be a group with identity e and let G' be a group with identity e'. Let f be a homomorphism of G onto G'.
    a) Show that $f(e) = e'$.
    b) Show that if $f(h_1) = e'$ and $f(h_2) = e'$, then $f(h_1 h_2) = e'$.
    c) Show that if $f(h) = e'$, then $f(h^{-1}) = e'$.
    d) Conclude that the kernel of f is a subgroup of G.
    e) Show that a and b belong to the same coset with respect to the kernel of f if and only if $f(a) = f(b)$.
    f) Use part (e) to show that the kernel of f is a normal subgroup of G.
    g) Denote the kernel of f by H. Let $a' \in G'$ correspond to the coset of H defined [part (e)] by $f(a) = a'$. Show that this correspondence is an isomorphism between G' and G/H.

2. Let f map the additive group of integers onto the additive group of integers modulo 4 by setting $f(n)$ equal to the remainder on dividing n by 4. Show that f is a homomorphism and find its kernel. Describe the quotient group determined by this kernel and describe the isomorphism between this quotient group and the range of f.

3. Show that there is no homomorphism of the symmetric group S_3 onto the group of order 3. [*Hint:* If there were one, its kernel would be a normal subgroup.]

4. For the group of symmetries of the square:
   a) Exhibit a homomorphism onto the Klein 4-group.
   b) Exhibit three different homomorphisms onto the group of order 2.
   c) Show that there is no homomorphism onto the cyclic group of order 4.
5. Show that for any n there is a homomorphism of the cyclic group of order $2n$ onto the cyclic group of order n. Describe its kernel.
6. In Chapter 5 we discussed several linear transformations on nongeometric vector spaces. In each of the following examples, regard the linear transformation as a homomorphism on the additive group; determine its kernel and describe the quotient space.
   a) The derivative transformation from the space of quadratic polynomials to the space of linear polynomials (see Section 5–6).
   b) The boundary transformation of Exercise 5, Section 5–6.
7. Suppose there is a homomorphism from a group of order n onto a group of order k.
   a) One of the relations $k \leq n$, $k \geq n$ must hold. Which?
   b) What is the order of the kernel?
   c) What is the order of the factor group generated by this kernel?
8. What is the kernel of an isomorphism?

7–6 RINGS

Since a group involves only one binary operation, it is one of the simpler algebraic systems. In the familiar algebra of real numbers we have two operations, addition and multiplication. Accordingly, we turn now to abstract systems with two operations.

When there are two operations in a system we expect them to be related in some way, and the standard relation is furnished by the distributive law. For real numbers we have

$$x(y + z) = xy + xz.$$

We say that this describes the fact that multiplication is distributive over addition. In general, for abstract systems with two operations, it is required that one be distributive over the other.

In group theory the operation is called multiplication, though it may well be something else. Similarly, two operations are usually called addition and multiplication. They are distinguished by the asymmetry of the distributive law. If operation A is distributive over operation B, then A is called multiplication and B is called addition.

To generate the two-operation systems commonly studied we require that addition be very well behaved. Indeed, the system with addition alone will always be an abelian group. By placing, successively, more and more restrictions on multiplication, we obtain a hierarchy of abstract algebraic systems.

We begin by requiring of multiplication only the closure postulate, associativity, and the distributive law (from both sides). The resulting system is called a ring. Specifically, a *ring* is a set R and two operations $+$ and $\cdot$ such that

1. $(R, +)$ is an Abelian group.
2. If $a \in R$ and $b \in R$, then $ab \in R$.
3. For all a, b, c in R,
$$a(bc) = (ab)c.$$
4. For all a, b, c in R,
$$a(b + c) = (ab) + (ac) \quad \text{and} \quad (a + b)c = (ac) + (bc).$$

The identity element in the group $(R, +)$ is denoted by 0 and the inverse of a in this group is written $-a$.

If $ab = ba$ for every a and b in R, then R is called a *commutative ring*. (The phrase abelian ring does not seem to be used.)

Even in a commutative ring, multiplication may still be short some key properties. In particular, there may be no multiplicative identity element. When there is one it is denoted by 1, and the ring is called a *ring with unity*. Specifically, the postulate is as follows.

A ring R is a ring with unity if there is a unique element 1 of R such that for every $a \in R$,
$$1a = a1 = a.$$

Looking at the properties of group multiplication suggests two other questions to raise about ring multiplication: Are there inverses? Does the cancellation law hold? In Section 7–2 the cancellation law for groups was proved by using the postulate on existence of inverses; so the same could be done here if we had inverses. It turns out that the cancellation law may hold, though, even if not every element has an inverse. So there are two successive restrictions that could be imposed on multiplication: a cancellation law and the existence of inverses. Systems satisfying these additional conditions are not called rings, however, and they will be examined later.

EXERCISES

1. Show that the set of all even integers with the usual definitions of addition and multiplication forms a commutative ring. Does it have a unity element?
2. Generalize Exercise 1. Consider a fixed integer n and all integer multiples of n. Show that this is always a ring and determine when it is a ring with unity.

3. The ring of integers modulo n consists of the integers $0, 1, 2, \ldots, n-1$, with the operations defined as follows. Form sums and products in the usual way; then divide by n and take the remainder.
   a) Show that for any n this is a commutative ring with unity.
   b) For each of the cases $n = 3, 4, 5$, set up the addition and multiplication tables.
   c) Show that for $n = 4$ the cancellation law fails.
4. Determine whether or not each of the following systems is a ring. For each ring determine whether or not it is commutative and whether or not it has a unity element.
   a) The set of all 2×2 matrices with the usual definitions of matrix addition and matrix multiplication.
   b) The set of all linear functions on the real-number system [functions f such that $f(x) = ax + b$] with addition defined in the usual way and multiplication defined to mean composition.
   c) As in part (b), except that all constant terms are zero; that is, functions f such that $f(x) = ax$.
   d) As in part (b), except that all coefficients a and b are restricted to be even integers.
   e) All quadratic functions [$f(x) = ax^2 + bx + c$] with the operations defined as in part (b).
   f) All power functions [$f(x) = x^a$] with addition defined to mean multiplication in the usual sense and multiplication defined to mean composition.
5. A ring isomorphism is a one-to-one mapping of one ring onto another that preserves both addition and multiplication.
   a) Define this idea precisely. [*Hint:* See the definition of group isomorphism in Section 7–3.]
   b) Show that the ring of Exercise 4(f) is isomorphic to the ring of all real numbers with the usual definitions of addition and multiplication.
   c) Show that the rings of Exercises 4(c) and 4(f) are isomorphic.
6. A vector space has two operations, addition and multiplication by scalars. Why is a vector space not a ring?

7–7 POLYNOMIALS

Consider the set of all polynomial functions

$$\sum_{k=1}^{n} a_k I^k.$$

Under the usual definitions of addition and multiplication of functions, these form a commutative ring with unity. The constant function I^0 is the multiplicative unit and the identically zero function is the additive identity.

An important feature of this ring is that it also has a cancellation law. Specifically, the cancellation law in a ring reads: "If $a \neq 0$ and $ab = ac$, then $b = c$." We can cancel anything except the additive identity. We can never hope to cancel 0 because $a0 = 0$ for every a.

A ring is said to *have no divisors of zero* if $ab = 0$ implies $a = 0$ or $b = 0$. The ring cancellation law may be written

$$a(b - c) = 0 \quad \text{and} \quad a \neq 0 \text{ implies } b - c = 0.$$

In this form it is clearly equivalent to the absence of divisors of zero.

An *integral domain* is a commutative ring with unity which has no divisors of zero. Thus the polynomial functions form an important example of an integral domain.

To solve an equation by factoring, we proceed as in the following example.
$$x^2 - x - 2 = 0; \quad (x - 2)(x + 1) = 0;$$
$$x = 2 \quad \text{or} \quad x = -1.$$

The last step here—deducing from the condition $(x - 2)(x + 1) = 0$ that either $x - 2 = 0$ or $x + 1 = 0$—is based on the fact that the polynomial ring is actually an integral domain. This example shows quite graphically how the abstraction of algebraic ideas clarifies the logical analysis of routine manipulative techniques.

The polynomials in two variables x and y also form an integral domain, and this example leads us to a very brief sketch of the role played by ring theory in the foundations of modern algebraic geometry. Consider the two polynomials
$$x^2 = y \quad \text{and} \quad x^2 + y^2 = 2.$$

If we set these two polynomials equal to zero, we get the two equations
$$y = x^2 \quad \text{and} \quad x^2 + y^2 = 2.$$

The loci of these two equations are shown in Fig. 7–6; they intersect at the two points $(-1, 1)$ and $(1, 1)$. Thus the two-point set $\{(-1, 1), (1, 1)\}$ is characterized by the pair of polynomials $x^2 = y$, $x^2 + y^2 = 2$. However, other sets of polynomials characterize the same set. For example, the pair
$$x^2 + y - 2, \quad x^4 - y$$

yields the same set of two points (Fig. 7–7).

We could also say that this two-point set is characterized by the set of all four polynomials listed here. That is, if we draw all four loci on the same graph, they all intersect in these two points. Clearly, if we choose them correctly, we can keep adding characterizing polynomials indef-

Fig. 7-6

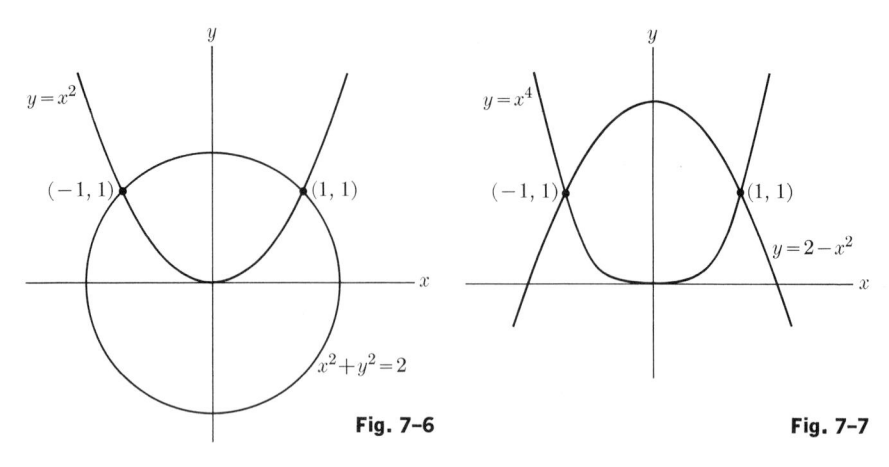

Fig. 7-7

initely. There are an infinite number of polynomials that vanish on our two-point set, and the point of view of modern algebraic geometry is to say that the algebraic representation of the point set is this infinite set of polynomials.

Let us look at the algebraic structure of such a polynomial set as a subset of the integral domain of all polynomials. Let C be a set of points in the plane and let S be the set of all polynomials P such that

$$P(x, y) = 0 \quad \text{for every} \quad (x, y) \in C.$$

If P and Q are two polynomials from S, then clearly

$$P(x, y) + Q(x, y) = 0 \quad \text{for every} \quad (x, y) \in C;$$

so $P + Q \in S$. That is, S is a subgroup of the additive group. Similarly, $PQ \in S$; so S is closed under both the ring operations, and we could say that it is a subring of the ring of all polynomials.

However, subrings are not so important in ring theory as subgroups are in group theory. The set S here has an even stronger multiplicative closure property that makes it significant in ring theory. Let $P \in S$ and $(x, y) \in C$ and let Q be any polynomial (in S or not); then

$$P(x, y)Q(x, y) = 0 \cdot Q(x, y) = 0.$$

That is, $PQ \in S$ if $P \in S$, no matter what Q is.

An *ideal* in a ring (or integral domain) is a subset that is a subgroup of the additive group and is closed under multiplication by any element of the entire ring.

An algebraic variety is a point set which is the set of common zeros of all elements of some ideal in the polynomial ring. The illustration given above involves an algebraic variety consisting of two points. The idea is more interesting in higher dimensions where varieties are curves, surfaces, etc. However, the present illustration introduces the idea without relying on details of higher-dimensional analytic geometry.

In ring theory, ideals rather than subrings play a role analogous to that of subgroups in group theory, and the counterpart of a normal subgroup is a 2-sided ideal. The reason for this is that 2-sided ideals are related to ring homomorphisms, just as normal subgroups are to group homomorphisms (see Exercise 6 below).

EXERCISES

1. Consider the integers modulo n. That is, add and multiply as usual, divide by n and take the remainder.
    a) Show that for each n this forms a commutative ring with unity.
    b) Set up addition and multiplication tables for each of the four cases $n = 3, 4, 5, 6$.
    c) Show that for $n = 4$ and 6 there are divisors of zero, while for $n = 3$ and 5 the system is an integral domain.
    d) For what integers n does the ring of integers modulo n form an integral domain?

2. Show that the set of all even integers is an ideal in the ring of all integers.

3. Generalize Exercise 2 to the set of all integer multiples of n.

4. In a noncommutative ring, a right ideal is a subgroup of the additive group that is closed under multiplication from the right (ab is in the ideal if a is in the ideal).
    a) In the ring of all 2×2 matrices, show that the set of all matrices of the form
    $$\begin{bmatrix} a & b \\ 0 & 0 \end{bmatrix}$$
    is a right ideal but not a left ideal.
    b) Describe a left ideal in this ring.

5. Let $P(x, y) = y - x^2$. The ideal consisting of all polynomial multiples of P describes what algebraic variety?

6. A mapping f of one ring onto another is a ring homomorphism if for every a and b in the domain
$$f(ab) = f(a)f(b) \quad \text{and} \quad f(a + b) = f(a) + f(b).$$
    a) Show that if $f(a) = f(b) = 0$, then $f(a + b) = 0$.
    b) Show that if $f(a) = 0$, then for any b, $f(ab) = f(ba) = 0$.
    c) Show how this proves that the kernel of a ring homomorphism is a 2-sided ideal.

7-8 FIELDS

In the discussion of rings we make addition a very "well-behaved" operation right from the start, and then successively impose more restrictions on multiplication to define different interesting systems. Specifically, in each of the standard two-operation structures, addition is always an abelian group operation, while the only blanket requirement on multiplication is associativity. Depending on the type of system studied, multiplication may or may not be commutative; it may or may not have an identity element; it may or may not have a cancellation law. Finally, if we want to require the existence of multiplicative inverses, we get out of ring theory and into field theory.

Look at the following example. We take the set (0, 1, 2) and define addition and multiplication by the following tables.

Addition	0	1	2		Multiplication	0	1	2
0	0	1	2		0	0	0	0
1	1	2	0		1	0	1	2
2	2	0	1		2	0	2	1

This ring "has everything." It has commutativity, a unity element, a cancellation law, and an inverse for everything except 0. Indeed, the entire set with addition is an abelian group and the set (1, 2) with multiplication is also an abelian group. This is an example of a field.

To be precise, a *field* is a set F closed under two binary operations $+$ and $\cdot$ satisfying these postulates.

1. $(F, +)$ is an abelian group with identity element 0.
2. If F' is F with 0 deleted, then $(F', \cdot)$ is an abelian group.
3. Multiplication is distributive over addition,

Note that the two-operation systems we have defined may be listed in increasing order of "good" behavior for multiplication as follows.

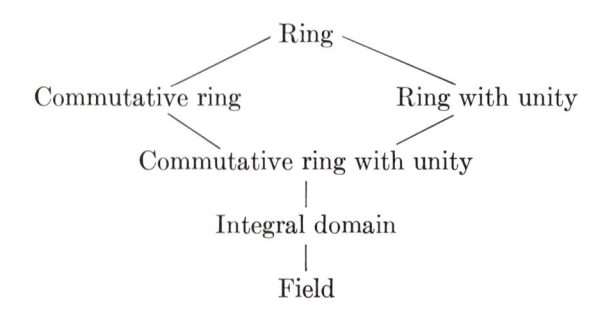

```
                        Ring
                       /    \
          Commutative ring    Ring with unity
                       \    /
                Commutative ring with unity
                           |
                    Integral domain
                           |
                         Field
```

The abstract systems we have studied exhibit various imitations of the real-number system, some of them more faithful imitations than others. So far as binary operations are concerned, a field exhibits all the properties of the real-number system. However, the little example with (0, 1, 2) above shows that a field may bear very little resemblance to the real-number system.

In order to characterize the real-number system postulationally, we must introduce the notion of inequality. In terms of abstract systems we define an *ordered field* to be a field in which there is a relation $<$ with these properties:

1. $a < b$ and $b < c$, then $a < c$.
2. For any a and b in the field, exactly one of the relations $a < b$, $b < a$, $a = b$ holds.
3. If $a < b$, then $a + c < b + c$.
4. If $a < b$ and $0 < c$, then $ac < bc$.

There are still several examples of ordered fields, and it takes one more postulate to give a unique postulational description of the real-number system. We state it here just to complete the discussion, although we shall not pursue the ideas involved at all. Let F be an ordered field, A a subset of F and b an element of F. We say that b is an upper bound for A if $a \leq b$ for every $a \in A$. We say that b is the least upper bound for A if b is an upper bound for A and $c < b$ implies c is not an upper bound for A. An ordered field is called complete if every nonempty set that has an upper bound has a least upper bound. Now the real-number system is a complete ordered field, and it can be proved that any two complete ordered fields are isomorphic. So the postulational description "complete ordered field" determines the real number system up to isomorphism.

In conclusion, let us look at a rather weird example of an ordered field. We might call it the "field of arithmetic without carrying." In ordinary arithmetic we add and multiply as follows:

$$\begin{array}{cc} 59.6 & 4.2 \\ \underline{34.7} & \underline{3.7} \\ 94.3 & 2\,9\,4 \\ & \underline{1\,2\,6} \\ & 1\,5.5\,4 \end{array}$$

Here the numbers are represented as a succession of digits with a decimal point to indicate where the units column is. In the field we are about to describe, an element will be written not as a succession of single digits but as a succession of real numbers, again with the units column appropriately marked. In writing such elements, we shall separate the

entries by commas (because there may be more than one digit per entry) and use a semicolon to spot the units column (because there may be a genuine decimal point in an individual entry). Thus, instead of 39.5, we shall write
$$3 , 9 ; 5.$$
Note, however, that
$$3.2 , 4 ; .006 , 57$$
is also a member of this field.

Addition and multiplication are done in this field without carrying. This presents no difficulties, since individual entries are not limited to single digits. For example, the arithmetic problems done above have different answers in this field.

$$\begin{array}{r} 5 , 9 ; 6 \\ 3 , 4 ; 7 \\ \hline 8 , 13 ; 13 \end{array} \qquad \begin{array}{r} 4 ; 2 \\ 3 ; 7 \\ \hline 28 , 14 \\ 12 , 6 \\ \hline 12 ; 34 , 14 \end{array}$$

Subtraction is done without borrowing by introducing negative individual entries:
$$\begin{array}{r} 5 , 2 ; 3 \\ 2 , 5 ; 7 \\ \hline 3 , -3 ; -4 \end{array}$$

Finally, long division can be done in this system (though specific examples are quite tedious), and it should be reasonably apparent that the system is a field. Inequalities are determined as for decimal expansions. Line up the semicolons and compare leading entries; if these are equal compare the next entries, etc. For example,

$$\begin{array}{cc} 5 , 3 ; 2 & 2 , -1 ; 42 \\ > 2 , 7 ; 13 & < 2 , 0 ; 13 \end{array}$$

With these definitions of $+$, $\cdot$, and $<$, the system forms an ordered field. Some of its peculiarities will be noted in the exercises below.

EXERCISES

1. Referring to Exercise 1, Section 7–7, show that whenever the ring of integers modulo n is an integral domain, it is also a field.
2. The polynomials form an integral domain that is not a field. Why?

3. Using the theorem on cancellation in groups (Section 7-2), show that every field is an integral domain.

4. Prove that, in a field, if an ideal contains an element other than 0, then it is the entire field. In the light of this, explain why homomorphism theory for fields is rather uninteresting.

5. Show that the set of all numbers of the form $a + b\sqrt{2}$ forms:
   a) an integral domain if a and b are restricted to be integers.
   b) a field if a and b are allowed to be any rational numbers.

6. Show that the rational numbers form an ordered field that is not complete. [*Hint:* The set of all rational numbers r such that $r^2 < 2$ does not have a rational least upper bound.]

7. Any field has a set of integers. These are defined as the multiplicative identity 1, then
$$1+1, \quad 1+1+1, \quad \text{etc.}$$

   a) In the field of arithmetic without carrying, the multiplicative identity is 1. What are the integers?
   b) Show that in this field 1, 0; is an upper bound for the set of all integers.

8. Let a and b be real numbers with $a < b$. Define successively
$$b_1 = \frac{a+b}{2}, \quad b_2 = \frac{a+b_1}{2}, \ldots, b_{n+1} = \frac{a+b_n}{2}, \ldots$$

Here $b_n \to a$ in that there is no real number c such that $c < b_n - a$ for all n. The field of arithmetic without carrying does not have this property.
   a) Let $a = 1$; and $b = 1, 0;$. Compute several "midpoints."
   b) Show that if $c = 250;$, then $c < b_n - a$ for all n.

COMPUTERS 8

8-1 ARTIFICIAL LANGUAGES

It is the purpose of this chapter to present the basic portion of one of the artificial languages that are used in communicating with an automatic digital computer. First let us get a broad look at what happens in the operation of a computer and what role such a language plays in this process.

The computer consists of a central processing unit (CPU) and an input-output (I-O) device. The CPU is the intricate system of thousands of transistors that control circuits and thereby record numbers and transmit them from one part of the unit to another. We shall not be concerned with the inner workings of the CPU at all. An I-O device is something that converts mechanical impulses into electrical ones to feed information into the CPU, and makes the reverse conversion to get information out.

One of the simplest I-O devices is a typewriter. The operator types in the usual way and every time he hits a key it sends an appropriate electrical signal to the CPU. It also prints like any other typewriter, but this is only so that the operator can see what he has done. As an output device the typewriter is operated electrically by the CPU and prints out the message.

Another commonly used I-O device is a card read-punch. This consists of a reader that scans punched cards and converts the punched information into appropriate electrical impulses and an electrically operated punch that produces new punched cards with the output information. There are many other I-O devices; often a system has several, and one uses one device for input and another for output. For the sake of simplicity we shall assume throughout this chapter that our computer has punched-card I-O and that we use it exclusively.

Now, of what does input and output consist? Output is simple to describe. It consists of answers. Input, on the other hand, is basically in two parts. It consists of a *program* and *data*. The program is a set of instructions to the machine to perform certain operations. The data are numbers on which the machine is to perform these operations. This serves to isolate the topic of this chapter. We are concerned here with techniques for writing simple programs.

8-1 ARTIFICIAL LANGUAGES

In the very early days of computers, programs had to be written in so-called machine language. To learn machine language one must understand the inner workings of the CPU; so to begin with, programming was a highly specialized job. Programming for the layman came in with the invention of the *compiler*. A compiler is itself a program (written in machine language) which instructs the CPU to translate into machine language a program written in a much simpler language. The artificial languages mentioned at the beginning of this section are the languages that have been invented to go with specific compilers.

Suppose we have written a program in one of these artificial languages. What do we have to do in order to use it? First, we get out the compiler, which is a deck of cards kept on file in the computation center. We put this on the card reader and put the deck containing our program on top. Then we punch the button and wait for output. This procedure is called *compiling*. The output of a compiling run is a deck containing our program in machine language. We are now ready for the *execution* run. We put our machine-language program on the reader, follow it by what is called the *subroutine* deck (to be found in the same file cabinet as the compiler), and then put the deck containing our data on top. Again we push the button and this time the output is our answers.

We outline this procedure by way of pointing out that when one is writing artificial language programs it usually pays to make them as general as possible. Remember, any change in your artificial-language program calls for recompiling; so if one program can be written to fit several problems this will usually save time and trouble.

There are a number of artificial computer languages in common use. We shall summarize here the rudiments of FORTRAN. This name is an abbreviation for "formula translation." There are several different FORTRAN compilers available, capable of translating various specialized commands. By and large the basic commands to be summarized here can be translated by any FORTRAN compiler.

First let us look at the "alphabet" in the FORTRAN language. This consists of the following characters, classified as indicated.

Alphameric characters:
   Alphabetic characters: A, B, . . . Z
   Numeric characters: 0, 1, 2, . . . 9
Special characters: + − * / , . ( ) =

It is important to learn the words *alphameric, alphabetic, numeric,* and *special* in this connection. Many rules of FORTRAN specify that only certain types of characters may be used in certain connections, and these technical terms are used in the statement of these rules.

FORTRAN is designed to look as much like algebra as possible, and in it we use letters to stand for unspecified quantities—quantities to be specified when the data are read and computation begins. To allow a little versatility, we can generally use anywhere from 1 to 5 characters to stand for a single quantity. For example, if we were going to read in some abscissas and ordinates, we might label them X and Y or we might label them ABS and ORD. These "words" are called FORTRAN *variables*. In writing a program we name our own variables, and it is useful to use mnemonics as much as possible.

Right at the beginning, however, there is one limitation on this. The CPU has two different units for doing arithmetic. One does *fixed-point arithmetic*. This is arithmetic with whole numbers with no provision for any decimal points. The other unit does *floating-point arithmetic*. In this every number must have a decimal point (at the end, if desired) and the location of the point is carried through all computations. Now, when a program names a variable, the CPU must reserve storage space for the number that is to be substituted. It has to know what kind of number to reserve storage for; so one of the first rules of FORTRAN has to do with the *mode* of a variable.

The name of a fixed-point variable must begin with I, J, K, L, M, or N. The name of a floating-point variable must begin with some alphabetic character other than these.

Note that this rule is modeled after our habits in algebra. The letters i through n are the ones commonly used to stand for integers, particularly in subscripts.

The computer does floating-point arithmetic as we would expect, usually expressing the answer to 8 significant figures with the decimal point in the appropriate place. In fixed-point arithmetic, addition, subtraction, and multiplication proceed according to plan, but fixed-point division introduces a slight peculiarity. Remember, the answer is coming out in fixed point, but the computer does not round off; it merely drops the fractional part. Thus, for example, in fixed-point arithmetic

$$\tfrac{5}{3} = 1.$$

Actually, once we note this feature we can frequently put it to good use.

EXERCISES

1. One of the FORTRAN rules (see Section 8–2) is that a variable must consist of 1 to 5 alphameric characters, the first of which must be alphabetic. Which of the following expressions qualify under this rule?

a) FORTRAN	b) ALPHA	c) X
d) Y2	e) A2B3	f) X(N)
g) 2AB	h) VAR	i) INT
j) NAME	k) A+B	l) 345
m) M,N	n) C13	o) (XY)

2. Another rule is that you cannot add, subtract, multiply, or divide variables of mixed mode (one fixed point, the other floating point). Which of the following operations are ruled out?

a) A+B	b) X2/ABC	c) I2−M3
d) AM+MA	e) (X+Y)/N	f) NAME + ADDRS
g) FIRST − LAST	h) ADD − SUBTR	i) (M+N)/J
j) (X−Y)/Z		

3. The following refer to fixed-point division.
   a) Let N assume the values 1, 2, 3, ... ; what are the values of N/2?
   b) Let N assume the values 2, 4, 6, ... ; what are the values of N/3?
   c) Set up a scheme in which a fixed-point variable assumes a regular succession of values and the values of a fraction come in groups of 2, then 3, then 2, then 3, etc.

8-2 I-O AND ARITHMETIC STATEMENTS

A FORTRAN program normally consists of a deck of cards; the message on a single card is referred to as a *statement*.

Clearly, any program must contain I-O statements. These will vary if there are several I-O devices available, but we have agreed to consider here only programs that use a card read-punch. So we have READ and PUNCH statements. To be interpreted by the compiler, these must follow a certain form that is best explained by an example:

$$\text{READ 101, A, B} \tag{1}$$

The number 101 following the key word is a reference to a FORMAT statement. These will be discussed in Section 8-6. Some compilers require FORMAT statements; others do not. Those that do not will ignore the reference number; so it is a good habit always to put a number after READ whether it refers to anything or not.

The comma following this number must be there. The compiler will not accept the statement unless it is.

Now the statement (1) means, "Read (the following format 101 in case there is such a thing) two floating-point numbers from the data. Store the first as A for future reference and store the second under the label B."

Output statements follow the same pattern. We are now in a position to write an extremely simple program. If we have a compiler that does not require FORMAT statements, the following program will compile and execute:

```
READ 101, A, B
PUNCH 101, B, A
STOP
END
```

The statement STOP means what you think it does. The statement END *must always be the last card* in a FORTRAN program. It is a message to the compiler, "OK, you've read it; now start compiling."

What does the little program above do? It tells the computer to read two floating-point numbers and punch them out in reverse order.

Normally we expect some computations between the reading and punching, and the simplest of these are called into play by arithmetic statements. The special characters

$$+ \ - \ /$$

are self-explanatory; they call for addition, subtraction, and division. Multiplication is denoted by *; that is, A times B is written

```
A*B.
```

The symbol AB would merely be a name for another variable, with no particular relation to A or B.

An arithmetic statement often introduces a new variable in terms of others that have already been introduced. Thus the following is a workable program:

```
READ 101, A, B, C, D
E = (A+B)/(C*D)
PUNCH 102, E
STOP
END
```

This calls for reading four floating-point numbers to be known as a, b, c, and d, computing

$$\frac{a+b}{cd},$$

and punching out the answer. Note that parentheses are used in FORTRAN arithmetic statements just as they are in algebra.

Now the following "program" will *not* compile:

```
READ 101, A, B
PUNCH 102, A+B
STOP
END
```

The intent is probably clear to the reader: "Read two numbers and punch out their sum." However, this is not clear to the compiler, and the following rules should be noted.

The name of a variable must consist of 1 to 5 alphameric characters, the first of which must be alphabetic.

The items to be read or punched in an I-O statement must be variables.

So the trouble with the sour "program" above is that A + B cannot be a variable because + is a special character, and it is illegal to embed computation instructions in an I-O statement.

One other operation can be described by a FORTRAN arithmetic statement. This is exponentiation; it is denoted by **. That is,

$$A ** B \qquad (2)$$

means A raised to the power B. This is the one operation in which mixed mode is allowed. That is,

$$A ** N \qquad (3)$$

is allowable even though it calls for mixing a floating-point number with a fixed-point one. So far as the computer is concerned, (2) and (3) are quite different forms, and it is well to remember the distinction that the computer makes. It computes (3) by multiplication and therefore preserves a negative sign for an odd power. It computes (2) by logarithms and gives the absolute value of A raised to the power B no matter what B may be.

Constants as well as variables may appear in arithmetic statements and here again we must be careful about mode. A floating-point constant must have a decimal point in it; a fixed-point constant must not. Thus, in FORTRAN, there is a difference between $2a$ and $2n$. The first is written

$$2. * A$$

and the second is

$$2 * N$$

Incongruous as it may look in English, we concluded the preceding paragraph with no punctuation at the end. It ended in a FORTRAN statement and FORTRAN does not have punctuation as such. The comma and period are special characters, in the same category as equals, plus, etc. They have their prescribed uses, but to put one at the end of a statement would cause the program to be rejected.

Given two numbers a and b, there are three commonly used "means" of a and b:

Arithmetic: $\dfrac{a+b}{2}$, Geometric: $\sqrt{ab}$, Harmonic: $\dfrac{2}{\dfrac{1}{a}+\dfrac{1}{b}}$.

The following program will read two floating-point numbers and compute and punch out their three means.

```
READ 101, A, B
ARITH = (A + B)/2.
GEOM = (A * B)**.5
HARM = 2./((1./A) + (1./B))
PUNCH 102, ARITH, GEOM, HARM
STOP
END
```

Note the careful use of decimal points in the floating-point constants. Note also the double parentheses in the expression for HARM. There are no brackets or braces in FORTRAN. While $2/[(1/a) + (1/b)]$ is easier to read as a whole, the expression in the program is quite precise. You can tell where you are with respect to parentheses by reading from left to right, counting the ('s and the)'s and keeping a net score. This is the way the computer does it.

The special character = is not really an equality symbol in the algebraic sense. For example, in the above program we could not write the instruction to compute the arithmetic mean in the form

$$(A + B)/2. = ARITH$$

because the following rules govern the formation of FORTRAN "equations."

The expression to the left of the special character = must be a single variable. That to the right must involve constants and variables that have previously been evaluated either by input or by previous computations.

The reason for this rule is simple enough. An arithmetic statement is a "compute and store" instruction. The right side tells the computer where to look for numbers and what to do with them. The left side tells it where to store the result.

EXERCISES

1. Which of the following are legitimate FORTRAN arithmetic statements? Check for mixed mode. Watch the rule for naming variables and the rule for forming "equations."

   a) MNSQ = (X**2 + Y**2)/2.
   b) XMNSQ = (X1**2 + X2**2)/2.
   c) DISCR = B**2 - 4*A*C
   d) F(X) = A*X**2 + B*X + C
   e) 3.*XMEAN = X1 + X2 + X3
   f) SUM = N1 + N2 + N3
   g) FOFX = (2.*X - 3.)**5
   h) N + 1 = J + K - L

2. Write a program that reads the coefficients a, b, c in the quadratic equation $ax^2 + bx + c = 0$ and punches out the solutions,

$$x_1 = -b + \sqrt{b^2 - 4ac}, \qquad x_2 = -b - \sqrt{b^2 - 4ac}.$$

Assume that the data will be such that the solutions are real.

3. A random variable x assumes the values x_1, x_2, x_3 with probabilities p_1, p_2, p_3, respectively. Write a program to find $E(x)$ and var (x).
4. Write a program that will read three fixed-point numbers and find all sums of pairs of them.
5. Write a program that will read three floating-point numbers and find all sums of squares of pairs of them.
6. Write a program that will read four floating-point numbers and punch out the product of the first two, the product of the first three, and the product of all four.

8-3 LIBRARY FUNCTIONS

We mentioned in Section 8-1 that after your program is compiled you put your machine-language program on the reader followed by what is called the subroutine deck. This is a deck that comes with the compiler. It consists of machine-language instructions for various operations that the machine will have to perform many times. For example, floating-point addition is far from being a basic machine operation; it requires quite a number of steps. So (for many machines) the floating add instructions are put in the subroutine deck. Then instead of repeating them every time they are needed in your program the compiler merely inserts an appropriate reference to the subroutine deck.

Instructions for computing values of a number of functions are also included in the subroutine deck, and these functions are known as the *library functions*. There is some variation from one compiler to another, but the following is a typical list of library functions and their FORTRAN call symbols.

    LOGF — logarithm (base e)
    EXPF — exponential (base e)
    SINF — sine (argument in radians)
    COSF — cosine (argument in radians)
    ATANF — arctangent (value in radians)
    SQRTF — square root
    ABSF — absolute value

These library function symbols are used in the following way. If we want to set $y = \sin x$ we put in the arithmetic statement

    Y = SINF (X)

Parentheses are used here as in functional notation in algebra. Note, however, that SINF (X) is *not* a variable name; it is a computation instruction. Thus
$$\text{SINF (X)} = A + B$$
is *not* allowed.

Composite functions are quite acceptable. For example,
$$Y = \text{LOGF (SINF (X))}$$
$$Z = \text{SQRTF (1. + COSF (X) ** 2)}$$
are legitimate arithmetic statements.

Note that even though they meet the specifications (1 to 5 alphameric characters with the first alphabetic), the library function names may *not* be used as variable names.

EXERCISES

1. Rewrite the program in Exercise 2, Section 8–2, using the SQRTF subroutine. [*Note:* This is usually faster and more accurate than taking **.5.]
2. Write a program that will compute $|\sin x|$ and $\sqrt{1 - \cos^2 x}$ and will then punch out the value of x, each of these two results, and the absolute value of their difference. [*Note:* Trigonometry says these results are equal, but the computer may not agree because of round-off error.]
3. Algebraically, $e^{\ln|x|} = |x|$. Write a program for a computer check on this modeled after the plan of Exercise 2.

8–4 CONTROL STATEMENTS

In the simple programs we have seen so far, the machine is expected to follow the instructions right down the line in the order in which they appear. To add versatility to programming it is useful to make it deviate from this straight path, and this is done through control statements.

When a FORTRAN program is punched onto cards, columns 1 and 6 are reserved for special purposes that we shall not discuss here. Columns 2–5 are for *statement numbers*, and the statement itself should begin in column 7. The statement numbers are put in so that we may instruct the computer, "Instead of going on to the next statement in the list, go instead to statement number so-and-so." Statement numbers do not have to come in order, and not all statements need be numbered. Indeed, it is a good plan not to use a statement number unless you are going to refer to it in a control statement. Numbered statements take more storage space to compile than do unnumbered ones.

The simplest control statement is the GO TO, illustration:

$$\text{GO TO 7}$$

This means just what it says, "Instead of continuing to the next statement in the list, go to statement number 7."

Another very useful control statement is based on the fact that the computer distinguishes very readily among negative, zero, and positive results. This leads to the IF statement. Sample:

$$\text{IF (ABSF (X - Y) - EPSLN) 7, 10, 15} \tag{1}$$

This is interpreted as follows.

$$\text{If } |x - y| - \epsilon \begin{cases} < 0, & \text{go to 7,} \\ = 0, & \text{go to 10,} \\ > 0, & \text{go to 15.} \end{cases}$$

One word of caution is in order. With floating-point variables an IF statement does not really give an effective three-way branch. Because of round-off errors, a genuine floating-point zero is seldom achieved. Thus the statement (1) would hardly ever send you to 10. The usual procedure is to make it a two-way branch:

$$\text{IF (ABSF (X - Y) - EPSLN) 7, 15, 15}$$

meaning

$$\text{If } |x - y| - \epsilon \begin{cases} < 0, & \text{go to 7,} \\ \geq 0, & \text{go to 15.} \end{cases}$$

With fixed-point variables, on the other hand, an IF statement gives a very effective three-way branch.

Clearly, with this sort of skipping around possible, you may come back to the same point several times in the course of a program. Sometimes you want to jump to different places on different returns to the same point in the program. This is achieved with the *computed* GO TO. Example:

$$\text{GO TO (5, 10, 7), N}$$

This means, "If at present $N = 1$, go to 5; if $N = 2$ on this trip, go to 10; if $N = 3$, go to 7."

As an illustration of some of these control statements, consider the following program to solve the quadratic equation $ax^2 + bx + c = 0$. Recall that the solution is

$$x = \frac{-b \pm \sqrt{b^2 - 4ac}}{2a}.$$

We have to determine whether the solutions are real or imaginary. If they are real, we want the two solutions punched out. If they are imaginary, the best we can do is have the machine punch out

$$\frac{-b}{2a} \quad \text{and} \quad \frac{\sqrt{4ac - b^2}}{2a},$$

and understand that the solution is the first of these $\pm i$ times the second.

222 COMPUTERS   8-4

In either case the punch-out is two numbers; so we also need a code number to indicate which interpretation we are to make of the result.

```
1   READ 101, A, B, C
    PUNCH 101, A, B, C
    DISCR = B**2 - 4. * A * C
    PART 1 = - B/(2.*A)
    PART 2 = SQRTF (ABSF (DISCR))
    IF (DISCR) 2, 3, 3
2   N = 2
    PUNCH 102, N, PART 1, PART 2
    GO TO 1
3   N = 1
    ANS1 = PART 1 + PART 2
    ANS2 = PART 1 - PART 2
    PUNCH 102, N, ANS1, ANS2
    GO TO 1
    END
```

Note that in this program we have not used the STOP statement. Here we have finished with an instruction to go to the READ statement. This is a standard way of terminating a program. The program above will continue to solve one quadratic equation after another as long as it finds more data cards with coefficients on them.

As another exercise in the use of control statements, consider the following problem. We take a number x and let y be the smaller of the two numbers $\sin x$ and $\cos x$. Then, we let z be the smaller of the two numbers $\sin 2y$ and $\cos 2y$. We want a record showing x, y, z, and indicating which trigonometric function was chosen at each stage. The following program will do this.

```
1   READ 101, X
    PUNCH 101, X
    L = 1
2   IF (SINF (X) - COSF (X)) 3, 3, 4
3   X = SINF (X)
    N = 1
    GO TO 5
4   X = COSF (X)
    N = 2
5   PUNCH 102, N, X
    GO TO (6, 1), L
6   L = 2
    X = 2. * X
    GO TO 2
    END
```

In addition to the computed GO TO, we have introduced here the often-used device of reusing a variable. Let us trace the progress of this computation. We read a number x, label it X and punch it out. Then we set $L = 1$ to control the computed GO TO and compare $\sin x$ and $\cos x$. We now have no more use for the number x; so (in statement 3 or 5, as the case may be) we store under the label X what we have called y in the statement of the problem. We then set N to indicate which function was chosen and punch out N and y. This brings us to the computed GO TO with $L = 1$; so we reset L for the next time around, store $2y$ under the label X and go to 2 to compare sines and cosines again. When we get to 5 this time we punch N and what is called z in the problem. The computed GO TO with $L = 2$ then sends us to the READ statement.

EXERCISES

1. The following is quite a good computer method for approximating a real root of a cubic equation. Let $f(x) = ax^3 + bx^2 + cx + d$ and take $x_1 < x_2$. If
$$f(x_1)f(x_2) > 0, \qquad (2)$$
there may be no root of $f(x) = 0$ between x_1 and x_2. If
$$f(x_1)f(x_2) < 0,$$
there must be one. If (2) holds for the initial choice of x_1 and x_2, replace them by $x_1 - 1$ and $x_2 + 1$ and try again. Once there is a root between x_1 and x_2, compute $(x_1 + x_2)/2$ and replace either x_1 or x_2 by this so that there is still a root in the interval. Write a program that will continue this until $x_2 - x_1 < 10^{-5}$, and then punch out the coefficients and the approximate root.

2. Write a program that will read three fixed-point numbers and punch them out in order of size.

3. Given numbers b and c, we want to solve the quadratic equation $x^2 + bx + c = 0$. If the roots are real, we call them p and q; if they are imaginary, we call them $p \pm iq$. We want to know p and q and know which interpretation to make of them. Then we want the same information on the solution of $x^2 + px + q = 0$. Write a program that will accomplish this.

4. Since $|\sin x| < |x|$ for $x \neq 0$, the succession of numbers x, $\sin x$, $\sin \sin x$, $\sin \sin \sin x$, ... is decreasing in absolute value. Write a program that will read a number x and compute iterated sines until either the result is less than 0.01 in absolute value or the sine operation has been repeated 100 times. Have it punch the initial x, the final result, and the number of iterations. [*Note:* The device for counting iterations is to introduce $N = 0$ before the process starts, then every time around pass the statement $N = N + 1$.]

8-5 DO LOOPS

We introduce here a programming device modeled after the algebraic device of the summation notation

$$\sum_{n=1}^{m} x_n.$$

This means, of course, "Add the numbers x_n as n runs through the integer values 1 through m, inclusive." More generally, we want to take numbers x_n and do something with them (probably something more complicated than simple addition) as n runs through the integer values $1 - m$.

The thing we would write in algebra as x_n is rendered into FORTRAN as X(N); for obvious reasons this is called a *subscripted variable*. Clearly, this is something new; so we should get the rules straight. A subscripted variable consists of a name followed by parentheses containing another name. The name inside the parentheses must be that of a fixed-point variable. That in front can be either a fixed- or floating-point variable name, depending on the mode desired for values of the subscripted variable. The fixed-point variable inside the parentheses is sometimes called the subscript, more often the *index*.

There is one other complication. Before a subscripted variable can be introduced there must be a DIMENSION statement for it. Example:

DIMENSION X(100), K(50)

The compiler interprets this as follows. "This program is going to contain subscripted variables named X and K. The index for X may run as high as 100 and that of K may run as high as 50; so reserve storage spaces for the 100 floating-point X's and 50 fixed-point K's that may have to be on call."

The statement that puts the subscripted variable to work is the DO statement. Example:

DO 10 N = 1, M

This means, "Set N = 1 and proceed through the program until statement 10 is reached. After executing 10, return here, set N = 2 and proceed to 10 again, etc. When 10 is reached with N = M, do not return here but proceed to the statement following 10."

Before looking at a sample program we should look at I-O statements for subscripted variables. The following statements instruct the computer to read X(1), X(2), ..., X(M):

DO 5 N = 1, M
5 READ 101, X(N)

On the other hand most (though not all) compilers provide for *list read* and *list punch* statements. The following example will accomplish the same thing as the pair of statements given above.

```
        READ 101, (X(N) N = 1, M)
```

For punching instructions the list statement and the do loop are not quite equivalent. We shall look at the distinction in Section 8–6.

Let us now look at a program to add floating-point numbers. We shall specify in the DIMENSION statement that there will not be more than 500 of them, but the actual number of summands in a specific problem will be specified as part of the data.

```
        DIMENSION X(500)
    1   READ 101, M
        READ 102, (X(N) N = 1, M)
        SUM = 0.
        DO 2 N = 1, M
    2   SUM = SUM + X(N)
        PUNCH 103, SUM
        GO TO 1
        END
```

An interesting and useful program can be based on Simpson's rule for approximating the value of an integral. For reasons that we shall not go into here, the following procedure gives a good approximation to

$$\int_a^b f(x)\, dx.$$

Divide the interval [a, b] into an *even* number n of equal subintervals by partition points

$$a = x_0, x_1, x_2, \ldots, x_{n-1}, x_n = b,$$

where

$$x_k = a + k(b - a)/n.$$

The approximation to the integral is given by

$$\frac{b-a}{3n} [f(x_0) + 4f(x_1) + 2f(x_2) + 4f(x_3) + 2f(x_4) + \cdots \\ + 2f(x_{n-2}) + 4f(x_{n-1}) + f(x_n)].$$

We shall need one new device here. This is a *change of mode* statement. The number n will be needed as fixed point to control the indexing, but it will also be needed as floating point to compute $(b - a)/(3n)$. We can arrange this as follows. We introduce a fixed-point variable N and read a value for it. Then we put in the statement

$$EN = N$$

We still have N when we want it, but we now also have the floating-point variable EN with the desired value.

Suppose we want approximations to

$$\int_a^b e^{-x^2/2}\, dx.$$

In the data we shall specify the limits of integration a and b and the number n of subintervals to be used. The approximation formula is more accurate for large n but the computer may not be, because of round-off error. Here is a program:

```
1    READ 101, A, B, N
     NN = N - 1
     EN = N
     H = (B - A)/EN
     SUM = 0
     L = 1
     X = B
2    Y = EXPF(-(X*X)/2.)
     GO TO (3, 3, 5), L
3    SUM = SUM + Y
     L = L + 1
     X = A
     GO TO (2, 2, 4), L
4    Z = - 1.
     DO 5 K = 1, NN
     X = X + H
     Z = - Z
     GO TO 2
5    SUM = SUM + (3. + Z) * Y
     ANS = SUM * H/3.
     PUNCH 102, A, B, N, ANS
     GO TO 1
     END
```

So far as this specific problem is concerned, the following shorter program will accomplish the same thing.

```
1     READ 101, A, B, N
      NN = N - 1
      EN = N
      H = (B - A)/EN
      SUM = EXPF(-(A * A)/2.) + EXPF(-(B * B)/2.)
      X = A
      Z = - 1.
      DO 2 K = 1, NN
      X = X + H
      Z = - Z
      Y = EXPF(-(X * X)/2.)
2     SUM = SUM + (3. + Z) * Y
      ANS = SUM * H/3.
      PUNCH 102, A, B, N, ANS
      GO TO 1
      END
```

In the longer version, all values of $e^{-x^2/2}$ are computed by going to statement 2. It requires some fancy control statements to get $e^{-a^2/2}$ and $e^{-b^2/2}$ via this route; so in the short version these are computed separately. Now each of these programs is good only for integrals of $e^{-x^2/2}$; if we want to change the function, we have to change one card in the long program and two in the short one. This distinction does not seem important because if we change anything we have to recompile. However, we present the longer program here because in Section 8-7 we shall show how to write a program in which the function can be changed without recompiling, provided all calls for function values go to the same spot in the program.

There are a few details in the Simpson's-rule program that merit comment. The variable NN is introduced because the upper limit of the do-loop index is to be $n - 1$ and N - 1 is not a variable. Limits on the index in a DO statement must be fixed-point constants or variables. Note also that we have a do loop with no subscripted variables. Most of the time the do-loop index is also a subscript, but this is not essential. So far as the DO statement is concerned, the index is merely a counting variable.

A final comment on the Simpson's-rule program is that on every trip around the loop in that program we go up to 5 and back down to 2. There are FORTRAN manuals (with misleading little diagrams in them) that say that once in a do loop you cannot transfer control to a statement outside the loop. What they mean to say is that controls must be such that proceeding from the DO statement you always get to the statement listed in the DO as the end of the loop. Physically this may carry you all over the program, but that is not important.

Consider next a simple little problem that introduces another technicality in the construction of do loops. We have two sets of numbers $x_1, x_2, \ldots, x_n$ and $y_1, y_2, \ldots, y_n$ and we want

$$\sum_{k=1}^{n} \min(x_k, y_k).$$

The working mechanism of this program will be as follows:

```
        SUM = 0.
        DO 3 K = 1, N
        IF (X(K) - Y(K)) 1, 1, 2
1       SUM = SUM + X(K)
        GO TO 3
2       SUM = SUM + Y(K)
3       CONTINUE
```

The real work in this loop is completed sometimes at statement 1, sometimes at 2. However, there must be one terminal statement for the loop. When, as here, we reach this terminal statement via a GO TO and there is nothing more to be done, CONTINUE is the appropriate statement.

A nice computer problem is that of finding the capital on which an annuity will be based. A man works for n years and in year k he pays x_k dollars into the company retirement fund. The money he has paid in draws interest at a rate r ($100r$ %) compounded annually. What is the accumulated capital after n years? Adding $100r$ % interest to a given amount of money merely multiplies that amount by $1 + r$; so compounding annually at the rate r for m years multiplies the original amount by $(1 + r)^m$. Therefore, algebraically, the answer to our problem is

$$\sum_{k=1}^{n} x_k (1 + r)^{n-k}.$$

(This assumes that both interest payments and contributions are credited at the end of the year; he receives $n - 1$ years' interest on his first contribution and none on the last.)

It is obvious how a program could be made to follow this formula, but the interesting thing about this as a computer problem is that the efficient way to program it is to start at the end of the employment period and back your way through the addition problem. The reason for this is that the big powers of $1 + r$ correspond to the chronologically first years. It is ridiculous to compute these separately. Even on a computer it is time-consuming to compute $(1 + r)^{40}$, throw it away and compute $(1 + r)^{39}$, etc. Instead we start from the back, save the interest factor each time and get the next one by a single multiplication. The program:

```
      DIMENSION X(50)
1     READ 101, N, R,
      READ 102, (X(K) K = 1, N)
      Z = 1. + R
      SUM = X(N)
      DO 2 K = 2, N
      SUM = SUM + X(N-K+1) * Z
2     Z = Z * (1.+ R)
      PUNCH 102, (X(K) K = 1, N)
      PUNCH 103, R, SUM
      GO TO 1
      END
```

Once we understand the ideas of subscripted variable and do loop, the ideas of *double subscript* and *nested set of do loops* are fairly easy to follow. A single example should suffice to introduce these notions, and one of the simplest is matrix multiplication. Recall that the matrix product

$$AB = C$$

is computed by the formula

$$c_{ij} = \sum_{k=1}^{n} a_{ik} b_{kj}.$$

The following program will multiply two square matrices.

```
      DIMENSION A(20,20), B(20,20), C(20,20)
1     READ 101, N
      READ 102, ((A(I,J)J=1,N)I=1,N),((B(I,J)J=1,N)I=1,N)
      DO 2 I = 1, N
      DO 2 J = 1, N
      C(I,J) = 0.
      DO 2 K = 1, N
2     C(I,J) = C(I,J) + A(I,K) * B(K,J)
      PUNCH 102, ((C(I,J) J=1,N) I=1,N)
      GO TO 1
      END
```

In the nested set of do loops above, the indices are set in the following order:

$$i = 1, j = 1, k = 1, 2, \ldots, n$$
$$j = 2, k = 1, 2, \ldots, n$$
$$\vdots$$
$$j = n, k = 1, 2, \ldots, n$$
$$i = 2, j = 1, k = 1, 2, \ldots, n, \quad \text{etc.}$$

This is frequently described by saying that the machine completes the inside loop first.

The statements to read the matrices A and B assume that the data will be arranged in the order

$$a_{11}, a_{12}, \ldots, a_{1n}, a_{21}, a_{22}, \ldots, a_{2n}, \ldots, a_{n1}, a_{n2}, \ldots, a_{nn};$$

that is, that the matrices will be listed by rows. In a sense, this program punches the answer out by rows also, though more will be said about this PUNCH statement in the next section.

The DIMENSION statement in the above program allows it to be used for matrices up to 20×20 in size. However, there are many computers on which this particular program would not compile because of inadequate storage space. Remember, the DIMENSION statement reserves storage space whether the problem is going to use it or not. So when we compile the above program we use up storage for $3 \times 20^2 = 1200$ floating-point numbers. Generally a floating-point number amounts to 10 digits (8 significant figures plus a 2-digit exponent to locate the decimal point). Thus our matrix program uses 12,000 digits of storage for the matrices alone. The program and subroutines must also be stored (approximately 10,000 digits) and at this stage many computer memories are exhausted. Computers are wonderful for working with matrices, but matrix storage can be a very vexing problem. For example, seldom can we afford the luxury of storing three complete matrices, as called for above. Various space-saving devices are used; see Exercise 10 below for samples.

EXERCISES

1. Write a program that reads $x_1, x_2, \ldots, x_n, y_1, y_2, \ldots, y_n$ and computes
$$\sum_{i=1}^{n} (x_i - y_i)^2.$$

2. Let x be a random variable, assuming values $x_1, x_2, \ldots, x_n$, with probabilities $p_1, p_2, \ldots, p_n$. Write a program to find $E(x)$ and var (x).

3. Write a program that will read a fixed-point number and determine whether it is odd or even. [*Hint:* Introduce an equivalent floating-point variable and compare half the floating-point number with half the fixed-point one.]

4. Write a program that will read n numbers and arrange them in increasing order. One possible procedure: Compare x_1 and x_2; relabel the smaller x_1 and the other x_2. Compare the new x_1 with x_3; relabel the smaller x_1 and the other x_3. When this process gets through x_n the resulting x_1 is the smallest of the given numbers. Repeat the process for the set $x_2, \ldots, x_n$, etc.

5. Write a program that will find the median of n numbers. [*Note:* For n odd, the median is the middle one in terms of size. For n even, the median is the average of the two middle ones.]

6. Write a program that reads $x_1, x_2, \ldots, x_n, y_1, y_2, \ldots, y_n$ and counts the number of values of k for which x_k and y_k have the same sign.

7. The trapezoidal rule for approximating
$$\int_a^b f(x)\, dx$$
is given by the formula
$$\frac{b-a}{2n}[f(x_0) + 2f(x_1) + 2f(x_2) + \cdots + 2f(x_{n-1}) + f(x_n)],$$
where
$$x_k = a + k(b-a)/n.$$

Write a program for this rule. Write it in such a way that there is only one statement calling for computation of values of the function f.

8. Given a function f, the function f^+ is defined by
$$f^+(x) = \begin{cases} f(x) & \text{if } f(x) \geq 0, \\ 0 & \text{if } f(x) < 0. \end{cases}$$
Write a trapezoidal-rule program for
$$\int_a^b f^+(x)\, dx.$$

9. An employees' committee wants to present data to a conference on revision of the pension plan. Their problem is described below. Write the program they need. Up until 5 years ago, the total contribution to the pension plan was 7% of salary. At that time it was increased to 10%. There are various proposals for further increases but they all involve an increase now and/or one three years hence. In the past the pension funds have been invested to draw 4.2% interest, compounded annually. There are various proposals to change the investment portfolio to increase the interest rate. All employees retire at age 65. To predict future salaries, the committee will assume an annual raise of $P\%$, but P should be adjustable from one run to another because there is some argument about what is realistic. The program should compute accumulated capital at retirement age given the following data: employee's present age, a list of past salaries, a plan for increasing pension contributions, a proposed future interest rate, a guess as to the future annual raise percentage.

10. Write matrix multiplication programs with the following space-saving features. Notation: Compute $AB = C$.
    a) Instead of storing the whole matrix C, store only one row of it. When row i of C has been computed, row i of A is no longer needed; store it there.
    b) Read all of B. Read only one row of A at a time; compute a row of C and punch it out; then read another row of A.

11. Suppose there is space available for 2500 floating-point numbers in storing the subscripted variables. How large matrices can be multiplied (a) by the

program in the text? (b) by the program of Exercise 10(a)? (c) by the program of Exercise 10(b)?

12. Write a program for solving linear-programming problems by the simplex method (Section 6–5).

   a) Write a "stripped-down" program that solves minimum problems only. That is, you have to carry the last row of the array but you do not have to label the entries.
   b) Add a routine for labeling the last-row entries and thereby solving the maximum problem.
   c) Put in instructions that will stop the machine and punch out an appropriate message if the problem is not solved after n passes, where n is in the data.
   d) Put in an error check in which the machine verifies relations (2)–(5) of Section 6–5 at the end of the run.
   e) Arrange it so that a code number in the data can call for the error check of part (d), either at the end of the run only or after each pass.

8–6 FORMAT

Each I-O statement that we have written has contained a number that so far has played no role in the program at all. This number is a statement number which refers to a so-called FORMAT statement. For example, if the program contains the statement

> PUNCH 101, A, B, N

there must (for many compilers) be a statement 101 which might read as follows:

> 101 FORMAT (2F12.5,I5)   (1)

 Physically the FORMAT statement can appear anywhere in the program. Some people put it right after the I-O statement; others collect all the FORMAT statements just before the END statement. It does not matter; the FORMAT statement is scanned when the I-O statement is executed, but it does not enter into the chain of executable statements at all.

 The function of the FORMAT statement is very simply described. With a PUNCH statement it tells the computer how to arrange the answers on the card. With a READ it tells it how to expect to find the data arranged.

 It remains to explain the hieroglyphics inside the parentheses in a FORMAT statement. There are three types of format:

> I — integer,
> F — floating point,
> E — exponential.

The notation I5 in the sample statement (1) above means, "Allot 5 columns for punching a fixed-point number." The notation F12.5 means, "Allot 12 columns for punching a floating-point number and give it to 5 decimal places." Thus the entire expression (2F12.5,I5) means, "You are going to punch two floating-point numbers and one fixed-point number. Put the first number in columns 1–12 and give 5 digits after the decimal point; put the second in columns 13–24 and give 5 decimal places; put the integer in columns 25–29." The machine will jam these entries up against the right-hand end of the allowable space; so the FORMAT statement (1) might produce the following punch-out (we use * here to indicate a blank space):

$$******.00123**-123.45678***12$$

The F-format is the most natural for floating-point numbers, but they may get "out of bounds." For example, -123456.78 cannot be printed in format F12.5 because it would have to read

$$-123456.78000 \qquad (2)$$

and this takes 13 spaces. The exponential format is less natural but more versatile. The number (2) could be written

$$-1.2345678E+05 \qquad (3)$$

meaning

$$-1.2345678 \times 10^5.$$

The statement

FORMAT (E16.7)

would produce the form (3) with two blank spaces in front.

With input format the primary concern is with fixed-point numbers. They must be punched on the data cards in the last columns allowed by the FORMAT statement because blank spaces at the end will be read as zeros (making your numbers grow tremendously). Input in F-format can be put in any columns allowed by the FORMAT statement because the decimal point on the data card determines the meaning of the entry.

With output format the chief concern is with F-format. It is the natural thing to use, provided you know approximately how big your answers are going to be. As noted above, the number (2) cannot be printed in F12.5. When such a case occurs on output, the machine goes on to the next card and punches the result in the form (3). Thus you get the information, but a carefully designed output design is probably destroyed. If numbers are unexpectedly small, you may lose them completely in F-Format. For example, in F12.5 the number .00000123 would merely be 0.00000.

One of the best illustrations of the use of FORMAT statements is the problem of punching out a matrix so it looks something like a matrix.

Suppose we could get only three numbers to a row. We would like to have a 3 × 3 matrix printed in the usual form:

———————   ———————   ———————

———————   ———————   ———————

———————   ———————   ———————

and the best compromise for a 4 × 4 would be something like this:

———————   ———————   ———————

———————

———————   ———————   ———————

———————

———————   ———————   ———————

———————

———————   ———————   ———————

———————

Actually, it is usually practical to get six numbers to a line. There are 80 columns on a card; so
$$\text{FORMAT (6F13.7)}$$
is legal. If the numbers are between 1 and 10, this will give us the 8 significant figures that most machines carry, allow one space for decimal point, one for sign, and leave three spaces between numbers.

The following sequence of statements will give matrix punch-out in the form suggested above.

```
       DO 5 I = 1, N
   5   PUNCH 102, (A(I,J) J = 1, N)
 102   FORMAT (6F13.7)
```

Let us analyze the steps in the execution of this. We set $I = 1$ and go to 5. There we proceed to punch $A(I, J)$ as J runs from 1 to N. Following 102, we do this six entries to the card, using as many cards as are needed to finish the list-punch command. If the last card is not used up when $J = N$, it is dropped out anyway. We then return to the DO, set $I = 2$ and repeat.

By contrast, a double list-punch,

```
      PUNCH 102, ((A(I,J)  J = 1,N) I = 1,N)
  102 FORMAT (6F13.7)
```

will not start a new card at the end of a row in the matrix. It will just punch six to the card until both I and J have reached the value N.

At the other extreme, a double do-loop,

```
      DO 5 I = 1, N
      DO 5 J = 1, N
    5 PUNCH 102, A(I,J)
  102 FORMAT (6F13.7)
```

will give only one number to the card, thereby listing the matrix in a single column. Even though the FORMAT statement provides for six numbers on a card, the PUNCH statement is fully executed by punching one number; so the card is dropped out.

Thus the effective way to punch out a matrix is to use a combination of do-loop and list-punch command. Without list-punch, the same effect can still be achieved, but it requires some tricky programming. See Exercise 6 below.

One other useful device in FORMAT statements is the X entry, meaning "skip." The statement

```
      FORMAT (F12.5, 10X, I4)
```

means, "floating-point number to 5 decimal places in columns 1–12, skip columns 13–22, fixed-point number in columns 23–26."

EXERCISES

1. Suppose $A = 2.53$, $B = 0.012$, $N = 57$, and the output commands are

```
      PUNCH 102, A, B, N
  102 FORMAT (2F12.5, I5)
```

   Reproduce the exact punch-out to be expected.

2. Suppose the machine has computed a "triangular" array of numbers a_{ij} ($i = 1, 2, \ldots, n; j = 1, 2, \ldots, i$). Write an output sequence and explain what the output will look like when it is printed.

3. In Section 8–5 there is written out a program for computing retirement annuity capital. (a) It calls for input FORMAT statements 101 and 102.

Write these. (b) Suppose $n = 15$, $r = .042$ and the contributions x_k start at $400 and increase by $20 a year. Write data to fit your FORMAT statements in part (a), indicating exactly how this is to be spaced on the data cards.

4. Add appropriate FORMAT statements to each program called for in the exercises in Section 8-5 and describe in each case what the output will look like.

5. At a certain university, registration records are kept on cards punched as follows:

Columns	Information
1–8	Student ID number
9–30	Student name
31	College
32	Sex
33	Marital status
34	Veteran status
35–36	Department code number
37–39	Course number
40	Lecture section
41–42	Recitation section
43–44	Lab section
45–47	Grade

The registrar wants to run a program to schedule final examinations by machine. In this program he needs as data student ID number, department code number, and course number. Rather than have these data punched by hand, he wants to read them from the master file card described above. Write a READ statement and a FORMAT statement that will accomplish this. [*Hint:* Use the "skip" device.]

6. Suppose your compiler will not accept the list-punch statement. Use the following suggestions to write an output sequence that will list a matrix by rows, six numbers to a line, starting a new line at the end of each matrix row. Determine how many entries in row i are yet to be punched. If there is only one, branch to an instruction to punch $a_{i,n}$. If there are two, punch $a_{i,n-1}, a_{i,n}$. Continue in this way, and if there are six or more, punch the next six entries.

8-7 FUNCTIONS

In this section we present a programming idea that can be useful in conjunction with programs (such as Simpson's rule—Section 8-5) in which there are repeated calls for values of some function. These ideas are of some mathematical interest outside the realm of computer programming because of the light they throw on the structure of elementary functions.

Our problem, so far as it concerns computers, is this. We want a spot in our program where we can feed in x and get out $f(x)$, and we want the program written in such a way that we can change the function f from one run to another without recompiling. This means that f must be specified in the data. Now data for a FORTRAN program must consist of numbers only; so the present project is in two parts. (1) We shall devise a numerical code for describing functions. (2) We shall present a program that will take the numerical code for f and convert it into instructions for accepting x and computing $f(x)$.

Functions in common use are constructed from a relatively small number of "building blocks" put together by means of certain basic operations. The basic components that we shall consider here are the FORTRAN library functions, the identity function, and the constant functions. The operations for putting these together are addition, subtraction, multiplication, division, and composition. To build up a complicated function, we put two things together and store the result for future reference; then we put two more things together and store, etc. The "things" that we put together may be basic components or previously constructed and stored combinations. Thus our numerical code will consist primarily of fixed-point numbers in blocks of four. In each block of four the first entry is a code for a combining operation; the next two are codes for the things to be combined; the last is a storage code.

The specific code we want to discuss is constructed as follows:

Operations

1. addition
2. subtraction
3. multiplication
4. division
5. composition

Library functions

11. logarithm
12. exponential
13. sine
14. cosine
15. arctangent
16. square root
17. absolute value

Special functions

21. identity function
30. constant function

Storage

101–115

There is one other factor to consider. If we put in a 30, meaning "constant," the computer will naturally wonder, "what constant?" So in addition to a string of $4n$ fixed-point numbers, we also need a list of floating-point numbers, one for each 30 entry, specifying what the constants are.

One example should explain the working of this code. Suppose we want instructions to compute
$$e^{-x^2} \sin 2x$$
from x. Coded instructions might look like this.

```
3 21 21 101    3 30 101 101    5 12 101 101
3 30 21 102    5 13 102 102    3 101 102 101
-1.    2.
```

Perhaps the following analysis is helpful

Block no.	Computes	Stores as
1	x^2	101
2	$-x^2$	101
3	e^{-x^2}	101
4	$2x$	102
5	$\sin 2x$	102
6	$e^{-x^2} \sin 2x$	101

Note the reuse of storage space when previously stored results are no longer required. We suggested above that the program will permit 15 different storage codes. Actually, fantastically complicated functions can be coded with only 4 or 5.

This is the code to be considered. Now how do we write the program? Note first of all that what we want is something to insert in another program. For example, in the Simpson's-rule program (first version) of Section 8–5 we find essentially the following sequence:

```
      L =
      X =
      GO TO 2
    2 Y = EXPF(-(X*X)/2.)
      GO TO ( , , ), L
```

That is, we set L and X and go to 2; this computes Y; then we go to an appropriate place determined by L. What we want to do here is replace the single statement 2 by a rather elaborate subprogram that will accept X and feed out Y where the function giving Y from X is determined by coded data.

Some input statements must be added to our program. Specifically we must read the coded description of our function and provide for additional subscripted variables. The new subscripted variables will be:

    I — the integers in the function code,
    C — the floating-point constants in the function,
  STOR — the stored intermediate function values.

Thus we add to the input section of the program the following statements.

```
      DIMENSION I(100), C(20), STOR(15)
      READ 201, NI, NC
  201 FORMAT (2I4)
      READ 202, (I(J) J=1, NI)
  202 FORMAT (20I4)
      READ 203, (C(J) J =1, NC)
  203 FORMAT (6F12.5)
```

The idea of the subprogram is that the numbers I(J) will be used to control branching so that, as a number x makes its way through the maze, it is converted into $f(x)$. There is one device in connection with DO statements that we have not used before. We shall write

```
      DO  599  J = 1, NI, 4
```

The additional entry here means, "Increment by fours; that is, set $J = 1$, 5, 9, 13, ...". Using this device we shall let J index the first integer in a block of four. For each setting of J we then proceed as follows.

1. Look at the third integer in the block and make the computation that it calls for. We go to I(J+2) first because if the operation is composition we must make this computation first and if the operation is anything else it does not matter.
2. If the operation is composition, we know I(J+1) must call for a library function. We find out which one and make the required computation. We then store the result under two labels:
   a) We store it as Y just in case the do-loop on J is completed and we are ready to feed back into the main program.
   b) We also store it as STOR(M), where M is determined by I(J+3), so it can be called in a subsequent round of the do-loop.
3. If the operation is not composition there are three more steps.
   a) We repeat the entire branching process of part 1 to find what I(J+1) is; then we make the required computation.
   b) We find what the operation is and combine the results of 1 and 3(a) as called for.
   c) We store this in two places, as in part 2.

240 COMPUTERS

The subprogram follows. The idea is that if you want a number operated on by the function coded in the data you store that number as X, set a control L to determine where the result is to be delivered, then go to 500 and the result will come out labeled Y.

```
500 KON = 1
    DO  599  J = 1, NI, 4
    K = J + 2
    R = X
    KK = 1
501 IF (I(K) - 30) 502, 530, 540
502 IF (I(K) - 20) 503, 503, 521
503 M = I(K) - 10
    GO TO (511, 512, 513, 514, 515, 516, 517), M
511 S = LOGF(R)
    GO TO 550
512 S = EXPF(R)
    GO TO 550
513 S = SINF(R)
    GO TO 550
514 S = COSF(R)
    GO TO 550
515 S = ATANF(R)
    GO TO 550
516 S = SQRTF(R)
    GO TO 550
517 S = ABSF(R)
    GO TO 550
521 S = R
    GO TO 550
530 S = C(KON)
    KON = KON + 1
    GO TO 550
540 M = I(K) - 100
    S = STOR(M)
550 GO TO (551, 554, 570), KK
551 K = J + 1
    IF (I(J) - 5) 552, 553, 552
552 KK = 2
    T = S
    GO TO 501
553 KK = 3
    R = S
    GO TO 503
```

```
554 M = I(J)
    GO TO (561, 562, 563, 564), M
561 Y = S + T
    GO TO 580
562 Y = S - T
    GO TO 580
563 Y = S * T
    GO TO 580
564 Y = S/T
    GO TO 580
570 Y = S
580 M = I(J + 3) - 100
599 STOR(M) = Y
    GO TO (    ), L
```

This device will work on any FORTRAN compiler. If the compiler provides for formal function subprograms, a considerable simplification of the main program can be effected. The interested reader may consult the appropriate FORTRAN specifications manual to see how this works.

It is instructive to consider doing this same thing for functions of two or more arguments. That is, suppose we want to feed in x and y and get out $f(x, y)$, where f is specified by code in the data. The code needs a little modification but not much. However, the modification required is of interest because of the light it throws on the structure of functions. If we are mapping number pairs into numbers, there is no such thing as an identity function. However, there are what might be called *selector functions*. We define functions S_1 and S_2 on number pairs as follows:

$$S_1(x, y) = x, \qquad S_2(x, y) = y.$$

That is, S_1 is the function that selects the first number from the pair on which it operates; S_2 selects the second number.

So, in coding these functions, we replace the 21 code for identity function by 21, 22, etc., for S_1, S_2, etc. We might as well go all the way to 29 in writing the program. This will take functions of nine arguments, and a function of two arguments is one of these that uses only 21 and 22.

By way of example, look at the code for the function that takes (x, y) and yields

$$\sqrt{x^2 + y^2}.$$

```
3 21 21 101    3 22 22 102    1 101 102 101
5 16 101 101
0.
```

No constants appear in this code, but we list one (which will never be used) so that the READ instruction will not hang up.

When it comes to writing the program, considerable simplification is achieved if we note that (as in the single-argument case) when $I(J) = 5$ (composition), $I(J + 1)$ must call for a library function. However, in the case of more than one argument, this is the only role that a library function can play.

There is another observation that does not contribute to program simplification but is of some interest. This is that (unless the function is constant) there must be selector functions in it somewhere. The selectors are the only functions in our repertoire that actually operate on number pairs.

These comments on what can occur where in the code are really comments on the structure of functions that are defined by algebraic formulas. Obviously our familiar formulas may be used to describe a multitude of functions, but, as noted above, there are limitations on the way these can be structured.

EXERCISES

1. From the following coded description of a function f find the formula for $f(x)$ in terms of x.

```
3   21   21   101       3   30   101   101       5   12   101   101
3   30   30   102       5   16   102   102       4   101  102   101
-.5      2.              3.1415926
```

2. For each of the following, describe f in the code discussed in this section.

   a) $f(x) = \sqrt{\dfrac{1 - x^2}{e^x - 3}}$

   b) $f(x) = \arcsin x$ [*Hint*: $\arcsin x = \arctan (x/\sqrt{1 - x^2})$.]
   c) $f(x) = \cos 2x \ln \sin 3x$
   d) $f(x, y) = e^{x-y} \sin (x + y)$
   e) $f(x, y) = e^{-(x^2+y^2)/2}$

3. In practice it is useful to add to our function code an operation 6 calling for integer exponentiation so that, for example,

```
             6   21   30   101
             7.
```

   would call for the computation of x^7.

   a) Write a call for x^7 in the code without this device.
   b) Modify the program in the text so as to incorporate this device in the code.

4. Write a subprogram that will take in x and y and feed out $z = f(x, y)$ from a coded description of f.

5. Write a program that will tabulate function values. Specifically, have it read a, b, k and a coded description of f. Have the output consist of two columns giving values of x and $f(x)$ as x runs through the values a, $a + k$, $a + 2k$, ..., b.

6. Write a program similar to that in Exercise 5 for tabulating values of x, y, and $f(x, y)$. Explain how the output of your program is to be read.

Answers to Selected Exercises

CHAPTER 1

Section 1-1

1. a) {1, 2, 3, 4, 5, 7, 9}   c) {7, 9}   e) {2, 4, 6, 8, 10}   g) {6, 8, 10}
4. a) A c) A e) $\emptyset$ g) $\emptyset$

Section 1-2

2. 210   4. $\binom{n}{r}$

Section 1-3

1. a) 50   d) $\frac{61}{144}$ g) 804   j) $\frac{36378}{40885}$

2. a) $\sum_{i=1}^{6}(2i-1)$ c) $\sum_{i=1}^{7}(2i-1)^2$

   e) $\sum_{i=0}^{n}(2i+2)$ g) $\sum_{i=1}^{n}\sqrt{1+i^2}$

   i) $\sum_{i=1}^{n}\left[\sqrt{1-c_i}\,(c_i - c_{i-1})\right]$

6. a) {1, 2, 3, 4, 5, 6, 7, 8, 9, 10, 11, 12, 13, 14, 15, 16, 17, 18, 19, 20}
   c) {2, 3, 4, 5, 6, 7, 8, 9, 10, 11, 12, 13, 14, 15, 16, 17, 18, 19, 20}
   e) {14, 15, 16, 17, 18, 19, 20, 21, 22, 23, 24, 29, 30, 31, 32, 33, 34, 35, 36, 37, 38, 39, 44, 45, 46, 47, 48, 49, 50, 51, 52, 53, 54, 59, 60, 61, 62, 63, 64, 65, 66, 67, 68, 69}
   g) {12, 13, 14, 15, 16}   i) $\emptyset$

Section 1-4

1.

a)	$f+g$	d)	f/g	f)	4	h)	f/f	j)	f^0
	2 0		2 -1				2 1		2 1
	0 4		4 0				0 1		0 1
	4 -3		1 $-\frac{3}{2}$				-3 1		-3 1
	1 -1						1 1		4 1
									1 1

2. a) Entire real number system   c) $a \leq -1$ and $a \geq 1$
   e) $-\sqrt{3} \leq a \leq \sqrt{3}$ g) $a \geq 1$
   i) Entire real number system except -1

3. a) $-2, 10, -\frac{5}{4}, \frac{22}{9}$ c) $11, -24, \frac{23}{8}, 3$
   e) $1-a^9$ g) $4-1=3, 9, 3, 1$

245

246 ANSWERS TO SELECTED EXERCISES

4. a) Square a number and subtract from the result three times the number.
   c) Cube a number and add 3 to the result.
   e) Cube a number and subtract the result from 1.
   g) Function that is constantly 3.
5. a) $f(a) = a^2 + 1$; all real numbers
   c) $f(a) = \dfrac{a^2 + 1}{a^3 - 1}$; all real numbers except $+1$
   e) $f(a) = (a + 1)^{1/2}$; all reals 'a' such that $a \geq -1$
   g) $f(a) = a + \dfrac{1}{a}$; all reals except 0
   i) $f(a) = \dfrac{1}{\sqrt{a+1}}$; all reals which are ≥ 0
7. a) $3I^3 + 11I^2 + 5I + I^0$

Section 1–5

1. a)
$f \circ g$	
4	2
1	−1
0	4
2	−3
−1	−1

   c)
$f \circ g \circ f$	
0	2
−3	−3
4	4
2	−1

   e)
$f \circ f$	
0	0
−3	−1
4	4
1	2

   g) 4   i) 4

2. a) $1 + 3a^2$, $3(1 + a)^2$
   c) $\sqrt{1 + \sqrt{1 - a}}$, $\sqrt{1 - \sqrt{1 + a}}$
   e) $1 + \dfrac{1}{2a\sqrt{a}}$, $\sqrt{1 + 2a^3}$
   g) $1 + (1 + a)$, a
3. a) $(I^2 - I^0)^{1/2}$
   c) $[I^0 + (I^2 + I^0)^{1/2}]^2$
   e) $(I^2 - 2I)^5$
   g) $[I^0 - (I^0 - I)^{1/2}]^{1/2}$
4. a) $I^5 \circ (I + I^2)$ c) $I^{1/2} \circ (I - I^3)$
   e) $I^2 \circ \{I^0 + [I^2 \circ (I^0 + I)]\}$
   g) $I^3 \circ \left(I^0 + \dfrac{I^0}{I^0 - I^2} \right)$
5. a) $(I^2 + I^0)^2 + I^0$
   c) $\dfrac{\left(\dfrac{I^2 + I^0}{I^3 - I^0}\right)^2 + I^0}{\left(\dfrac{I^2 + I^0}{I^3 - I^0}\right)^3 - I^0}$
   e) $[\{[(I + I^0)^{1/2} + I^0]^2 + I^0\}^{1/2} + I^0]^2$
   g) $\left[I + \dfrac{I^0}{I} \right] + \dfrac{I^0}{I + \dfrac{I_0}{I}}$
   i) $\dfrac{I^0}{I^0 + \left(\dfrac{I^0}{I^0 + I^{1/2}}\right)^{1/2}}$

Section 1–6

4. a) Variable   c) Meaningless   e) Number
   g) Meaningless   i) Meaningless   k) Meaningless
   m) Function   o) Number   q) Variable
   s) Meaningless   u) Meaningless   w) Number
   y) Meaningless

5. a) $I^2 \circ (I^0 + I^{1/2}) \circ x$ c) $[3I^0 + I^4 \circ (2I^0 - I)] \circ x$
   e) $I^3 \circ \{2I^0 + [I^0 - I^{1/2} \circ (I + 4I^0)]\} \circ x$
   g) $I^2 \circ [2I^0 - I^{1/2} \circ (I^0 - I^3)] \circ x$
   i) $I^{1/2} \circ [I - I^{1/2} \circ (I^0 - I)] \circ x$

6. a) $\sqrt{1+x}$ c) $[2(1-x) - (1-x)^2]^2$
   e) $(x - x^2) - (x - x^2)^2$ g) $(1-x)^{3/2}$
   i) $[(3x^2 - 2x)^3 - (3x^2 - 2x)^2]^3$

7. a) $x + y$ c) $x(p)y(p)$ e) $a^3 + a^2$
   g) $I^2 \circ x + I^2 \circ y$ i) $I^0 + I^{1/2}$

9. a)   c)

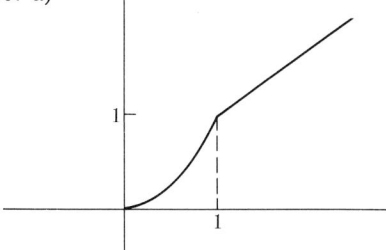

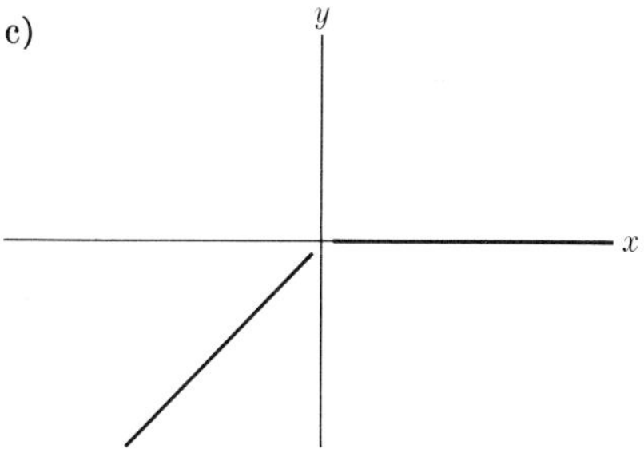

   e)

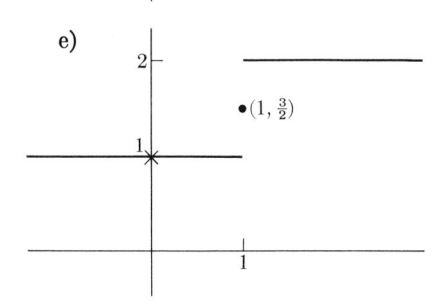

Section 1–7

1. a) $\frac{1}{3}$ c) No slope   e) $-\frac{1}{2}$
   g) $-\frac{1}{3}$ i) 1

2. a) $m, 0, h$ c) $m, 0, h$ f) $0, h, m$
   h) $m, h, 0$ k) $m, 0, h$ m) $h, m, 0$

3. a) $2x - y - 1 = 0$ c) $x + 5y = 0$ e) $y + 4 = 0$
   g) $x + 5y + 28 = 0$ i) $x - 3 = 0$

4. b) $m = -\frac{5}{4}, b = -\frac{7}{4}$ d) $m = 0, b = \frac{4}{3}$ f) $m = -\frac{1}{5}, b = 2$
   h) $m = \frac{3}{2}, b = \frac{9}{2}$ j) $m = \frac{5}{7}, b = 0$

248 ANSWERS TO SELECTED EXERCISES

CHAPTER 2

Section 2–1

1. a)

Year	C. on weekend	Even year
1954, 1960, 1966	T	T
1955, 1965	T	F
1952, 1956, 1958, 1962, 1964	F	T
Other years	F	F

c)

Year	Leap year	Div. by 3
1956	T	T
1952, 1960, 1964	T	F
1953, 1959, 1962, 1965	F	T
Other years	F	F

e)

Year	C. on lecture day	Even year	Leap year
1956, 1962	T	T	T
1952, 1958	T	T	F
1951	T	F	F
1954, 1960, 1964, 1966	F	T	F
1953, 1959, 1965	F	F	T
Other years	F	F	F

g)

Year	C. on lab day	Even year	1950's
1952, 1956, 1958	T	T	T
1962	T	T	F
1951	T	F	T
1954	F	T	T
1960, 1964, 1966	F	T	F
1953, 1955, 1957, 1959	F	F	T
Other years	F	F	F

2.

a)

	Total is 6
(1, 5), (2, 4), (3, 3), (4, 2), (5, 1)	T
Others	F

c)

Outcome	Total is 4	First die is 4
(1, 3), (2, 2), (3, 1)	T	F
(4, 1), (4, 2), (4, 3), (4, 4), (4, 5), (4, 6)	F	T
Others	F	F

e)

Outcome	1st is odd	Both dice same	Total 6
(3, 3)	T	T	T
(1, 1), (5, 5)	T	T	F
(1, 2), (1, 3), (1, 4), (1, 5), (1, 6), (5, 1) (3, 1), (3, 2), (3, 4), (3, 5), (3, 6) (5, 2), (5, 3), (5, 4), (5, 6)	T	F	F
(2, 2), (4, 4)	F	T	F
(2, 4), (4, 2)	F	F	T
Others	F	F	F

Section 2-2

2. c) Either it is not a year or the date is divisible by 3.
   e) Christmas is not on a lab day and either it is an even numbered year or the date is divisible by 3.
   g) Christmas is on a lab day and it is not true that either it is an even numbered year or it is in the 1950's.

3. a) $p \wedge q$ c) $\sim p \wedge \sim q$ e) $p \wedge q$ g) $\sim(p \wedge q)$

Section 2-3

1. a) TTFT   c) TFFF   e) TTFT
   g) FTTT   i) TTFTFTFT   k) FTFTFFFT

Section 2-4

1. a) FTTT   c) TFFT   e) TTFT
   g) TFTTTTTT   i) TFTTTTTT

Section 2-5

3. (a), (b), (d), (e), (h)   5. (b), (e), (f)
8. a) $q \vee \sim p$ b) $\sim q \vee p$

Section 2-8

1. (a), (b), (e), (h) are valid.
   (c), (d), (f), (g), are invalid.

2. a) $\sim q \to \sim p$
   $r \to \sim q$
   $\sim s \to \sim r$
   $\sim s$
   $\therefore p$ (Invalid)

   b) $p \to q$
   $r \to \sim q$
   $\therefore \sim p \vee \sim r$ (Valid)

   c) $q \to p$
   $q \to r$
   $\sim r$
   $\therefore \sim p$ (Invalid)

   d) $p \to q$
   $q \to r$
   $r \to s$
   $\therefore p \to s$ (Valid)

CHAPTER 3

Section 3-2

1. a) $\int_0^2 (2I - 3I^2)$ c) $\int_3^5 I^{1/2}$ e) $\int_0^{10} I^{1/2}$
   g) $\int_0^2 (5I^0 + 2I)^3$ i) $\int_1^2 I^3$

2. a) $\frac{1}{3}$ c) $\frac{5}{2}$ e) $\frac{b^4 - a^4}{4}$
   g) $\frac{16}{3}$ i) $\frac{b^{k+1} - 1}{k+1}$

3. a) Positive   c) Negative   e) Positive
   g) Positive   i) Positive

ANSWERS TO SELECTED EXERCISES

Section 3-3

1. a) $15I^4 - 6I^2$
   c) $15I^{14} - 15I^0$
   e) $I^0 - \frac{1}{4}I^{-3/4}$
   g) $\frac{3}{4}I^{-1/4} + \frac{4}{3}I^{1/3}$
   i) $2I + \frac{1}{2}I^{-1/2}$
   k) $24I^2 + \frac{2}{3}I^{-2/3}$
   m) $\frac{1}{2}I^{-1/2} + \frac{1}{2}I^{-3/2}$
   o) $-\frac{8}{3}I^{-4/3} - \frac{1}{6}I^{-4/3}$
   q) $I^0 + I^{-2}$
   s) $-3I^{-4} + 4I^{-5}$
   u) $-2I^{-3} + 3I^{-4} - 15I^{-6}$
   w) $\frac{\sqrt{3}}{2}I^{-1/2} - \frac{1}{\sqrt{3}}I^{-2}$
   y) $\frac{1}{2}I^{-1/2} - \frac{3}{2}I^{-3/2} + \frac{15}{2}I^{-5/2}$

2. a) 1
   c) $7a^6$
   e) $\frac{1}{3}a^{-2/3}$
   g) $-2a^{-3}$
   i) $-\frac{1}{2}a^{-3/2}$

Section 3-4

1. a) $-\frac{4}{3}$
   c) 48
   e) $-\frac{1}{12}$
   g) $\frac{147}{20}$
   i) $\frac{63}{4}$
   k) $4 + 3\sqrt{2}$
   m) $\frac{23}{3}$

2. a) $\frac{49}{12}$
   c) 2

Section 3-6

1. a) $3x^2 - 6x$
   c) $25t^{24} - 25$
   e) $2y + \frac{1}{2}y^{-1/2}$
   g) $\frac{9}{4}u^{-1/4} + \frac{10}{3}u^{-1/3}$
   i) $4x + \frac{3}{2}x^{-1/2}$
   k) $6y + \frac{\sqrt{3}}{2}y^{-1/2}$
   m) $\frac{1}{3}v^{-2/3} - \frac{1}{3}v^{-4/3}$
   o) $-2x^{-3/2} + \frac{1}{4}x^{-3/2}$
   q) $2 - 2z^{-2}$
   s) $-2t^{-3} - 3t^{-4}$
   u) $-2y^{-2} + 6y^{-3} - 15y^{-4}$
   w) $(2u)^{-1/2} - (2u)^{-3/2}$
   y) $-x^{-3/2} - 2x^{-2}$

Section 3-7

1. a) $I^{1/2} \circ (I^2 - I^0)$
   c) $I^2 \circ [I^0 + I^{1/2} \circ (I^2 + I^0)]$
   e) $3I^5 \circ (I^2 - 2I)$
   g) $I^{1/2} \circ [I^0 - I^{1/2} \circ (I^0 - I)]$

2. a) $\dfrac{x}{\sqrt{1+x^2}}$
   c) $x(1 - x^2)^{-3/2}$
   e) $12x(x^3 - 3x^2 + 5)^3(x - 2)$
   g) $(3x - 1)(3x^2 - 2x + 1)^{-1/2}$
   i) $\frac{1}{3}x^{-2/3}(1 - x^{1/3})^{-2}$
   k) $\frac{1}{2}[x - (1 - x)^3]^{-1/2}[1 + 3(1 - x)^2]$
   m) $\frac{1}{2}[(1 - x)^{-3/2} - (1 + x)^{-3/2}]$
   o) $-\frac{1}{2}[x + (1 - x)^{-1}]^{-3/2}[1 + (1 - x)^{-2}]$
   q) $\frac{2}{3}[x^{2/3} - x^{-2/3}]^{-2/3}[x^{-1/3} + x^{-5/3}]$
   s) $[x^{-1} - (1 - x)^{-1}]^{-2}[x^{-2} + (1 - x)^{-2}]$

3. a) $4(x - 1)(1 - \frac{1}{4}t^{-1/2})$
   c) $4xt$
   e) $\frac{1}{2}x^{-1/2}(8t - 3)$
   g) $3t(1 + x)^{-1/2}$
   i) $24x^{-4}(1 + 4t^2)^{-1/2}t$
   k) $(1 - x)^{-2}(1 - 2t)$
   m) $6x$
   o) $2u^{-1/2}t$
   q) $-9ux^2(x^3 + 4)^{-1/2}t^{-2}$
   s) $6ut^{-1/2}$

Section 3-8

1. a) $\dfrac{-2x}{3y^2}$ c) $\dfrac{6x^2}{1+6y}$

   e) $\dfrac{3x(1+x^2)^2}{y^3-1}$ g) $\dfrac{5-6x}{3+8y}$

Section 3-9

1. a) $\tfrac{1}{3}[2^{3/2} - 1]$ c) $\tfrac{3}{4}[2^{2/3} - 1]$ e) $\tfrac{2}{15}$
   g) $\tfrac{3}{2}(2 - \sqrt{2})$ i) $\tfrac{2}{5}$ k) 0
   m) $5 \cdot 2^{-2/3}$

2. a) $\tfrac{4}{15}$ c) $\tfrac{5787}{10}$ e) $\tfrac{9}{140}$ g) $\sqrt{3}/4$

Section 3-10

1. a) $(0, 0)$ min c) $(0, -4)$ min
   e) $(-1, -2)$ min g) $(2, 0)$ min
   i) $(2, -2)$ min k) $(1, 2)$ max

   m) $\left(-\dfrac{b}{2a}, \dfrac{4ac - b^2}{4a}\right)$ min o) $(-1, 2)$ max, $(1, -2)$ min

   q) $(0, 1)$ max, $(2, -3)$ min s) $(0, 0)$ min, $(2, 4)$ max
   u) $(0, 0)$ min, $(\tfrac{1}{4}, \tfrac{5}{256})$ max, $(2, -4)$ min
   w) $(0, 0)$ max, $(4, -128)$ min, $(-1, -3)$ min
   y) $(0, 3)$ min, $(1, 6)$ max, $(-4, 131)$ max

Section 3-11

1. $A = \tfrac{37}{96}, C = \tfrac{47}{96}, E = \tfrac{23}{96}, G = \tfrac{1}{8}, I = \tfrac{1}{2}, K = \tfrac{77}{96}$
2. $A = 12, B = 4$
3. a) $\tfrac{48}{5}$ c) 8 e) $\tfrac{96}{5}$
   g) $\tfrac{37}{12}$ i) $\tfrac{1}{750}$ k) $\tfrac{3}{4}$
   m) $\tfrac{2}{3}$ o) $\tfrac{125}{6}$ q) $\tfrac{8}{3}$

Section 3-12

1. a) $\pi\left(\dfrac{4x^7}{7} - \dfrac{2x^6}{3} - \dfrac{3x^5}{5} + \dfrac{x^4}{2} + \dfrac{x^3}{3}\right)\Big|_{-1}^{-1/2}$

   c) $\pi\left(\dfrac{x^3}{3} - x^2 + x\right)\Big|_{-1/2}^{0}$

   e) $\pi\left(\dfrac{4x^7}{7} - \dfrac{2x^6}{3} - \dfrac{3x^5}{5} + \dfrac{x^4}{2} + \dfrac{x^3}{3}\right)\Big|_{0}^{1/2}$

   g) $\pi\left(\dfrac{x^3}{3} + x^2 + x\right)\Big|_{-1}^{1}$

   i) $\pi\left(\dfrac{4x^7}{7} - \dfrac{2x^6}{3} - \dfrac{3x^5}{5} + \dfrac{5x^4}{2} - x^3 - 2x^2 + 4x\right)\Big|_{0}^{1/2}$

   k) $\pi\left(\dfrac{4x^7}{7} - \dfrac{2x^6}{3} - \dfrac{3x^5}{5} + \dfrac{5x^4}{4} - x^3 - 2x^2 + 4x\right)\Big|_{1/2}^{1}$

Section 3-13

1. 8, 8
5. 60 by 30
9. 10 by 10 by 5
13. $4\sqrt{3}$ by $12 + 4\sqrt{3}$ by $6 - 2\sqrt{3}$
17. $\dfrac{48}{\pi + 4}$ by $\dfrac{24}{\pi + 4}$
21. $\dfrac{A - b - t}{2(a + B)}$

3. $\dfrac{16}{3}, \dfrac{32}{3}$
7. 78 by 82
11. $r = 1, h = 8/\pi$
15. $5(4^{1/3})$ by $5(4^{1/3})$ by $25/2^{4/3}$
19. 120

CHAPTER 4

Section 4-2

1. a) $\frac{1}{2}$ c) $\frac{1}{2}$
2. a) $\frac{1}{3}$ c) 0.40   e) 0
3. a) $\Pr[3] = \frac{2}{30}$, $\Pr[8] = \frac{4}{30}$ c) $\frac{1}{6}$
   $\Pr[4] = \frac{2}{30}$, $\Pr[9] = \frac{4}{30}$
   $\Pr[5] = \frac{4}{30}$, $\Pr[10] = \frac{2}{30}$
   $\Pr[6] = \frac{4}{30}$, $\Pr[11] = \frac{2}{30}$
   $\Pr[7] = \frac{6}{30}$,

Section 4-3

1. b) $\frac{1}{6}$ c) $\frac{1}{3}$
2. b) $\frac{5}{30} = \frac{1}{6}$ c) $\frac{1}{3}$
3. b) $\frac{1}{3}$
5. a) 0.5342   c) 0.6   e) 0.007   g) 0.3795

Section 4-4

1. a)

t	1	2	3	4	5	6
$f_x(t)$	$\frac{1}{6}$	$\frac{1}{6}$	$\frac{1}{6}$	$\frac{1}{6}$	$\frac{1}{6}$	$\frac{1}{6}$

t	1	2	3	4	5	6
$f_y(t)$	$\frac{1}{6}$	$\frac{1}{6}$	$\frac{1}{6}$	$\frac{1}{6}$	$\frac{1}{6}$	$\frac{1}{6}$

t	2	3	4	5	6	7	8	9	10	11	12
$f_{x+y}(t)$	$\frac{1}{36}$	$\frac{2}{36}$	$\frac{3}{36}$	$\frac{4}{36}$	$\frac{5}{36}$	$\frac{6}{36}$	$\frac{5}{36}$	$\frac{4}{36}$	$\frac{3}{36}$	$\frac{2}{36}$	$\frac{1}{36}$

t	2	3	4	5	6	7	8	9	10	11	12
$f_{x-y+7}(t)$	$\frac{1}{36}$	$\frac{2}{36}$	$\frac{3}{36}$	$\frac{4}{36}$	$\frac{5}{36}$	$\frac{6}{36}$	$\frac{5}{36}$	$\frac{4}{36}$	$\frac{3}{36}$	$\frac{2}{36}$	$\frac{1}{36}$

t	1	2	3	4	5	6	8	9	10
$f_{xy}(t)$	$\frac{1}{36}$	$\frac{2}{36}$	$\frac{2}{36}$	$\frac{3}{36}$	$\frac{2}{36}$	$\frac{4}{36}$	$\frac{2}{36}$	$\frac{1}{36}$	$\frac{2}{36}$

t	12	15	16	18	20	24	25	30	36
$f_{xy}(t)$	$\frac{4}{36}$	$\frac{2}{36}$	$\frac{1}{36}$	$\frac{2}{36}$	$\frac{2}{36}$	$\frac{2}{36}$	$\frac{1}{36}$	$\frac{2}{36}$	$\frac{1}{36}$

b) x and y are identical and independent.
c) $x + y$ and $x - y + 7$ are identical and not independent.

Section 4–5

1. a) $\dfrac{7}{2}$ c) $\dfrac{7n}{2}$
4. a) $\dfrac{85}{13}$ b) $\dfrac{850}{13}$
6. b) $\dfrac{1}{3}, \dfrac{1}{3}$ d) $\dfrac{1}{n}$ e) $\dfrac{n+1}{2}$

Section 4–6

1. a) $\dfrac{35}{6}$ b) $\dfrac{35n}{12}$
5. a) $\dfrac{1}{2}, \dfrac{1}{4}$ b) $\dfrac{n}{2}, \dfrac{n}{4}$

Section 4–7

1. $\binom{5}{2}(\tfrac{1}{6})^2(\tfrac{5}{6})^3$
3. a) $\binom{10}{9}(\tfrac{5}{36})^9(\tfrac{31}{36})^1 + \binom{10}{9}(\tfrac{1}{6})^9(\tfrac{5}{6})^1 + \binom{10}{9}(\tfrac{5}{36})^9(\tfrac{31}{36})$
   b) $\binom{10}{8}(\tfrac{5}{36})^8(\tfrac{31}{36})^2 + \binom{10}{8}(\tfrac{1}{6})^8(\tfrac{5}{6})^2 + \binom{10}{8}(\tfrac{5}{36})^8(\tfrac{31}{36})^2$
   c) $\displaystyle\sum_{r=5}^{10} \binom{10}{r}(\tfrac{5}{36})^r(\tfrac{31}{36})^{n-r} + \binom{10}{r}(\tfrac{1}{6})^r(\tfrac{5}{6})^{n-r} + \binom{10}{r}(\tfrac{5}{36})^r(\tfrac{31}{36})^{n-r}$

Section 4–8

1. a) *Bernoullian trial analysis*
      Trial: office extension
      Success: requests outside line during given 5-minute period
      Random occurrence in time analysis
      Time: time
      Occurrence: outside line requested
      Stated time: 5 minutes
   b) 7, 9   c) 2, 3
2. 9

CHAPTER 5

Section 5–1

1. b)
$$AB = \begin{bmatrix} 1 & 3 & -2 \\ 1 & 2 & 0 \end{bmatrix}, \quad BC = \begin{bmatrix} 1 & 1 \\ 4 & -1 \end{bmatrix},$$

$$BD = \begin{bmatrix} 1 & 1 & 4 \\ 4 & -3 & 0 \end{bmatrix}, \quad CA = \begin{bmatrix} 0 & -1 \\ 1 & 0 \\ 2 & -2 \end{bmatrix},$$

$$CB = \begin{bmatrix} 1 & 3 & -2 \\ 0 & -1 & 2 \\ 2 & 4 & 0 \end{bmatrix}, \quad DC = \begin{bmatrix} 1 & -2 \\ 4 & 1 \\ 4 & -3 \end{bmatrix}$$

254 ANSWERS TO SELECTED EXERCISES

2. a) $\begin{bmatrix} u \\ v \end{bmatrix} = \begin{bmatrix} 2 & -3 \\ 4 & -1 \end{bmatrix} \begin{bmatrix} x \\ y \end{bmatrix}$

c) $\begin{bmatrix} u \\ v \\ w \end{bmatrix} = \begin{bmatrix} 2 & -3 & 1 \\ 1 & -2 & 3 \\ 4 & -1 & 5 \end{bmatrix} \begin{bmatrix} x \\ y \\ z \end{bmatrix}$

Section 5-2

1. $A^{-1} = \begin{bmatrix} \frac{1}{7} & -\frac{3}{14} \\ \frac{2}{7} & \frac{1}{14} \end{bmatrix}$, $\quad B^{-1} = \begin{bmatrix} -\frac{2}{5} & \frac{3}{5} \\ -\frac{1}{5} & \frac{4}{5} \end{bmatrix}$,

$AB = \begin{bmatrix} -7 & 9 \\ 14 & -8 \end{bmatrix}$, $\quad (AB)^{-1} = \begin{bmatrix} \frac{4}{35} & \frac{9}{70} \\ \frac{1}{5} & \frac{1}{10} \end{bmatrix}$,

$BA = \begin{bmatrix} -16 & -6 \\ -9 & 1 \end{bmatrix}$, $\quad (BA)^{-1} = \begin{bmatrix} -\frac{1}{70} & -\frac{3}{35} \\ \frac{9}{70} & -\frac{8}{35} \end{bmatrix}$,

$A^{-1}B^{-1} = \begin{bmatrix} -\frac{1}{70} & -\frac{3}{35} \\ \frac{9}{70} & -\frac{8}{35} \end{bmatrix}$, $\quad B^{-1}A^{-1} = \begin{bmatrix} \frac{4}{35} & \frac{9}{10} \\ \frac{1}{5} & \frac{1}{10} \end{bmatrix}$

Section 5-3

3. a) Not a vector space b) A vector space
4. No
5. Not a vector space

Section 5-4

1. a) $\begin{bmatrix} -1 & -2 \\ -2 & -3 \end{bmatrix}$ c) $\begin{bmatrix} \frac{2}{3} & \frac{1}{3} \\ \frac{1}{3} & -\frac{1}{3} \end{bmatrix}$

2. a) $\begin{bmatrix} -1 & -2 \\ -2 & -3 \end{bmatrix} \begin{bmatrix} 3 \\ 2 \end{bmatrix} = \begin{bmatrix} -7 \\ -12 \end{bmatrix}$, $\begin{bmatrix} -3 & -2 \\ 2 & 1 \end{bmatrix} \begin{bmatrix} 3 \\ 2 \end{bmatrix} = \begin{bmatrix} -13 \\ 8 \end{bmatrix}$

b) $\begin{bmatrix} \frac{2}{3} & \frac{1}{3} \\ \frac{1}{3} & -\frac{1}{3} \end{bmatrix} \begin{bmatrix} 4 \\ -3 \end{bmatrix} = \begin{bmatrix} \frac{5}{3} \\ \frac{7}{3} \end{bmatrix}$, $\begin{bmatrix} \frac{2}{3} & -\frac{1}{3} \\ \frac{1}{3} & \frac{1}{3} \end{bmatrix} \begin{bmatrix} 4 \\ -3 \end{bmatrix} = \begin{bmatrix} \frac{11}{3} \\ \frac{1}{3} \end{bmatrix}$

4. b) $\frac{4}{5}$ and $\frac{7}{5}$

Section 5-5

1. a) $\begin{bmatrix} 1 & 2 \\ -3 & 1 \end{bmatrix}$ c) $\begin{bmatrix} -21 & 35 \\ -14 & 23 \end{bmatrix}$

Section 5-6

2. a) $\begin{bmatrix} \frac{4}{5} & \frac{2}{5} & \frac{2}{5} \\ \frac{3}{5} & -\frac{1}{5} & -\frac{1}{5} \end{bmatrix}$ b) $\frac{6}{5}(x+2) + \frac{7}{5}(2x-1)$

4. a) $\begin{bmatrix} \frac{1}{3} & 0 & 0 \\ 0 & \frac{1}{2} & 0 \\ 0 & 0 & 1 \\ 0 & 0 & 0 \end{bmatrix}$

  b) $\begin{bmatrix} \frac{1}{3} & 0 & 0 \\ 1 & \frac{1}{2} & 0 \\ 1 & 1 & 1 \\ 0 & 0 & 0 \end{bmatrix}$

c) $-\frac{1}{2}$

6. a) $\begin{bmatrix} \frac{1}{2} & \frac{2}{5} & \frac{3}{10} \\ \frac{1}{2} & \frac{3}{5} & \frac{7}{10} \end{bmatrix}$

  b) $s_1 = 44\frac{1}{2}$, $s_2 = 60\frac{1}{2}$

c) $\begin{bmatrix} 1 & 0 & 0 \\ 0 & 1 & 0 \end{bmatrix}$

Section 5–7

2. b) $T_1[aI^2 + bI + cI^0] = 2aI + bI^0$,

$$T_2^*[a \ b \ c] = \begin{bmatrix} \dfrac{a}{2} & b \end{bmatrix}$$

c) $T_2[ax + b] = \dfrac{aI^2}{2} + bI$,

$T_1^*[a \ b] = [2a \ b \ 0]$

4. a) $\begin{bmatrix} 4 \\ -6 \end{bmatrix}$ b) 10 c) $[6 \ -7 \ -3]$ d) 10

6. $[\frac{1}{2}a_1 + \frac{1}{2}a_2, \frac{2}{5}a_1 + \frac{3}{5}a_2, \frac{3}{10}a_1 + \frac{7}{10}a_2]$

7. None of the sets

CHAPTER 6

Section 6–1

2. $z_1 \geq 0$; $z_2 \geq 0$, $3z_1 + z_2 \leq 50$, $z_1 + 2z_2 \leq 25$

4. If x is number of regular martinis and y is number of extra-dry martinis, $x \geq 0$; $y \geq 0$, $2x + y \leq 200$, $4x + 5y \leq 800$.

Section 6–2

2. The Smith-Jones strategies are
   a) 150 to 30, b) 0 to 180, c) 150 to 30.

Section 6–3

2. a) $A = \begin{bmatrix} 1 & 1 \\ 1 & 2 \\ 1 & 3 \end{bmatrix}$, $B = \begin{bmatrix} 180 \\ 200 \\ 240 \end{bmatrix}$, $C = [1 \ 1.5]$

   Minimize CX.

2(c) $A = \begin{bmatrix} 1 & 1 \\ 1 & 2 \\ 1 & 3 \end{bmatrix}$, $B = \begin{bmatrix} 180 \\ 200 \\ 240 \end{bmatrix}$, $C = [1 \quad 2.5]$

Minimize CX.

3(b) $A = \begin{bmatrix} 1 & 2 \\ 1 & 5 \end{bmatrix}$ $B = \begin{bmatrix} 45 \\ 100 \end{bmatrix}$, $C = [\frac{100}{3} \quad \frac{400}{3}]$

Minimize CX.

CHAPTER 7

Section 7-1

1. b) Not commutative
   c) The inverses of I, R_1, R_2, A_1, A_2, A_3 are respectively I, R_2, R_1, A_1, A_2, A_3.
2. c) Commutative
   d) The inverses of I and R are respectively I and R.
3. c) Commutative
   d) The inverses of I, R_1, D_1, D_2 are respectively I, R_1, D_1, D_2.
4. a) Commutative. The inverses of I, R_1, R_2, R_3 are respectively I, R_3, R_2, R_1.
   c) Commutative. The inverses of I, R_2, H, and V are respectively I, R_2, H, and V.

Section 7-2

1. a) Commutative, identity $= 0$, $x^{-1} = -x$
   c) Commutative, identity $= 1$, $a^{-1} = 1/a$
   e) Not commutative, identity $=$ identity function I. If $f(x) = ax + b$, $f^{-1}(x) = (x - b)/a$.
4. Factorial n

Section 7-3

2. a) Group I, $f(I) = e$, $f(R_1) = a$, $f(R_2) = b$, $f(R_3) = c$
   c) Group IV, $f(I) = e$, $f(f_1) = a$, $f(f_2) = b$, $f(f_3) = c$
   e) Group IV, $f(I) = e$, $f(f_1) = a$, $f(f_2) = b$, $f(f_3) = c$
11. a) $T_e(x) = ex$, $T_a(x) = ax$, $T_b(x) = bx$, $T_c(x) = cx$
    c) $T_R = \{T_x \mid x \in R, T_x(a) = xa\}$

Section 7-4

1. The subgroup $\{I, P_{213}\}$:

Left cosets

	I	P_{213}
P_{132}	P_{132}	P_{312}
P_{231}	P_{231}	P_{321}

Right cosets

	P_{132}	P_{312}
I	P_{132}	P_{312}
P_{213}	P_{231}	P_{321}

The subgroup $\{I, P_{321}\}$:

Left cosets

	I	P_{321}
P_{213}	P_{213}	P_{312}
P_{231}	P_{231}	P_{132}

Right cosets

	P_{213}	P_{312}
I	P_{213}	P_{312}
P_{321}	P_{231}	P_{132}

The subgroup $\{I\}$: The left and right coset is all of S_3.

6. The quotient group G/H consists of two elements; the first is H itself and the second is all odd integers.

Section 7–5

2. Kernel of f = all integers divisible by 4
   = K say.

   Z/K consists of four members: the first member is all multiples of 4, the second is all numbers of the form $4x + 1$, the third is all numbers of the form $4x + 2$, and the fourth is all numbers of the form $4x + 3$ (x an integer). If $Z/K = \{K, K_1, K_2, K_3\}$, then the isomorphism between Z/K and the range of f is defined by

   $$g(K) = 0, \quad g(K_1) = 1, \quad g(K_2) = 2, \quad g(K_3) = 3.$$

5. Let G_1 and G_2 be two cyclic groups of order $2n$ and n, respectively, with respective generators a and b. Then $G_1 = \{a, a^2, a^3, \ldots, a^{2n}\}$, $G_2 = \{b, b^2, b^3, \ldots, b^n\}$.

   Let $1 \leq k \leq 2n$. Define $f(a^k) = b^k$ for each k. Then

   $$\begin{aligned} f(a^k a^l) &= f(a^{k+l}) \\ &= b^{k+l} = b^k b^l \\ &= f(a^k) f(b^l). \end{aligned}$$

   $\therefore f$ is a homomorphism.

   If $b^p (1 \leq p \leq n)$ is an identity of G_2, then the kernel of f is $\{a^p, a^{n+p}\}$.

7. a) $k \leq n$
   b) If p elements of the first group are mapped to the identity in the second group, then the order of the kernel is p.
   c) The order of the factor group generated by this kernel is n/p.

Section 7–6

1. The even integers under usual addition form an abelian group and the usual operation of multiplication on integers is associative and the product of two even integers is even. Multiplication is both left and right distributive over addition. There is no identity for this commutative ring.

4. a) Ring, not commutative, with identity = $\begin{bmatrix} 1 & 0 \\ 0 & 1 \end{bmatrix}$
   c) Commutative ring with the identity function I as identity
   e) Not a ring

CHAPTER 8

Section 8–1

1. (b), (c), (d), (e), (h), (i), (j), and (n) are OK.
2. (d), (e), (f), and (g) are ruled out.

Section 8–2

1. (b), (c), (g) are OK.

3.
```
READ 101, X1, X2, X3, P1, P2, P3
EXP = X1*P1 + X2*P2 + X3*P3
VAR = X1**2*P1 + X2**2*P2 + X3**2*P3 - EXP**2
PUNCH 102, EXP, VAR
STOP
END
```

5.
```
READ 101, A, B, C
SAB = A**2 + B**2
SAC = A**2 + C**2
SBC = B**2 + C**2
PUNCH 102, A, B, SAB
PUNCH 102, A, C, SAC
PUNCH 102, B, C, SBC
STOP
END
```

Section 8–3

2.
```
READ 101, X
A = ABSF (SINF (X))
B = SQRTF (1. - COSF (X)**2)
C = ABSF (A - B)
PUNCH 102, X, A, B, C
STOP
END
```

Section 8–4

2. 5
```
    READ 101, I, J, K
    IF (I - J) 2, 2, 1
1   M = I
    I = J
    J = M
2   IF (J - K) 4, 4, 3
3   M = J
    J = K
    K = M
```

```
     4    PUNCH 102, I, J, K
          GØ TØ 5
          END

4.1       READ 101, X
          N = 0
          Y = X
     2    X = SINF (X)
          IF (ABSF (ABSF (X) - .01))4, 3, 3
     3    N = N + 1
          IF (N - 100) 2, 4, 4
     4    PUNCH 102, Y, X, N
          GØ TØ 1
          END
```

Section 8-5

```
2.        DIMENSIØN X(50), P(50)
     1    READ 101, N
          READ 102, (X(I)I = 1,N), (P(I)I = 1,N)
          PUNCH 102, (X(I)I = 1,N)
          PUNCH 102, (P(I)I = 1,N)
          EX = 0.
          DØ 2 I = 1, N
     2    EX = EX + P(I)*X(I)
          EXSQ = 0.
          DØ 3 I = 1, N
     3    EXSQ = EXSQ + P(I)*X(I)**2
          VARX = EXSQ - EX**2
          PUNCH 103, EX, VARX
          GØ TØ 1
          END

4.        DIMENSIØN X(100)
     1    READ 101, N
          READ 102, (X(I)I = 1,N)
          NN = N - 1
          DØ 3 J = 1, NN
          JJ = J + 1
          DØ 3 I = JJ, N
          IF (X(I) - X(J)) 3, 3, 2
     2    Y = X(J)
          X(J) = X(I)
          X(I) = Y
     3    CØNTINUE
          PUNCH 102, (X(I)I = 1,N)
          GØ TØ 1
          END
```

6.   DIMENSION X(100), Y(100)
    1   READ 101, N
          READ 102, (X(I)I = 1,N), (Y(I)I = 1,N)
          K = 0
          DO 3 I = 1, N
          IF (X(I)*Y(I)) 3, 3, 2
    2   K = K + 1
    3   CONTINUE
          PUNCH 101, K
          GO TO 1
          END

10. a)   DIMENSION A(35,35), B(35,35), C(35)
    1   READ 101, N
          READ 102, ((A(I,J)J = 1,N)I = 1,N),
                    ((B(I,J)J = 1,N)I = 1,N)
          L = 1
    2   DO 3 I = 1, N
    3   PUNCH 102 (A(I,J)J = 1,N)
          GO TO (4,1), L
    4   L = 2
          DO 5 I = 1, N
    5   PUNCH 102 (A(I,J)J = 1, N)
          DO 7 I = 1, N
          DO 6 J = 1, N
          C(J) = 0.
          DO 6 K = 1, N
    6   C(J) = C(J) + A(I,K)*B(K,J)
          DO 7 J = 1, N
    7   A(I,J) = C(J)
          GO TO 3
          END

(*Note:* This will punch out all three matrices.)

10. b)   DIMENSION A(49), B(49,49), C(49)
    1   READ 101, N
          READ 102, ((B(I,J)J = 1,N)I = 1,N)
          DO 3 I = 1, N
          READ 102, (A(J)J = 1,N)
          DO 2 J = 1,N
          C(J) = 0.
          DO 2 K = 1,N
    2   C(J) = C(J)+A(K) * B(K,J)
    3   PUNCH 102 (C(J)J = 1,N)
          GO TO 1
          END

(*Note:* This punches out only the matrix *C*.)

ANSWERS TO SELECTED EXERCISES   **261**

11. a) 28×28 b) 35×35 c) 49×49

Section 8-6

1.   *****2.53000******.01200***57
3. a) 101 FORMAT (I2, F5.4)
    102 FORMAT (16F5.0)
   b) 15*.042
    *400.*420.*440.*460.*480.*500.*520.*540.*560.
    *580.*600.*620.*640.*660.*680.

(*Note:* * here indicates a blank space. The second part of (3b) is written on two lines here but it will all go on one card.)

5.   READ 101, K, L, M
   101   FORMAT (I8,26X,I2,I3)

Section 8-7

2. a) 3   21   21   101   2   30   101   101   2   12   30   102
    4   101   102   101   5   16   101   101
    1.   3.
   c) 3   30   21   101   5   14   101   101   3   30   21   102
    5   13   102   102   5   11   102   102   3   101   102   101
    2.   3.
   e) 3   21   21   101   3   22   22   102   1   101   102   101
    3   30   101   101   5   12   101   101
    −.5

5. Use the DIMENSION and READ statements given in the text. Then proceed to

     1   READ 101, A, B, H
    101   FORMAT (3F12.0)
           X = A − H
     2   X = X + H
           GO TO 500

Now insert the subprogram given in the text with the final statement (following 599) omitted. Then proceed to

           PUNCH 102, X, Y
    102   FORMAT (F16.8, 10X, F16.8)
           IF (X − B)2, 1, 1
           END

Index

Abscissa, 23
Algebraic variety, 206
Antiderivative, 71
Archimedes, 60
Area, 90
Argument, 55
    valid, 56
Associative, 186
Axiom, 58

Basis, 141
Bernoullian trials, 120
Biconditional, 44
Binomial coefficients, 5
Binomial theorem, 6
Boolean lattice, 52

Cancellation law, 190
Central limit theorem, 128
Central processing unit, 212
Chain rule, 78
Commutative, 186
Compiler, 213
Complement, 3
Component, 141
Conclusion, 56
Conditional, 42
Conditional probability, 108
Conjunction, 35
Constraint, 165
Contrapositive, 46
Converse, 47
Corner point, 170
Coset, 196

Data, 212
Derivative, 67
Determinant, 136
Differential, 82
Differentiation, 67

Disjunction, 35
Domain, 10
Dual problems, 177
Dual transformation, 162
Duality theorem for linear programming, 178

Elements, 1
Event, 102
Expectation, 115
Expected value, 115

Fallacy, 56
Field, 208
    ordered, 209
Fixed-point, 214
Floating-point, 214
FORTRAN characters
    alphabetic, 213
    alphameric, 213
    numeric, 213
    special, 213
FORTRAN statements
    arithmetic, 216
    computed GO TO, 221
    DIMENSION, 224
    DO, 224
    FORMAT, 232
    GO TO, 220
    IF, 221
    PUNCH, 216
    READ, 215
Function, 10
    composite, 18
    constant, 15
    identity, 15
    polynomial, 15
Function space, 140
Fundamental theorem of calculus, 71

INDEX

Generator, 194
Group, 188
  abelian, 188
  quotient, 198
  symmetric, 189

Homomorphism, 200

Ideal, 206
Implication, 42
Independent events, 109
Integral, 63
Integral domain, 205
Integration by substitution, 85
Intersection, 2
Input-output, 212
Isomorphism, 193

Kernel, 200
Klein's 4-group, 194

Lagrange Theorem, 199
Law of large numbers, 127
Leibnitz, 60
Limit, 61
Limits of integration, 63
Limits of summation, 8
Linear equation, 29
Local maximum, 88
Local minimum, 88
Locus, 23
Logical equivalence, 40
Logical implication, 42
Logical independence, 37

Mapping, 22
Matrix, 131
  identity, 135
  inverse, 135
Minimum problem, 175

Negation, 35
Newton, 60

Order of a group, 189
Ordered pair, 10
Ordinate, 23

Pascal's triangle, 4
Permutation, 189
Poisson distribution, 124

Postulate, 58
Premise, 55
Probability measure, 104
Program, 212

Range, 10
Ring, 203
  commutative, 203
  with unity, 203

Sample space, 101
Set, 1
  convex, 166
  singleton, 2
  vacuous, 2
Simplex algorithm, 180
Simpson's rule, 225
Solid of revolution, 94
Space, 3
Statement, 35
Subgroup, 196
  normal, 197
Subroutine, 213
Subset, 1
  proper, 1
Summation index, 7
Summation sign, 7
Symmetries, 185

Transformation, 148
  linear, 149
Transpose, 134
Truth set, 24
Truth table, 38
Truth values, 35

Union, 2

Variables, 22
  component, 142
  coordinate, 23
  FORTRAN, 214
  random, 112
    identical, 113
    independent, 113
  subscripted, 224
Variance, 118
Vector space, 139
Venn diagram, 50
Volume, 93

ABCDEFGHIJKL 6098